Shell Connections

NEW PLAYS
FOR YOUNG PEOPLE

Connections Series

The Chrysalids
adapted by David Harrower from the novel by John Wyndham

More Light Bryony Lavery

After Juliet Sharman Macdonald

Gizmo Alan Ayckbourn
Don't Eat Little Charlie Tankred Dorst with Ursula Ehler

Eclipse Simon Armitage
Friendly Fire Peter Gill

Cuba Liz Lochhead
Dog House Gina Moxley

Brokenville Philip Ridley
The Pilgrimage Paul Goetzee

NEW CONNECTIONS: NEW PLAYS FOR YOUNG PEOPLE
(*Asleep Under the Dark Earth* by Sian Evans, *The Chrysalids* adapted by David Harrower from the novel by John Wyndham, *Cuba* by Liz Lochhead, *Dog House* by Gina Moxley, *Eclipse* by Simon Armitage, *The Golden Door* by David Ashton, *In the Sweat* by Naomi Wallace and Bruce McLeod, *More Light* by Bryony Lavery, *Shelter* by Simon Bent, *Sparkleshark* by Philip Ridley, *Travel Club* and *Boy Soldier* by Wole Soyinka, *The Ultimate Fudge* by Jane Coles)

NEW CONNECTIONS 99: NEW PLAYS FOR YOUNG PEOPLE
(*After Juliet* by Sharman Macdonald, *Can You Keep a Secret?* by Winsome Pinnock, *The Devil in Drag* by Dario Fo, translated and adapted by Ed Emery, *Don't Eat Little Charlie* by Tankred Dorst with Ursula Ehler translated by Ella Wildridge, *Early Man* by Hannah Vincent, *Friendly Fire* by Peter Gill, *Gizmo* by Alan Ayckbourn, *King of the Castle* by Christina Reid, *The Pilgrimage* by Paul Goetzee, *Taking Breath* by Sarah Daniels)

INTERNATIONAL CONNECTIONS: NEW PLAYS FOR YOUNG PEOPLE
(*The Actor* by Horton Foote, *The Bear Table* by Julian Garner, *The Exam* by Andy Hamilton, *Gold* by Timothy Mason, music by Mel Marvin, *Illyria* by Bryony Lavery, *Lady Chill, Lady Wad, Lady Lurve, Lady God* by Kay Adshead, *Nuts* by Fausto Paravidino, trs. Luca Scarlini and Zachery James Kinney, *Olive* by Tamsin Oglesby, *Starstone* by Christian Martin, trs. Penny Black, *Take Away* by Jackie Kay, *Team Spirit* by Judy Upton)

Shell Connections

NEW PLAYS
FOR YOUNG PEOPLE

A copy of this anthology has been placed in every secondary school in the UK through the generous support of the Foyle Foundation

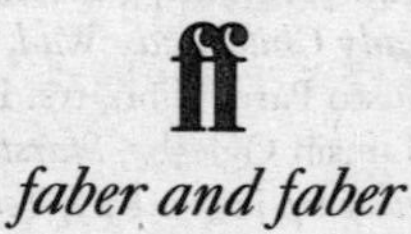

faber and faber

First published in 2003
by Faber and Faber Limited
3 Queen Square London WC1N 3AU

Typeset by Country Setting, Kingsdown, Kent CT14 8ES
Printed in England by Mackays of Chatham plc, Chatham, Kent

A CIP record for this book is available from the British Library

0-571-22014-2

2 4 6 8 10 9 7 5 3 1

Contents

Preface

The *Shell Connections* programme has everything: exciting new plays, committed and inspired performers and an audience that wants to be challenged, provoked and entertained. It's a model of what the theatre should be, and of what I hope the National Theatre will be in the years to come.

It's all the more exciting for starting in youth theatre companies and schools all over the world. I love the way it connects us at the National with the artists and audiences of the future, and I love the way it inspires so many young people to discover how urgent and necessary the theatre can be.

Shell's generous sponsorship enables the National to engage directly with young talent across the country, and we invariably find great bursts of creative energy and intelligence wherever we go.

It's no surprise that so many of our best playwrights have been eager to write for *Connections*. They know what's good for them. I can't wait to discover what riches have been unearthed this year.

NICHOLAS HYTNER
Artistic Director of the National Theatre

Introduction

Shell Connections is the [illegible] [illegible] plays [illegible] each [illegible] throughout the UK [illegible] selected [illegible]

[illegible]

[illegible] and [illegible]

[illegible] at ACT (the American Conservatory Theater) in San Francisco [illegible] residency at the O'Neill Playwrights' Conference, Connecticut [illegible] Constance Congdon and Mark Ravenhill. Their plays were written and [illegible] there in August [illegible]. At the same time [illegible] worked with ACT on the [illegible] piece and [illegible] had its American premiere at the [illegible] Theatre, San Francisco, that same month.

Introduction

Shell Connections is the most imaginative, significant, large-scale new plays programme for teenagers in the world. Throughout the UK, Ireland, Italy, the USA, Scandinavia, Japan and Australia thousands of young actors perform in several hundred local premières of ten specially commissioned new plays.

This fifth anthology of *Connections* plays is as wide-ranging and eclectic as its predecessors. It features ten works from some of the finest writers of our time. This volume brings you new plays from Philip Ridley, Laura Ruohonen, Jon Fosse, Lucinda Coxon, Constance Congdon, Christopher William Hill, David Farr, Maya Chowdhry, Sarah Daniels and Mark Ravenhill.

When commissioning the plays, our admiration for the writers' work was of paramount importance. We particularly wanted to include contemporary writers from countries that have become involved with the programme, so we approached Norway and Finland's best-known writers, Jon Fosse and Laura Ruohonen. They wrote in their mother tongues and were speedily and expertly translated by David Harrower (for Jon Fosse's *Purple*) and David Hackston (for Laura Ruohonen's *An Island Far from Here*). Craig Slaight, our American collaborator at ACT (the American Conservatory Theatre) in San Francisco organised a residency at the O'Neill Playwrights' Conference, Connecticut, for Constance Congdon and Mark Ravenhill. Their plays were written and workshopped there in August 2002. At the same time, we worked with ACT on the Sarah Daniels piece and *Dust* had its American première at the Zeum Theatre, San Francisco, that same month.

Multiplex was developed in association with the Theatre Royal, Plymouth, where Christopher William Hill is currently Writer in Residence. All the plays were then workshopped at the National Theatre with a consultative group of young people from across London who had been nominated by their drama teachers.

There were 165 schools and youth theatres which had successfully applied to join the programme. In autumn 2002 the plays were ready for the next step in the process, where the groups chose the play they most wanted to do. At a weekend retreat in Keswick, Cumbria, the groups' leaders, plus the writers and facilitating directors, workshopped all the plays. This meant everybody was able to start the rehearsal process in the best way possible – having talked about the play directly with its writer and with expert advice on hand from directors. The notes accompanying the plays in this anthology are based on what happened in those workshops.

In March 2003 the plays were premièred at a venue local to each group and all 165 productions were visited by a team from the National. The Shell Connections Festival was launched at Newcastle Theatre Royal on 28 March 2003, and continued at Belfast's Lyric Theatre, Cambridge Arts Theatre, Clwyd Theatr Cymru, Keswick's Theatre by the Lake, Scarborough's Stephen Joseph Theatre, Nottingham Playhouse, Plymouth's Theatre Royal, Edinburgh's Royal Lyceum Theatre, Bath's Theatre Royal, London's Albany Stage, Brighton Pavilion Theatre and London's Tricycle Theatre. The 2003 cycle culminated in a fantastic summer festival in July in the Cottesloe and Olivier Theatres at the National, London.

But it doesn't stop there. With the publication of this volume many more schools and theatre groups around the world have the chance to read and produce the plays for years to come. You'll find the work here offers a whole range of cast sizes and presents a multiplicity of settings:

the dark side of the moon, a multiplex cinema, the tarot universe, Roman London and the eve of Queen Elizabeth II's Golden Jubilee. There's lots of comedy, quests for courage, fame and fortune, tales of sinister parallel worlds and magical happenings. You're going to be spoilt for choice.

SUZY GRAHAM-ADRIANI
National Theatre
March 2003

BROKENVILLE

Philip Ridley

Philip Ridley returns to the *Connections* portfolio after the huge success of his play *Sparkleshark* in the 1997 cycle. He was born and still lives in the East End of London where he writes books, stage plays and screenplays for both adults and children. Philip has won both the *Evening Standard*'s Most Promising Newcomer to British Film and the Most Promising Playwright Awards (the only person ever to receive both prizes), eleven international awards for his self-directed screenplay *The Reflecting Sun*, the Smarties Prize and WH Smith's Mind-Boggling Books Award, as well as being short listed for the Carnegie Medal, and nominated for the Whitbread Prize. Philip is currently under commission by Paines Plough Theatre Company and the Royal Court.

Characters

Child

Satchel

Glitter

Quiff

Bruise

Tattoo

Old Woman

Stories are for joining the past to the future.
Stories are for those late hours of the night
when you can't remember how you got
from where you were to where you are.
Stories are for eternity, when memory is erased,
when there is nothing to remember except the story.

Tim O'Brian

Night.

Twinkling stars.

Ethereal moonlight reveals –

A ruined house: no ceiling, near-demolished walls, smashed windows, stairway. Several piles of rubble. A big puddle.

Signs of family life are scattered everywhere: framed photographs, toys, etc. Also, a bed, table, chairs. Everything damaged by some nameless catastrophe. In the moonlight this becomes a dreamscape of broken memory.

A ten-year-old boy is in the building, holding a music box. His clothes – T-shirt, jeans and trainers – all bear signs of whatever has gone before. He will be known, quite simply, as Child.

Child gets into bed, tucks blanket round him, then opens music box.

A gentle, haunting lullaby starts to play.

Child opens book of fairy tales. The pages are scorched and torn, but he stares as if reading, finding comfort in this instinctive ritual. Child sinks lower into bed and pulls blanket up round him.

Gradually, he drifts into sleep . . .

Pause.

A fifteen-year-old male enters, clutching satchel and torch. He is wearing a dishevelled school uniform. He has an intense, studious manner, enhanced by his short hair and glasses. He will be referred to as Satchel.

Satchel searches the ruined house with his torch. The light comes to rest on Child.

Slowly, Satchel approaches Child.
Child is gently moaning in his sleep.
The music box continues playing . . .

Satchel goes to puddle. He stares into it for a while, then sits nearby. He continues gazing into water.

Pause.

A fourteen-year-old female enters, clutching torch. She is wearing a dress (decorated with silver sequins) and silver stilettos. Her face is fully made-up (albeit a little smudged) and there is glitter in her hair. She will be referred to as Glitter.

Glitter Anyone here?
Satchel Me. Who're you?
Glitter I'm . . . I don't remember.

Approaches Satchel.

What's your name?
Satchel Forgotten.

Slight pause.

Glitter I . . . I've got glitter in my hair.
Satchel I'm holding a satchel.
Glitter What's in it?

Satchel looks in satchel.

Satchel Pens. And a . . . a notebook.
Glitter It might have your name in.

Satchel flicks through notebook.

Satchel Blank pages.

Glitter aims torch at Child.

Glitter I heard the . . . what's it called?

Hums to music.

Satchel Music.
Glitter Music. Yes.
Satchel I heard it too.
Glitter Nothing to do with you, then?
Satchel What?
Glitter The child.
Satchel No.

Slight pause.

Were you at a party?
Glitter Party?
Satchel Your dress. Hair.
Glitter Oh . . . suppose I must've been.

Slight pause.

What happened?
Satchel Where?
Glitter Everywhere.
Satchel Don't remember.
Glitter No. I don't. Nothing.

Indicates Satchel's wristwatch.

What's the time?
Satchel It's stopped. Midnight.

A fourteen-year-old male enters, clutching torch. He is well built and wearing jeans, leather jacket and white T-shirt. He will be referred to by the style of his hair: Quiff.

Satchel (*with Glitter*) Who's there?

Glitter (*with Satchel*) Who's there?
Quiff Who're you first?

Approaches Satchel and Glitter.

Satchel I've got a satchel.
Glitter I've got glitter in my hair.

Quiff goes to puddle, looks at reflection and combs hair.

Satchel You hear the music too?
Quiff What if I did?
Glitter Can you remember your name?
Quiff 'Course I can.
Satchel What is it, then?
Quiff . . . Not telling.
Glitter He's forgotten.
Satchel We've all forgotten.
Quiff Everyone liked my quiff. Remember that much. Everyone wanted to . . . to . . .

Slight pause.

Stuff with lips.
Satchel . . . Kiss?
Quiff Yeah. Kiss. But . . . more.
Glitter More?
Quiff Longer. Tongues.
Glitter Snog?
Quiff Snog. That's it. Everyone wanted to snog me.
Glitter I don't.
Quiff (*indicating Satchel*) He does.
Satchel Don't!
Quiff Liar!

Child starts murmuring in his sleep again.
Quiff aims torch at Child, then goes to him.

Quiff Anything to do with you two?

Glitter What?
Quiff The kid.
Glitter (*with Satchel*) No. Not ours.
Satchel (*with Glitter*) No, no.

Quiff takes blanket from Child and wraps it round his shoulders.

Glitter (*at Satchel*) Should we stop him?

Quiff sits in corner and continues combing his hair.

Satchel You got a watch?
Quiff Eh?
Glitter The time.

Quiff looks at his wristwatch.

Quiff Midnight.
Satchel It's not.
Quiff Can tell the bloody time.
Satchel You'll find it's stopped.

Quiff puts wristwatch to ear.

Satchel Am I right?
Quiff Leave me alone.

A fifteen-year-old female enters, clutching a torch. She is wearing a dark dress, dark cardigan, an engagement ring, and a single earring. There's a bruise on her left leg. There's a becalmed melancholy about her. She'll be referred to as Bruise.

Satchel (*with Glitter*) Who's there?
Glitter (*with Satchel*) Who's there?
Bruise Just me, just me.

Slight pause.

Who're you?
Satchel Got a satchel.

Glitter Got glitter.

Slight pause.

Satchel He's got a quiff.
Bruise Well . . . I've got a bruise.
Glitter How that happen?
Bruise . . . Forgotten.

Aims torch at Child.

That music. I heard it from . . . wherever I was. It's so . . .
Glitter Beautiful?
Bruise No. I mean, yes. It is. But that's not the word.

Slight pause.

A thing for children.
Glitter Nursery rhyme?
Bruise To help them sleep.
Satchel Lullaby.
Bruise Lullaby! Of course!

A fifteen-year-old male enters, holding a torch. He is stocky, with a closely shaven head, and wearing army-surplus-style trousers and shirt. A tattoo is visible on his arm. There's a bandage stuck over his left eye. He'll be referred to as Tattoo.

Satchel (*with others*) Who's there?
Glitter (*with others*) Who's there?
Bruise (*with others*) Who's that?
Tattoo I'll ask the questions. Who're you?
Satchel . . . Satchel.
Glitter Glitter.
Tattoo (*at Bruise*) You?
Bruise . . . What?
Tattoo Name!
Glitter She's got a bruise.
Bruise Yes. I'm Bruise.

Tattoo (*at Quiff*) You?
Satchel Quiff.
Tattoo Ain't he got a tongue?
Satchel Oh, he's got a tongue, yes.

Slight pause.

Glitter What've you got?
Tattoo Eh?
Satchel For your name.
Tattoo Name? My name's . . .

Slight pause.

Glitter Is that a tattoo?
Tattoo Looks like it is.
Satchel Show me.

Looks at tattoo.

What is it?
Tattoo Some . . . thing.
Bruise What's it mean?
Tattoo . . . Forgotten.

Winces at pain in eye.

Glitter What happened?
Tattoo Not sure.
Satchel He's forgotten.
Glitter Everything's forgotten.
Bruise Should bathe it. Your eye.
Satchel Use the puddle.

Tattoo goes to puddle and bathes eye.

Satchel You got the time?
Tattoo Watch stopped.
Satchel (*with Glitter*) Midnight.
Glitter (*with Satchel*) Midnight.

Old Woman enters, clutching torch. She is in her eighties, wearing many layers of frayed jumpers, and walks with the aid of a stick. Like the others, her clothes bear signs of whatever has gone before.

Satchel (*with others*) Who's there?
Glitter (*with others*) Who's there?
Bruise (*with others*) Who's that?
Tattoo (*with others*) Identify yourself.
Old Woman Don't get your knickers in a twist. An old woman. That's all.

Aims torch at them.

Who're you lot?
Satchel Satchel.
Glitter Glitter.
Bruise Bruise.
Tattoo Tattoo.
Old Woman (*at Quiff*) Lost your tongue?
Satchel No, he's got a tongue.
Tattoo He's Quiff.
Old Woman (*indicating Child*) What about this one?
Bruise He's not ours.
Satchel No.
Tattoo Nothing to do with us.
Old Woman One of the lost, eh?

The music box has been winding down.
Now it stops.
Child wakes in panic and jumps from bed.

Old Woman Don't be scared. (*at others*) Stop shining your bloody torches at him!

Approaches Child.

It's all right.

Child backs away.

Old Woman I'm not going to hurt you.

Moves closer to Child.

You're safe now.

Gradually, Old Woman makes her way to Child. She wraps her arms around him.

Old Woman He's petrified. And cold. Make a fire, someone.

Pause.

Can't you help a child? Eh? Forgotten how to do that? – Oi! Tattoo! Fire!

Tattoo All right, all right.

Starts looking for firewood.

Old Woman (*at Bruise*) Wakey-wakey! A fire needs things to burn. Remember?

Bruise Oh . . . yes. Sorry.

Starts looking.

Old Woman Don't burn anything that hasn't been damaged. Just broken stuff. This is still someone's home. Hear me?

Bruise Of course, yes.

Tattoo All right, all right.

Tattoo and Bruise start making pile of objects in middle of room.

Satchel You know the time?

Old Woman No.

Bruise You know what happened?

Old Woman No.

Glitter You know where we are?

Old Woman No, no, no. Why all the questions? The time? Sometime! What happened? Something! The place? At the moment it's a cold place – Coldville!

Ha! How's that? – Where's that bloody fire?
Tattoo Nearly there.

Child is watching Tattoo and Bruise search.
Old Woman keeps her eye on Child.
Slight pause.

Bruise finds dead bird.
Child points at it.

Old Woman What?

Child still points.

Old Woman What you got there?
Bruise A bird.
Satchel Cockatoo.
Old Woman Someone's pet probably.

Child reaches out for dead bird.

Slight pause.

Old Woman Give it to him.

Bruise gives Child the dead bird.

Old Woman Light the fire! Come on. Chop-chop.
Tattoo Got any matches?
Old Woman No.

Slight pause.

Tattoo (*at Quiff*) What about you?
Quiff What?
Tattoo Matches? Lighter?
Quiff What if I have?
Tattoo Quickly!

Quiff gives lighter to Tattoo.
Tattoo sets fire to pile of objects.
Child starts whimpering at firelight.

Old Woman Only a little fire. Don't worry.
Tattoo What's he afraid of?

Child continues to whimper.
Old Woman notices book of fairy tales.

Old Woman What's this . . .? Fairy stories? You like fairy stories?

Child calms a little.

Old Woman Want me to tell you one?

Slight pause.

Well?

Child nods.

Old Woman A story it shall be!

Opens book and reads.

'There was a land called . . .'

Peers closer.

Oh . . . the pages are burnt.

Child begins whimpering again.

Old Woman Don't panic. I'll think of something.

Slight pause.

There was once a land where everything . . . everything was in ruins. Like this place. No one knew what had caused everything to be broken. But broken it was. And this land was called . . . was called . . .

Child begins to whimper.

Satchel Brokenville?
Old Woman What –? Oh, yes! Very good. Brokenville. Now we're getting somewhere. There was once a land

called Brokenville. And, like all fairy-tale lands, it had a . . .

Child begins to whimper.

Satchel Castle?
Old Woman Exactly! (*at Child*) You see the top of that wall? The jagged brick? That's just what the turrets looked like . . . Now what?

Child plucks feather from the dead bird and gives it to Old Woman.

Old Woman A feather?
Satchel He wants a story about a feather.

Child nods.

Old Woman Well, if that's what you want, that's what you'll get. Let's see . . .

Slight pause.

In Brokenville Castle there lived a king.
Satchel And queen?
Old Woman Of course. The King and Queen of Brokenville. And the Queen . . . oh, she loved the King very much.
Satchel And the King loved her.
Old Woman No. The King couldn't stand the sight of her. In fact, she made him puke.
Satchel Why?
Old Woman Battles and wars! That's all the King's life had been. Wars and battles. And so now his heart . . . well, he had no heart.
Satchel Just one big nothing.
Old Woman No love.
Bruise Poor Queen.
Old Woman Oh, she was very upset.

Satchel What did she do?

Slight pause.

What did the Queen –?

Old Woman Give me a chance, cleverclogs!

Slight pause.

A wizard! That's it! The Queen went to see a wizard. And she said, 'I love the King more than life itself, but the King . . . well, I make him puke. Tell me, Wizard, what can I do to make the King love me?'

Satchel What does he say?

Old Woman You tell me . . . Wizard Satchel.

Satchel Me? But . . . oh, I forget how to –

Old Woman 'Forget!' said the Wizard. 'Forget all about the King.' But the Queen said, 'I can't forget the King. Not just like that. You'll have to think of something better. Hear me? You'll have to try harder, Wizard Satchel.'

Pause.

Child begins to whimper.

What about a magic song?

Satchel Good idea! I'll teach you a magic song.

Old Woman 'And have I got to sing it to the King?' asked the Queen.

Satchel That's right. Every night. As he sleeps.

Old Woman 'Then what?' asked the Queen.

Slight pause.

Chop-chop.

Satchel If, after singing this song . . . forty times, you still make the King puke, then . . . well, you won't be bothered.

Bruise Why?

Satchel Because . . .

Old Woman Because after singing the song forty times, said Wizard Satchel, if the King doesn't love you, then you will stop loving him. Right?

Satchel Right.

Old Woman What d'you think of that . . . Queen Bruise?

Bruise . . . Me? Why me?

Old Woman It's about singing to a husband.

Bruise So?

Old Woman You're wearing an engagement ring.

Bruise Oh . . . is that what it is?

Glitter Is it real gold?

Tattoo Why'd you get married?

Satchel Did you have to?

Quiff Where's your bloke now?

Bruise I don't remember. Nothing. Why? Why?

Old Woman Don't worry about remembering. Just sing.

Satchel Sing to the King and stop loving.

Bruise But . . . is it possible? You know? To sing a song and stop loving? Just like that?

Old Woman It's magic. Anything's possible. Sing.

Slight pause.

Bruise . . . Nothing.

Old Woman Something will come. Some fragment. Trust me.

Pause.
Then –

Bruise
Rock . . . a-bye, baby . . .
on the treetop.
When the wind . . . blows
the cradle will rock.
When the bough breaks
the cradle will fall.

Down will come baby
cradle and all.

Pause.

Old Woman For forty nights the Queen sang this song. And for forty mornings she asked the King . . .

Bruise . . . Love me?

Old Woman And for forty mornings the King replied . . .

Old Woman looks at Tattoo.
Child looks at Tattoo.
Others look at Tattoo.

Tattoo . . . Me?

Old Woman Oh, do wake up. (*at Child*) The King was notoriously hung-over in the mornings. (*at Tattoo*) Do you love this girl?

Tattoo No.

Old Woman Said the King.

Slight pause.

And then, on the night the Queen sang her magic song for the fortieth time, she felt something shift inside her.

Bruise Shift?

Old Woman Kick.

Bruise I'm . . . pregnant.

Tattoo Pregnant!

Old Woman Gasped King Tattoo.

Bruise Love me now?

Tattoo No.

Bruise Good.

Tattoo What's going on?

Bruise When . . . when my baby's born – oh, yes! My baby will love me. I know I'm young. But I'm gonna be the best mum in the world. It's my body. My choice! Hear me? Don't care what any of you bloody think! Go to hell!

Slight pause.

Tattoo winces with sudden pain in eye.

Old Woman The next day King Tattoo felt a pain in his eye.
Satchel Pain got worse and worse.
Old Woman It started to bleed.
Satchel Big clots of black blood.
Glitter Then a frog jumps out!
Tattoo A frog?
Old Woman King Tattoo was surprised.
Tattoo King Tattoo thinks it's stupid.
Old Woman Next day he had a lump on his arm.

Slight pause.

What d'you do?
Tattoo Eh?
Old Woman That lump on your arm. Like a boil. We want to know what you're going to do about it. (*at Child*) Don't we?

Child nods.

Tattoo Lance it.
Satchel He cuts it open.
Old Woman What jumps out?
Tattoo . . . A frog?
Old Woman Very good. And now you've got to find out what's wrong with you. (*at Child*) Right?

Child nods.

Tattoo But . . . how?
Old Woman Ask the Wizard, stupid. Go on.

Slight pause.

Chop-chop.
Tattoo What's wrong with me?

Satchel What're the symptoms?
Tattoo Frog growing.
Satchel You're suffering from . . . Frog Growing Disease.
Tattoo Mmm, I see.
Old Woman Ask what it means, King Tattoo. Go on.
Tattoo What does Frog Growing Disease mean?
Satchel You're dying.
Tattoo I'm not.
Old Woman Ask him why, King Tattoo?
Tattoo Why?
Satchel Because . . . no one loves you.
Tattoo They do!
Satchel Who?
Tattoo Her! Queen Bruise.
Bruise You make me puke.
Tattoo Other people then.
Satchel Who? Give me phone numbers.

Slight pause.

Tattoo I . . . can't remember.
Satchel Then you're dying.
Old Woman Say it!

Slight pause.

Tattoo I'm dying.
Old Woman There's an alternative, you know.
Tattoo What?
Old Woman Tell him, Wizard Satchel.

Slight pause.

Satchel If . . . if you manage to find something that loves you, then the frogs will stop growing. You'll live.
Tattoo And . . . if I don't find something?
Old Woman Your heart will stop beating when your child is born.

Pause.

Bruise Search, then.
Tattoo I am.
Old Woman You don't find love sitting on your backside.

Tattoo takes a few steps round the building. As he reaches the puddle –

Old Woman One day, as the king walked along the bank of a river, he heard a cry for help. He looked and saw . . .
Glitter A fish!
Old Woman Trapped in some weeds.
Tattoo So . . . what happens?
Old Woman You tell us.
Tattoo I cook it?
Bruise It's love you're after, not dinner.
Tattoo Rescue it!
Old Woman Then you say . . .
Tattoo I . . . rescued you, Little Fish. So now I want you to . . . to . . .
Bruise He can't say it.
Tattoo Can!
Satchel Can't!
Tattoo Can! Can!
Old Woman Prove it!
Tattoo . . . Love me.

Slight pause.

Old Woman But Little Fish replied . . .

Looks at Child.

Yes, you. What did the fish reply?

Child whispers in Old Woman's ear.

Old Woman Little Fish says, no.
Tattoo Why?
Old Woman Because you don't want love. Not *real* love. You just want gratitude. (*at Child*) Right?

Child nods.

Bruise Clever fish.
Old Woman And Little Fish swam away from the King as fast as he could. Splash, splash.

Child makes splashing noises.

Old Woman Oh, very good.

Slight pause.

The next day the King found . . . (*at Child*) What?

Child points at sky.

Old Woman The sky?

Child shakes head.

Satchel A cloud?
Bruise The sun?
Glitter The moon?
Old Woman A star!

Child nods, then falls to the ground.

Glitter (*with Bruise*) A fallen star!
Bruise (*with Glitter*) A fallen star!

Child nods.

Bruise What d'you do, King Tattoo?
Tattoo Rescue it.
Old Woman Throw it back to the sky. Go on.

Tattoo throws star up.

Bruise He'll ask you to love him now.

Tattoo Love me, Fallen Star.
Old Woman But the Fallen Star said . . .

Child whispers in Old Woman's ear.

Old Woman Ha! Very good! 'Twinkle, twinkle.' Which roughly translates as: Why should I love a pillock like you?
Tattoo What you call me?
Old Woman Answer the question!
Tattoo No!
Old Woman (*with Bruise*) Answer!
Bruise (*with Old Woman*) Answer!

Slight pause.

Tattoo Because . . . I'm very strong. No one else could . . . throw you back like I did. That's why you should love me. How's that?

Child whispers in Old Woman's ear.

Tattoo What's he say?
Old Woman 'Twinkle, twinkle.'
Tattoo What's that mean?
Old Woman You don't want love. You want admiration. And Fallen Star turned its twinkling away from the King.

Child looks away from Tattoo.

Bruise Clever star.
Tattoo Well, I dunno what to do next.
Old Woman The King was on the brink of giving up when he found an egg.

Slight pause.

Find it!
Bruise Go on!
Old Woman (*with Satchel*) Go on!

Satchel (*with old Woman*) Go on!
Tattoo Stop bloody bossing me around! I don't like it. Sod ya stupid story!

Child is distressed by sudden outburst.

Old Woman You're upsetting the child.
Bruise (*with Satchel*) Find it!
Satchel (*with Bruise*) Find it!
Old Woman Chop-chop!

Child's distress is increasing.

Tattoo All right, all right, I'm looking.

Starts looking.

There ain't no egg.
Old Woman Anything young will do.
Tattoo . . . Young?

Old Woman indicates Child.

Slight pause.

Tattoo approaches Child.
Child whimpers in panic.

Old Woman Shush. It's all right. He won't hurt you. (*at Tattoo*) Will you?
Tattoo 'Course I won't.

Slight pause.

Hello, Little Egg.
Old Woman (*at Child*) You see? He's not as scary as he looks.

Child calms.

Tattoo What now?
Old Woman You tell us.

Slight pause.

Tattoo I'll . . . I'll take this Little Egg . . . somewhere safe. Secret.
Old Woman The forest?
Tattoo Yeah.
Old Woman And look after it?
Tattoo Yeah.
Old Woman And when it hatches?
Tattoo I'll make it love me.
Old Woman Very good. So that's what the King did. He stayed in the forest and looked after Little Egg. Until, one day, he heard a hatching sound . . . (*at Child*) Hatching sound, if you please.

Child makes a hatching sound.

Old Woman And he saw?
Tattoo An eye!

Child makes hatching sound.

Old Woman What now?
Tattoo A beak!

Child makes hatching sound.

Tattoo A baby bird!

Child opens mouth.

Tattoo What's it doing?
Old Woman He's hungry.
Bruise Feed him.
Tattoo With what?
Satchel Chewed worms.

Slight pause.

Old Woman Go on.

Tattoo chews.
He goes to hand imaginary worms to Child.

Old Woman Not like that.
Glitter Like a bird.
Bruise Beak to beak.

Slight pause.

Old Woman Chop-chop.

Tattoo leans towards Child.
Closer . . .
Closer . . .

Bruise Baby Bird is fed!
Old Woman And, after forty days of caring for his Baby Bird, the King asked . . .

Slight pause.

Tattoo . . . Love me?
Old Woman And Baby Bird replied . . .

Child whispers in Old Woman's ear.

Old Woman Yes!
Bruise You sure?
Old Woman He's sure.
Tattoo Back to the Castle!
Old Woman King Tattoo put Baby Bird in a cage. And he kept it secretly in his room.
Glitter Why?
Old Woman So it can never love anyone else.
Tattoo Good idea.

Bruise tuts irritably.

Old Woman Queen Bruise – oh, she was becoming very wound up.
Bruise What's in your room?

Tattoo Something that loves me.
Bruise You? Loved? Ha!
Old Woman One day the Queen's child was born.
Bruise What –? Oh, yes. My baby.
Glitter Boy or girl.
Bruise Boy. Hoped for a boy. Look at his little hands.
Old Woman Look, King Tattoo.
Bruise His fingers. See?
Tattoo Yeah.
Bruise So perfect. And look! Here! A birthmark on his leg. See?
Tattoo Yeah.
Bruise Your son.
Tattoo My . . . son.
Bruise We'll look after it together.

Slight pause.

Old Woman King Tattoo went to see Wizard Satchel.
Tattoo I do?
Old Woman Baby born? You alive?
Tattoo Oh, yeah. Right . . . Hey, Wizard Satchel. I'm still alive. And look! No frogs. That means I ain't going to cop it. Right?
Satchel We all cop it eventually.
Tattoo You know what I mean.
Satchel You won't cop it.

Slight pause.

Old Woman So . . . the King went back to Baby Bird's cage and opened the door.
Tattoo Clear off! Don't need you any more. Migrate or something.
Old Woman Baby Bird flew out of its cage.

Child flaps his arms.

Old Woman Oh, very good.

Tattoo Goodbye, Baby Bird.

Slight pause.

Satchel And . . . that's the end of the story?
Old Woman Not sure. (*at Child*) Is it?

Child shakes his head.

Old Woman 'Course not! I know! Being in that cage for so long must've driven Baby Bird bonkers. Right?

Child nods.

Old Woman Baby Bird flew around the Castle in a frenzy.
Satchel Catch it!
Bruise Catch it!
Glitter There it goes!
Tattoo What's going on?
Old Woman And then . . . one feather . . .

Holds up feather.

Goes into the open mouth of the baby Prince.
Bruise You can't.
Old Woman Can! One feather goes into the baby's mouth. No one noticed. By the time Baby Bird had been driven from the Castle, the feather had –
Bruise Don't! Please!
Old Woman The feather had choked the Prince.
Bruise No!
Old Woman Your child is dead!

Slight pause.

Happy with that?

Child nods.
Child takes feather from Old Woman.
Child puts feather in fire.
Pause.

Old Woman We should look for more things to burn. (*at Child*) What d'you think?

Child nods.

Old Woman Don't want the fire to go out, do we? – Oi! Satchel!
Satchel Yeah, yeah, all right. (*at Child*) Wanna help?
Old Woman (*at Child*) Well?

Child nods.

Old Woman Go on, then.

Child looks for things.

Old Woman Oi! Quiff! Make yourself useful.

Quiff doesn't move.

Satchel gasps at something he's found.

Old Woman What?
Satchel No, no, it don't matter.

Child tries to see.

Old Woman Show him!
Satchel But it's not –
Old Woman Show him!
Satchel It's a human tooth. Satisfied?

Gives tooth to Child.
Slight pause.

Child leads Satchel to fire.

Satchel Wh . . . what's he want?
Old Woman The story of the tooth. (*at Child*) Right?

Child nods.

Old Woman Gather round, everyone. Chop-chop.

Child and Satchel sit round fire.
Others gather round.
Pause.

Satchel There was once a land called Brokenville.
Old Woman Very good. Go on.
Satchel And . . . in this land there was . . .
Bruise Queen Bruise?
Satchel Yes.

Child shakes his head.
He whispers in Old Woman's ear.

Bruise What's wrong?
Old Woman No queen.

Slight pause.

Satchel In Brokenville there was a king –

Child shakes his head.
He whispers in Old Woman's ear.

Old Woman No king.
Satchel Where are they, then?

Child whispers in Old Woman's ear.

Old Woman Oh, that's wonderful. (*at others*) The Queen collects seashells. But Brokenville Beach is miles and miles from the Castle. And very difficult to get to. In fact, it's the most difficult place to get to in the whole of the Kingdom.
Satchel And the most beautiful, I bet.
Glitter So the King has taken her there. The Queen. With soldiers to help.
Bruise He does it once a year.
Old Woman And while the King and Queen are gone . . . guess who they leave in charge?

Child whispers in Old Woman's ear.

Old Woman Their son.
Quiff Prince Quiff!

Child claps excitedly.
Quiff moves towards the fire.

Old Woman What a dishy prince.
Glitter Oh, don't. He's vain enough already.
Quiff If you've got it, flaunt it.
Old Woman Go on, then, you vain Prince. Flaunt!
Quiff You ever seen hair like this? Have you? It's bloody perfection. And look at my eyelashes? Girls would die to have lashes like these. And cop an eyeful of this –

Lifts T-shirt.

If this six-pack don't get you drooling, you ain't got drool.
Glitter Oh, gimme a break.
Satchel Every morning the Prince would look at his reflection in the mirror and say . . .
Quiff . . . Eh?
Bruise The story, the story.
Glitter What does the vain Prince say when he looks in the mirror?
Old Woman And use the puddle.
Quiff For what?
Satchel The mirror, you bimbo.

Slight pause.

Quiff (*at Satchel*) Wanna touch me?
Satchel What?
Quiff My skin – just here. Stroke it. With your finger. Like this. You know you want to.

Slight pause.

Go on.

Slowly, Satchel reaches out to touch Quiff.
Just as his finger is about to make contact –

Quiff (*jumping back*) Sorry. You're too ugly to touch me!
Glitter That's nasty!
Bruise Bully.
Satchel (*at Quiff*) You think I'm just a joke, don't you!
Quiff Er . . . yeah.
Bruise Don't upset yourself.
Satchel Take more than him to upset me.
Quiff Oh, yeah, ugly?
Satchel Shut up! Shut up!
Bruise Get your own back.
Glitter Do something.
Satchel What can I do? Eh? Against him? Nothing!

Satchel turns away.

Old Woman There's plenty you can do . . . when you're the one telling the story.

Slowly, Satchel turns to face them all.
Slight pause.

Satchel The Prince . . . he spent all his time gazing into the mirror, saying, 'Kiss me! Kiss me! Kiss me!'
Quiff What?
Old Woman Do it.
Quiff No way.

Child starts whimpering.

Old Woman Look what you're doing! The story! Do it!
Bruise (*with Glitter*) Chop-chop!
Glitter (*with Bruise*) Chop-chop!
Quiff Kissmekissmekissme.

Child begins to calm.

Old Woman Use the puddle!

Quiff goes to puddle.

Satchel And say it properly.
Quiff Kiss me! Kiss me! Kiss me!

Child claps.

Satchel And then, one day, the Prince kissed the mirror so hard it cracked. He cut his lip.

Child whispers in Old Woman's ear.

Old Woman Describe the wound.
Satchel Oh . . . it wasn't really a wound. Just a tiny nick. Like when you shave.
Quiff You? Shave? Ha!
Old Woman I bet something crawled inside the cut, didn't it?
Satchel Yeah.
Tattoo Something very small.
Old Woman I think we gathered that much.
Satchel A spider.
Old Woman Very good. Then?

Slight pause.

Did it do something to the Prince?
Satchel It . . . it went into his bloodstream.
Old Woman Aha!
Satchel It . . . made the Prince very ill.
Old Woman Aha!
Satchel It made his hair start to fall out.
Quiff No way! No!
Old Woman Oh, the Prince was angry.
Satchel But it did no good.
Glitter More hair fell out.
Bruise Handfuls.
Quiff No!
Satchel Until he was bald.
Glitter Well done, Satchel.
Bruise Yeah. Well done.

Quiff I'm not playing any more!

Storms to corner.

Old Woman If you don't like the story, change it.

Pause.

Bruise He ain't got the brains to change it.
Glitter All surface, that's him.
Old Woman He's just a bimbo.

Quiff returns from corner and –

Quiff The King and Queen – they've gone to . . . to – where?
Satchel Brokenville Beach
Quiff And I'm in charge?
Old Woman The kingdom is yours.
Quiff And the people?
Old Woman We're your humble subjects.
Quiff Shave your heads!
Glitter He . . . he can't do that. Can he?
Bruise I'm sure he can't.
Satchel I'm sure he can.
Old Woman He can.
Quiff Get shaving.
Satchel So . . . the humble subjects shaved their heads.
Quiff Ha! Clever or what? I'm the most gorgeous thing in the land again.

Looks at reflection in puddle.

Kiss me! Kiss me! Kiss me!
Satchel And then Prince Quiff got thinner.
Quiff Thinnner?
Glitter No six-pack.
Satchel He locked himself in his room and cried for . . . oh, let's see . . . twenty-eight days and twenty-eight nights.

Old Woman Go to your room.
Bruise (*with Glitter*) Chop-chop.
Glitter (*with Bruise*) Chop-chop.

Quiff goes to corner.

Old Woman (*at Child*) Wonder what he's going to do, eh? Prince Quiff was very clever before. Wonder if he can do it again.

Quiff returns from corner.

Quiff Stop eating!
Bruise What?
Quiff Get as thin as me.
Glitter Oh, this is just silly.
Old Woman This is the law.
Satchel Everyone stopped eating until they were as thin as the Prince.

Quiff looks at his reflection.

Quiff Kiss me! Kiss me! Kiss me!
Satchel And then he spat out a tooth.

Holds up tooth.

Glitter His teeth are falling out.
Satchel The Prince locked himself –
Quiff I'm going.

Goes to corner.

Glitter Wait for it . . .

Slight pause.

Quiff returns from the corner.

Quiff Pull your teeth out.
Glitter Knew it!
Satchel And the Prince travelled the land looking at the piles of teeth or hair.

Quiff Kiss me! Kiss me! Kiss me!
Satchel Now cough blood.
Quiff Blood?
Satchel Lots.
Glitter He's dying.
Quiff I'm not!
Old Woman You are!
Quiff Satch?
Old Woman Go to your room.
Quiff It's *his* story.

Points at Satchel.

Old Woman Go! Go!

Quiff goes to corner.

Bruise What's he gonna do?
Old Woman Don't know. (*at Child*) Do we?

Quiff returns from corner.

Quiff Kill yourselves.
Satchel What?
Quiff If I'm gonna cop it, so are you.

Child shakes his head and whispers in Old Woman's ear.

Old Woman He says you can't do that.
Quiff But I'm using the story. Like you said.
Old Woman You're using it the wrong way.
Satchel Yeah. You're being too . . . obvious.
Bruise Vulgar.
Glitter You big kid!
Tattoo Rebellion!
Old Woman What –? Oh, yes. Very good. Rebellion in Brokenville. Come on, everyone.
Quiff What you gonna do?
Old Woman (*at Child*) What d'you think?

Child whispers in Old Woman's ear.

Old Woman Attack the Castle!
Tattoo Arm yourselves.

Child whispers in Old Woman's ear.

Old Woman Get the Prince!
Glitter Then what?

Child whispers in Old Woman's ear.

Old Woman Tear him to pieces.
Quiff No!
Tattoo Yes!

Quiff backs away from them.

Old Woman Don't let him escape!
Tattoo Catch him! Catch him!
Satchel (*with Tattoo*) Don't let him escape! Catch him! (*etc., etc.*)
Glitter (*with Tattoo*) Let me get my hands on him! Catch him! (*etc., etc.*)
Bruise (*with Tattoo*) He's a bad Prince! Teach him a lesson! (*etc., etc.*)

Tattoo, Satchel, Glitter and Bruise are closing in on Quiff.

Quiff Don't touch me! Don't! Please!
Tattoo Kill him!
All (*except Quiff and Child*) Kill! Kill! Kill! Kill! Kill!
Quiff (*screaming*) Noooooooooo!

Silence.
Slight pause.
Then –

Child – who has been enjoying the whole thing – now claps ecstatically.

Old Woman (*at Child*) You enjoyed that, didn't you?

Child nods, then whispers in Old Woman's ear.

Old Woman Feed him to the birds.

Slight pause.
Then –

Hauntingly, they all make squawking noises.
They all flash their torchlight everywhere.
Slowly, their squawks fade away . . .

Pause.

Glitter Perhaps the Prince's blood is magic.
Old Woman Magic?
Glitter Perhaps it . . . well, perhaps it made everyone's hair grow back.
Bruise And their teeth.
Satchel That's good. I like that.
Old Woman (*at Child*) What d'ya think?

Child shakes his head.

Glitter But why?
Old Woman He's right. You're alive. That's enough.
Quiff No magic blood.

Slight pause.

Old Woman Where's the tooth?
Satchel Here.

Child takes tooth from Satchel, then puts it on the fire.
Slight pause.
Child points.

Old Woman What?

Child still points.

Bruise Something over here?

Goes to some shelves.

The vase?

Child shakes his head.

Bruise This?

Holds up a damaged hand mirror.
Child nods.

Glitter What is it?
Bruise A mirror.

Child sits in front of fire.

Old Woman (*at Bruise*) You know what to do.

Bruise goes to fire.
Others gather round her.
Slight pause.

Bruise There was once a . . .
Glitter Princess Glitter?
Bruise No.
Tattoo King Tattoo?
Bruise Yes.

Slight pause.

But he was a blind king.
Tattoo Why?
Bruise Because you once had a queen. And you didn't love her enough. The Queen died of a broken heart. And, once she was dead, you . . . you realised just how much you really cared for her and . . . and . . . you cried your eyes out!

Child claps excitedly.

Bruise Every day the King walked in the garden of the Castle.

Old Woman The garden was the Queen's.
Bruise She planted everything. Smell her flowers, King.
Tattoo Wish I could see it.
Bruise Your son describes it to you.

Slight pause.

Old Woman Prince Quiff?
Quiff Thought I was dead.
Old Woman New story, new prince.

Tattoo puts a hand on Quiff's shoulder.
Child claps with delight.

Tattoo Describe the garden, Prince Quiff.
Quiff Oh . . . it ain't bad. Yellow climbing flowers – oh, what they called?
Tattoo Roses?
Quiff They're the ones! Roses. All over the joint. Yellow roses. Red roses. And there's tiny roses all round the border. And butterflies. And ladybirds. And the smell! Wicked! How's that?
Old Woman Surprisingly good.
Glitter Yeah.
Bruise There was nothing King Tattoo liked to do more than sit in his dead Queen's garden and smell all those wicked roses.

Tattoo sniffs.

Tattoo Very . . . flowery.

Slight pause.

Bruise And then, one day, a dragon flew out of the sky.
Old Woman (*at Child*) They're scary, those dragons.
Satchel Where'd it come from?
Old Woman From . . . from the nearby mountains.
Bruise And this was the first time the Dragon had ever flown so close to the Castle. And d'you know why?

Child shakes head.

Quiff The . . . smell of the roses?

Bruise Exactly. You see, the roses had been growing. More and more each year. And now the wicked smell had reached the mountains. And there's nothing dragons like more than to eat roses.

Old Woman How's the King feel about this?

Tattoo I'm bloody livid.

Quiff Go to the Wizard.

Tattoo You bet I will. (*at Child*) Right?

Child nods approvingly.
Tattoo goes to Satchel.

Tattoo That Dragon's gonna eat all my garden. Do something!

Satchel Take my advice. Give it a corner of your garden. Grow roses in this corner just for the Dragon. I'm sure it'll be happy to leave the rest of your garden alone. I know dragons. They ain't greedy.

Tattoo I'm not having some overgrown lizard spoiling my view.

Bruise You can't see it!

Tattoo Beside the point! Where's my son?

Slight pause.

Prince Quiff!

Quiff Oh . . . sorry. Here. Wotchya, King.

Tattoo Kill the Dragon.

Quiff But the Wizard said –

Tattoo No 'buts'. It's an order. Chop the Dragon's head off.

Quiff It only wants a few bushes.

Tattoo Not one petal.

Slight pause.

Bruise So . . . Prince Quiff got the biggest sword he could find and went to the mountains.

Slight pause.

Old Woman Go on.
Bruise (*with Glitter*) Chop-chop!
Glitter (*with Bruise*) Chop-chop!
Quiff If this messes my quiff there'll be trouble.

Quiff picks up table leg and starts climbing pile of rubble.

Quiff Dragon!
Old Woman Louder.
Quiff Dragon!
Satchel Louder.
Quiff Dragon! Dragon! Dragon!
Bruise Then he saw something. On top of the mountain. It was very large and . . . made of twigs.
Quiff What?
Old Woman You're the one up the mountain.
Quiff . . . A nest.
Bruise Anything inside?
Quiff Eggs.
Old Woman How many?
Quiff Nine.

Child whispers in Old Woman's ear.

Old Woman Describe them.
Quiff They're . . . they're huge. All swirling with millions of colours. Like when you get oil on water.

Child claps approvingly.

Bruise And that's when the Dragon attacked.
Quiff Why?
Bruise Protecting its nest.
Quiff I ain't hurting anything.

Satchel The Dragon don't know that.
Bruise The Prince stabbed the Dragon.
Quiff Take that!
Bruise The Dragon chased the Prince back down the mountain.
Quiff Mind my quiff, you Dragon.

Descends rubble.

You can't beat me! Look at my muscles! My stomach! Six-pack or what?
Glitter Oh, get on with it.

Quiff swings table leg.

Quiff There!
Bruise What you done?
Quiff Chopped its head off.

Picks up piece of rubble.

Bruise Take it to the King.

Quiff drops rubble in front of Tattoo.

Quiff Look at it, Dad! Well, you can't. You're blind. But if you could you'd see the head of the scariest dragon ever. But me – yeah, Prince Quiff – I fought it and won. No problem! What a fight it was.
Tattoo You did a good job, son.
Quiff The Dragon didn't stand a chance against my muscles.
Old Woman But the Prince had to forget the Dragon.
Quiff Why?
Glitter Time to grow up.
Bruise And marry.
Quiff Marry!
Old Woman A Princess!
Glitter . . . Me?
Quiff Who'd want to marry you? Not me.

Glitter And who'd want to marry you? Not me.
Bruise King Tattoo will decide.
Tattoo Get hitched, you two.

Slight pause.
Glitter takes a step towards Quiff.

Old Woman Closer.

Glitter takes another step.

Old Woman Closer. (*at Quiff*) You too!

Quiff takes a step.
Glitter takes a step.
Eventually, they stand next to each other.

Satchel The Prince and Princess are married.

Throws torn paper like confetti.
Others cheer and clap.
Slight pause.

Old Woman Honeymoon!
Glitter (*with Quiff*) Honeymoon?
Quiff (*with Glitter*) Honeymoon?

Slight pause.

Quiff Wotchya, Princess.
Glitter Wotchya, Prince.
Old Woman Kiss!
Glitter (*with Quiff*) Do what?
Quiff (*with Glitter*) Do what?
Satchel Snog time!
Quiff But . . . I don't fancy her.
Glitter And I don't fancy him.
Old Woman It's for the story.

Quiff and Glitter look at each other awkwardly.
Gradually, they lean towards each other.

Just as it looks as if they might actually kiss –

Quiff Did I tell you about the Dragon?
Glitter Zillions of times.
Quiff My sword went right into its eye. Yellow jelly spurted out.
Glitter All right, all right, enough.
Quiff I stabbed the other eye.
Glitter How are we gonna move the story forward if you keep going on about the Dragon?
Bruise The Princess was very upset. She loved the Prince very much –
Glitter Hang on!
Bruise And more than anything she wanted his child.
Glitter (*with Quiff*) Now hang on!
Quiff (*with Glitter*) Now hang on!
Old Woman It's for the story. You love the Prince and want his child.
Tattoo And I want an heir.
Old Woman There! Perfect!

Slight pause.

Glitter Prince . . . I love you so much and –
Quiff I don't want a baby.
Glitter But I love you and the King –
Quiff I don't want a baby.
Glitter Oh, I give up.

Slight pause.

Tattoo I'll go to the Wizard.
Old Woman Good thinking.
Satchel Wizard Satchel here.
Tattoo The Princess loves the Prince so much and she wants to have his baby but –
Quiff I don't want a baby.
Tattoo You see? What can we do, Wizard Satchel?

Slight pause.

Well?

Old Woman Why don't you make a mirror, Wizard Satchel?

Bruise gives mirror to Satchel.

Satchel A mirror! Right. Good idea. Well . . . it's a magic mirror, obviously. Now . . . what can it do?

Tattoo Don't you know?

Satchel There's lots of spells, you know.

Slight pause.

Got it! Take this mirror to Prince Quiff. When he looks in it, he'll forget all about the Dragon.

Gives mirror to Tattoo.

Tattoo So . . . what? The Prince has to look in the mirror all day? That's the spell?

Satchel Got it! Gradually, break off tiny bits of the mirror. So small the Prince won't see. And keep doing that until the mirror's all gone. By that time . . . well, the Prince will have forgotten all about the Dragon. There! How's that?

Tattoo It'll do.

Satchel One more thing. The mirror can be a dangerous magic. Don't look into it yourself.

Tattoo I can't. I'm blind.

Satchel Then there's no problem.

Bruise So the King took the mirror to the Prince.

Hands mirror to Quiff.
Quiff looks in mirror and –

Quiff Wicked!

Tattoo What can you see?

Quiff Wicked!

Satchel And what about your battle with the Dragon?

Quiff Who cares?

Child claps his hands in approval.

Old Woman Very good.

Bruise The King went to the Princess and told her about the magic mirror.

Tattoo All we've got to do is break off little bits when the Prince ain't looking. Soon there'll be no mirror. The Prince will be free of Dragon memories and you will have that baby.

Bruise You've forgotten something.

Tattoo What?

Child whispers in Old Woman's ear.

Old Woman Good boy. Not to look in the mirror.

Bruise So, that night, Princess Glitter broke a tiny piece from the mirror and looked in it.

Glitter Oh, amazing!

Bruise And then – a noise in the sky!

Tattoo What's going on now?

Old Woman A dragon!

Bruise More than one. Because, when the Prince had returned from killing the Dragon, he forgot about one thing. Guess what?

Child rushes to Bruise and whispers in her ear.

Bruise You are a clever boy! The nest!

Child whispers in her ear again.

Bruise With eggs. Exactly. And now the dragons have hatched and grown up and . . .

Child sniffs loudly.

Bruise They smell the roses.

Child flaps arms as if flying.

Bruise They're coming to eat the garden.
Old Woman Well done.
Bruise The dragons are coming!
Old Woman The dragons are coming!

Child runs around flapping arms.

Tattoo Prince! Son! Do something!
Quiff Wicked!
Tattoo Princess?
Glitter Amazing!
Tattoo Oh, stop looking in the mirror!
Satchel I warned you!
Bruise Before long there was no garden left. The dragons . . . oh, they ate every single rose.

Child whispers in Bruise's ear.

Bruise And more?

Child points at Satchel.

Bruise They ate Wizard Satchel?
Quiff Bad luck, Satch.

Child points at Glitter.

Bruise And Princess Glitter.
Quiff Ha, ha.

Child points at Quiff.

Bruise And Prince Quiff.
Quiff I'm dead again.
Tattoo Me too?

Child shakes his head.

Bruise Not the King?

Child whispers in Bruise's ear.

Bruise The King lives on. He tells everyone the story. How he once had the most beautiful garden in the kingdom. And lost it. Because he wouldn't share a petal.

Old Woman And that's the end?

Child nods.

Old Woman Who's got the mirror?

Glitter holds up mirror.

Old Woman You know what to do.

Glitter puts mirror on fire.
Child points at Bruise.

Old Woman But . . . she's just told a story.

Child touches Bruise's earring.

Old Woman He wants your earring.

Bruise gives earring to Child.

Glitter Is that a real diamond?

Bruise Shouldn't think so.

Child takes earring to Tattoo.
He grabs Tattoo's hand and leads him to fire.
Everyone gathers round.
Slight pause.

The stories are gradually becoming more and more like pieces of theatre. Everyone moving around, miming actions. An ever more inventive use of objects in house as props. The use of fire and torches to increasing dramatic effect.

Tattoo There was once a . . . queen.

Bruise Queen Bruise.

Tattoo She lived with her son.

Quiff Prince Quiff.

Tattoo And they lived in a Castle. But this Castle . . . well, it was very special.

Glitter (*with Satchel*) How?

Satchel (*with Glitter*) How?

Tattoo It . . . it was made of gold . . . and diamond.

Holds up earring.

Glitter (*with Satchel*) Why?

Satchel (*with Glitter*) Why?

Bruise I made it that way.

Quiff What for?

Bruise For you, of course. When you were born – oh, I was so happy. I wanted to keep you with me for ever. Safe. So I created this Castle of Treasure. Look at it! A wonder of the kingdom.

Quiff *This* place?

Bruise Look again. Stained-glass windows.

Quiff That means I can't see outside.

Bruise Why would you want to?

Slight pause.

And the walls are decorated with gold leaf. Images of trees made of emeralds. Apples of rubies. You see? Across the ceiling a map of the heavens. A million diamonds make the stars. The moon is purest silver with craters of mother-of-pearl. The rising sun a swirling mix of gold and platinum. You see? And across the floor . . . a river made of crushed sapphires. The ripples are rarest crystal. See?

Quiff It's amazing.

Bruise Oh, let it amaze. Amaze so much you never want to leave. Look! Your clothes are silk and stitched together with hair from unicorns. And here – let me massage your temples with this perfume. It takes a million crushed roses to produce one drop.

Slight pause.

Happy?

Quiff Yeah.

Bruise And you'll always stay with me?

Quiff Yeah.

Slight pause.

What happened to Dad?

Bruise Wh–what?

Quiff The King. What happened to him?

Bruise I've told you a million times.

Quiff Tell me again. It's such a wicked story.

Slight pause.

Bruise A long time ago – before you were born – I wanted to go to the seaside.

Quiff That's the most beautiful place in Brokenville, ain't it?

Bruise And the most difficult to get to. But I heard it had the most precious blue coral in the whole kingdom.

Quiff So the King took you.

Bruise That was the plan, yes. But we didn't get very far.

Quiff What happened?

Bruise We got lost in the forest outside.

Quiff What's the forest like?

Bruise A terrible place.

Quiff Do the trees look like this? All emerald leaves and ruby apples?

Bruise Oh, no. Real trees are ugly. They don't shine at all. And for seven days and nights the King and me stumbled round these ugly, dull trees. No idea where we were going. The King got so hungry he picked mushrooms and ate them raw.

Quiff Didn't it make the King ill?

Bruise In a way. The next day he started hearing a voice.

Quiff What voice?

Bruise A woman's voice. Or so he said.

Quiff *You* couldn't hear it?

Bruise 'You're imagining things,' I told the King. 'I'm not,' said the King. 'The voice wants me to join her in her hut at the centre of the forest.' 'Then it's a witch,' I told him. 'Cover your ears!'

Quiff Did he?

Bruise 'Course not. The next day, I fainted with hunger and exhaustion. When I came round the King had gone. I searched and searched the forest. And then – quite by accident – I saw the Castle. What luck!

Quiff And the King was never found?

Bruise His body was. About a week later. Dead. Birds had pecked out his eyes.

Quiff And – don't tell me – you were pregnant.

Bruise It must've happened on that last night I was with the King. I thought, Well, I won't lose my child to the forest. So I transformed the Castle into this wonder. All the treasure in Brokenville went into its making. Just for you, my son.

Quiff Can I see it?

Bruise What?

Quiff The forest.

Bruise After all I've just said?

Quiff Just once?

Bruise No.

Tattoo But the Prince wanted to see the forest more than anything. He searched for gaps in the golden walls of the Castle.

Quiff None!

Tattoo In the stained-glass windows.

Quiff None!

Tattoo So he decided to make one.

Quiff picks up a spoon.

Tattoo He stole a platinum spoon from the dinner table. That night, when the rest of the castle was sleeping, he went to the stained-glass window and –

Quiff Break it!

Glitter You'll wake the Queen.

Old Woman You'll have to grind away the glass.

Quiff That'll take ages.

Tattoo For nine years the Prince grinds and grinds at a small area of glass – no bigger than a thumbprint – until a hole appears.

Quiff At last!

Tattoo He looks through it.

Quiff . . . Darkness.

Satchel You'll have to wait till morning.

Quiff Hang on! Something's crawling through the hole.

Glitter A spider!

Quiff Oh, it's wicked! Look at it go! There!

Bruise What's going on?

Quiff Nothing.

Bruise Don't lie to me – Ouch!

Quiff What's happened?

Satchel The spider bit her.

Glitter It's poisonous.

Bruise Who says?

Old Woman We all do.

Quiff You look ill.

Bruise I do?

Old Woman Best go to bed.

Quiff helps Bruise to bed.

Bruise Don't go to the forest.

Satchel The Queen's getting sicker by the second.

Bruise Don't go to the forest.

Glitter She's motionless.

Bruise Don't go to the –
Old Woman Frozen!

Bruise freezes.
Child claps.

Quiff Open the gates!

Takes a step through hole in wall.

I'm in the forest. It's wicked.
Tattoo He found a dead blackbird.
Quiff Wicked!
Glitter A twig.
Quiff Wicked!
Tattoo And he took all these wicked things back to the Castle.

Quiff comes back into building.

Quiff Look, everyone. The Queen said it was a terrible place outside. But it's not. Look. It's –
Glitter Wicked?
Quiff Full of treasure.

Slight pause.

I want a cloak made out of . . . dead birds.

Child claps.

Quiff A crown made out of . . . twigs.

Child claps more.

Quiff And I want . . . leaves in my hair. And my skin covered with dirt.

Child claps even more.
Old Woman joins in.

Old Woman Very good, very good.
Satchel (*with Glitter*) Yeah. Well done.

Glitter (*with Satchel*) Good stuff, yeah.

Slight pause.

Quiff The forest is a wonder of the kingdom. I'm gonna live in it for ever. I'm gonna eat squirrels and mushrooms. Drink rainwater. For the first time in my life I'm happy. Really happy.
Bruise Where's my son?
Tatttoo Then – to everyone's surprise – the Queen woke up.
Bruise I'm better now. Prince Quiff! Son!

Quiff approaches Bruise.

Satchel He wore a cloak of dead birds.
Glitter Crown of twigs.
Tattoo Dirt on his skin.
Bruise Noooooooooooo!

Child laughs.
Slight pause.

Tattoo That night the Queen went to –
Satchel Me again!
Bruise My son is –
Satchel Bonkers!
Bruise What can I do?
Satchel Whatever made him bonkers must be destroyed.
Bruise . . . The forest?
Satchel Bingo!
Bruise But how?
Satchel Up to you.

Child points at fire.

Bruise Burn it?

Child nods.

Old Woman (*at Bruise*) Do it!

Child takes burning stick from fire and gives it to Quiff.

Quiff Me?
Old Woman Ah, yes. Very good. You!
Quiff But why? I love the forest.
Old Woman Exactly!

Slight pause.

Quiff goes to window.

Quiff So long, forest.

Throws burning stick out of window.

Tattoo A tree catches fire.
Satchel Another!
Glitter Another!
Bruise Another!
Old Woman Another! Another!
Tattoo Until the whole forest is burning! Burning!

They relax as if the story's over.
But Child is restless.
He whispers in Tattoo's ear.

Tattoo The air's full of sparks.
Bruise So . . . what next?

Child rushes to Bruise and whispers in her ear.

Bruise The Castle is burning.
Quiff We can run away.

Child whispers in Quiff's ear.

Quiff My clothes are burning!

Child whispers in Bruise's ear.

Bruise Mine too!
Quiff (*with Bruise*) Help!

Bruise (*with Quiff*) Help!

Child whispers in Old Woman's ear.

Old Woman Your skin is burning.
Bruise (*with Quiff*) No!
Quiff (*with Bruise*) No!

Child is becoming hysterical now.
He is whimpering out loud.

Old Woman Shush! Calm down.

Old Woman holds Child.
Others cluster round Child.

Gradually, Child calms.
Long pause.

Old Woman (*at Child*) Is this your house?

Child nods.

Quiff What happened to your mum and dad?
Old Woman What happened to any of us? Can any of you remember? Anything? Eh?

Slight pause.

Just tell stories. That's all we can do in this place.

Child whispers in Old Woman's ear.

Old Woman You sure?

Child nods.

Old Woman He says . . . perhaps something's not burnt. In the last story. Not everything is destroyed.
Tattoo What?

Child whispers in Old Woman's ear.

Old Woman A leaf.

Bruise Just . . . a leaf?
Glitter And that's the end?
Old Woman No. It's the beginning.

Child takes earring from Tattoo and puts it on the fire.

Old Woman Next story, someone.

Glitter breathes into her hands.

Glitter A breath. How's that?

Child nods enthusiastically.

Old Woman Well, I can't wait for this one.
Glitter In the forest lives an ugly witch.

Everyone looks at Old Woman.

Old Woman Typical.

Quiff laughs.

Glitter And this ugly witch fell in love with a prince.

Quiff stops laughing.

Glitter Every day the Witch goes to the Prince and says –
Old Woman I've got a beautiful little hut in the middle of the forest. You'd like it if you gave it a chance. I'll cook you my speciality. Squirrel and mushroom pie. Come on. Kiss me! Kiss me! Kiss me!

Approaches Quiff.

Quiff squeals and runs.

Others laugh.

Quiff Shut it, you lot.
Glitter The Prince goes to King Tattoo and tells him about the Witch.
Quiff She's rampant.

Tattoo Oh, I remember her from years ago. In those days she used to live here.
Quiff In the Castle?
Tattoo She used to do magic to entertain us.
Quiff What happened?
Tattoo One day the land was invaded. I begged the Witch to help. Asked her to make . . . a powerful weapon.
Quiff What did she say?
Old Woman I'm a good witch. My magic must not be used to hurt.
Quiff Did the enemy have powerful weapons?
Tattoo They could destroy a whole village.

Snaps fingers.

Like that!
Quiff But surely . . . once the Witch saw all that she must've changed her mind.
Old Woman I'm a good witch. My magic must not be used to hurt.
Quiff So the war dragged on?
Tattoo For years and years.
Quiff We won though?
Tattoo Eventually, yeah. But . . . oh, so many wars and battles. Piles of bodies everywhere. People torn apart.
Quiff Hope you taught the Witch a lesson.
Tattoo I banished her.
Quiff That all?
Tattoo What else could I do? (*at Old Woman*) You'll stay in the forest from now on.

Slight pause.

Quiff Go on!
Tattoo Go on!

Old Woman moves further away.

Quiff And stay there, you old bag.
Old Woman Don't you dare call me that.

Slight pause.

You know I love you, gorgeous Quiffy. Come here.

Slight pause.

Please.

Quiff joins Old Woman.

Old Woman I can't sleep for thinking about you. You haunt me, you sexy beast. Your eyes are so . . . oh, look at them. I would kill for lashes like that. Please . . . let me touch your wicked skin with my finger.
Quiff No way.
Old Woman Then . . . oh, I've got it! Yes! Let me hold my hand in front of your lips and feel your breath.

Old Woman looks at Glitter.
Glitter smiles and nods.

Quiff Not even a breath! No!
Glitter And then, one day, the land is invaded again . . .
Tattoo Prince! Son! Hear that?
Quiff Invasion!
Tattoo Explosions! Bombs! Sounds like the enemy has even bigger weapons this time.
Quiff Villages gone –

Snaps fingers.

Like that!
Tattoo Cities too.
Quiff What can we do?
Tattoo No idea.

Slight pause.

Quiff Got it!

Goes to Old Woman.

Listen, Witchy, if I let you hold your hand in front of my mouth like you wanted . . . will you make me a really powerful weapon?

Old Woman I'm a good witch. My magic must not be used to hurt.

Quiff turns to leave.

Old Woman Wait! Let me feel!

Quiff And I'll get a weapon?

Old Woman Oh, yes.

Feels Quiff's breath and lets out an ecstatic cry.

Glitter And so . . . the Witch made the weapon.

Quiff Big explosion! Fire! Ash falling like snow!

Tattoo Millions of their people are dead.

Quiff Wicked!

Tattoo But they keep on fighting.

Quiff How come?

Tattoo Their weapons are even more powerful. What can we do?

Slight pause.

Quiff goes to Old Woman.

Quiff Hey! Witchy! If I let you . . . touch my quiff, will you make me a more powerful weapon?

Old Woman I'm a good witch. My magic must not be –

Quiff turns to leave.

Old Woman No! Wait! I'll do it! Just . . . oh, let me touch that wicked quiff.

Quiff Don't mess it though.

Old Woman strokes hair and lets out an ecstatic cry.

Glitter The weapon is made.
Quiff King! Dad! Look! Explosions like you've never seen. Boom! Whole areas of ground where nothing will grow for zillions of years.
Tattoo Very impressive.
Glitter But the enemies' weapons are still stronger.
Quiff No way.
Tattoo 'Fraid so . . . What can we do? Any ideas?
Quiff . . . Bloody hell!

Goes to Old Woman.

If I let you touch my finger –
Old Woman Deal!

Grabs Quiff's finger.

Tattoo Victory!
Quiff It's . . . it's not the end yet.
Satchel It's not?
Quiff I've got an idea.
Glitter Blimey.
Tattoo Spill the beans.
Quiff Why don't I go back to the Witch . . . and ask her to make The Most Powerful Weapon of All?
Tattoo The Most Powerful Weapon of All?
Quiff No one will ever invade us again. They wouldn't dare. A weapon to end all wars.
Tattoo Good idea. But . . . will she do it?
Quiff She's under my spell. She won't be able to say no.

Quiff goes to Old Woman.

Old Woman I'm surprised to see you again.
Quiff If I let you feel my skin, will you make me The Most Powerful Weapon of All?
Old Woman The Most Powerful Weapon of All? For feeling your skin? I can't. The price is too high.

Turns to leave.

Quiff Wait! I'll let you touch me anywhere.
Old Woman Anywhere?

Slight pause.

No. I can't.

Turns to leave.

Quiff I'll let you . . . hold me in your arms.

Slight pause.

I'll let you . . . kiss me.

Slight pause.

With tongues.
Old Woman . . . No. I can't.

Turns to leave.

Quiff I'll take my clothes off. Show you all my muscles. I'll stay the night with you in your hut. And you can do anything you like to me.
Old Woman Anything?
Quiff Anything.
Old Woman Get in that hut!

Slight pause.

Glitter In the morning . . . the Witch had changed. She was no longer old and ugly.
Quiff You're gorgeous too.
Old Woman (*with Glitter*) I know.
Glitter (*with Old Woman*) I know.

Old Woman looks at Glitter, smiles and nods.

Glitter The way I used to look – that was a curse. All I needed was for someone to . . . love me.

Quiff I . . . I still need The Most Powerful Weapon of All, you know.

Glitter Of course. But . . . well, making it will take a little time. And be a bit painful. For me. So . . . until it's made you've got to stay with me in the forest. Deal?

Quiff Deal.

Glitter holds hand out to Quiff.
Slowly – oh, so slowly – he takes it.
They begin strolling around.

Glitter Fancy something to eat?

Quiff Mushroom pie?

Glitter With squirrel.

Quiff Not hungry.

Slight pause.

Glitter I like your hair.

Quiff Really?

Glitter Suits you.

Quiff Thanks. I . . . I like yours too.

Glitter Really?

Quiff And your eyes.

Glitter My eyes.

Quiff They're . . . shiny. And – look! I can see me in them.

Quiff and Glitter are face to face now, very close.
Perhaps they might kiss.
Slight pause.
Then –

Glitter Ouch!

Quiff What's wrong?

Glitter A pain.

Quiff Where?

Glitter Belly.

Quiff What can I do?
Glitter Help me lie down.

Quiff helps Glitter to the ground.

Quiff Help! Someone!
Glitter Don't worry. It's only – Ahhh!
Quiff Anyone!
Glitter Look between my legs.
Quiff Do what?

Child rushes to Quiff and whispers in his ear.

Quiff A baby!
Glitter A boy.
Quiff My son.
Glitter Take him to the river.
Quiff He can't swim yet.
Glitter To *wash* him.
Quiff Oh, yeah. Right.

Goes to puddle.

Get you good and clean, little baby.

Slowly, as Quiff bathes imaginary baby, something changes in him.
He calms, becomes thoughtful.
Pause.

Glitter What's wrong?
Quiff Oh . . . nothing.
Glitter Look at his little fingers.
Quiff . . . They're wicked.
Glitter And look! A birthmark on his leg.
Bruise Don't let anyone hurt him.
Quiff I won't.
Glitter Cross your heart?
Quiff Cross my heart.
Bruise And hope to die?

Quiff . . . Yeah.
Bruise Say it.

Slight pause.

Old Woman Say it.
Quiff Hope to die.
Glitter Now take it to the King – this baby.
Bruise Your child.
Old Woman And tell him – at last – we have made it.
Quiff What?
Glitter (*with Old Woman*) The Most Powerful Weapon of All.
Old Woman (*with Glitter*) The Most Powerful Weapon of All.

Child claps with delight and lifts a shell into the air.

Satchel A shell!
Old Woman (*at Quiff*) Quickly!
Quiff A Prince!
Glitter Princes!

There should be a natural fluidity and exhilarating speed to the storytelling now. Movement, use of found objects, torchlight, fire – everything used to create image after image. The evolution from static narration to full-blown theatre is now complete.

Glitter Look at my hair. My sparkly eyes. I'm gorgeous.
Quiff Looks ain't everything.
Glitter Fancy a snog, Prince?
Quiff . . . No.
Glitter Liar!

Approaches Quiff.

Come on! You know you want to.

Slowly, Quiff leans forward.
Just as he's about to kiss Glitter –

Glitter Hang on! We're brother and sister.
Quiff Brother and sist –? Oh, don't play games.
Glitter Like you, you mean.
Quiff I've grown up now.
Glitter Ha!
Quiff Have!
Bruise Don't let her wind you up, son.
Quiff She thinks I'm just a joke.
Bruise Your sister thinks everyone's a joke.
Tattoo Including me.
Bruise She's got you wrapped round her little finger.
Tattoo She's just a tease.
Quiff With *you*?
Tattoo Ain't ya noticed?
Quiff But . . . you're the King. Her dad!
Bruise She's after the Kingdom.
Tattoo Oh, I don't think it's that.
Bruise 'Course it is. Don't be a fool.
Tattoo But he's the Prince. The Kingdom will be his. How can she get the Kingdom by flirting with me?
Bruise Oh, I don't know. My head's spinning. I need an aspirin.
Quiff I'll go down to the beach and find you a shell.
Bruise A shell?
Quiff For your collection.
Bruise Collection? My shell collection! Yes! Thank you. See you later.

Quiff searches near puddle.
Glitter approaches and watches him.

Glitter What you up to?
Quiff Looking for a shell for the Queen.

Holds up shell.

Think she'll like this?
Glitter Who cares?

Quiff points.

Quiff Look!
Glitter . . . What?
Quiff A whale!
Glitter Boring.
Quiff It's not.
Glitter Tell me one interesting thing about a whale.
Quiff . . . Wizard Satchel knows something.
Satchel I do?
Glitter I'm waiting.

Child whispers in Satchel's ear.

Satchel Right! How the first whale was made! OK. Ready?
All (*except Child*) Ready!
Satchel A long time ago there were lots and lots of wizards. In fact, you couldn't throw a lobster without hitting one. Anyway . . . one day, just to pass the time, all these wizards got together and decided to have a game. A sort of contest. To see who could change themselves into the most spectacular creature. Lots and lots of creatures were created that day.
Quiff Like what?
Satchel Creatures with two beaks and a hundred legs. Creatures with . . . horns that glowed in the dark. There was even a giant flying sea horse.
Quiff Where're they now?
Satchel Don't exist.
Quiff Why?
Satchel As soon as a wizard turned himself into one of these remarkable creatures he turned himself back again.
Quiff Why?
Satchel He might forget what it was like being a wizard.
Quiff Wicked!

Satchel One day, a wizard turned himself into a very big creature that swam in the sea.

Quiff A whale!

Satchel All the other wizards cheered and clapped. They'd never seen such a remarkable creature. A few of them got carried away and turned themselves into whales too. They swam and splashed in the sea. Dived down to shipwrecks. Then swam up, faster and faster, until – wooosh! They shot out of the ocean. Then crashed back down – splasshhh! – sending waves all over the place. They enjoyed themselves so much they forgot how to change themselves back into wizards. And then . . . well, they forgot they'd ever been wizards at all.

Quiff What a wicked story. I'm gonna skim stones.

Glitter What?

Quiff Skim stones across the ocean. Look! Watch this one bounce! One! Two! Three! Four! Nearly reached that bit of blue coral. It's so beautiful and . . . pure. That's my ambition, you know. To reach blue coral.

Glitter You really have changed.

Walks away.

Quiff Don't go.

Glitter Hear the Prince, Dad?

Tattoo What's wrong with him?

Glitter Wants to kiss me?

Tattoo He's an affectionate brother.

Glitter He don't want that sort of kiss.

Tattoo What you getting at?

Glitter Oh, not now, Dad. Running away from the Prince has knackered me out.

Tattoo Running away?

Glitter Going to my room.

Sits on bed.

Quiff and Glitter look at each other.
Slight pause.

Glitter Did you hit it?
Quiff What?
Glitter Blue coral.
Quiff Nah.
Glitter Keep trying.

Slight pause.

Quiff You look down in the dumps.
Glitter . . . Yeah.

Quiff sits next to Glitter.
Slight pause.

Quiff What's up?
Glitter It's . . . oh, I dunno how to say.
Quiff Try.
Glitter Well . . . it's just that sometimes I feel like I'm the wrong character in the right story.
Quiff And sometimes the right character in the wrong story. But never –
Glitter (*with Quiff*) The right character in the right story.
Quiff (*with Glitter*) The right character in the right story.

They lean close to each other.

Glitter Perhaps . . . we just have to be ourselves.
Quiff Whatever the story is.
Glitter Whoever we are.

They lean closer.
Closer . . .
Then –

Tattoo You're brother and sister, don't forget.

Glitter He . . . he forced his way into my bedroom.
Quiff No way!
Glitter Liar!
Tattoo I've had enough of you pestering your sister.
Quiff Pestering!
Glitter Banish him!
Tattoo Too right!
Glitter Go on, then.
Tattoo You're banished!
Quiff Mum!
Bruise What's going on?
Glitter The King's banished the Prince.
Bruise He can't do that.
Tattoo Done it!
Glitter If you don't like it, he'll banish you too.
Bruise Wouldn't dare.
Glitter Dad?
Tattoo You're banished!
Bruise Goodbye, then.
Glitter Goodbye.
Quiff Goodbye.
Glitter Goodbye.

Bruise and Quiff walk a bit further away.

Glitter Keep going.

Bruise and Quiff walk outside the building.

Glitter Help me put this sharktooth necklace on, Dad.

Picks up piece of string and hands it to Tattoo. Tattoo ties it round her neck.

Glitter How'd I look?
Tattoo Very tasty.
Bruise You're her dad, don't forget.
Glitter Can I have all Mum's jewellery?
Tattoo Sure.

Glitter And my brother's weapons?
Tattoo Anything you want.
Glitter Anything?
Tattoo Anything.
Glitter The sun.
Tattoo Eh?
Glitter Well, just a piece of it. I'm not greedy. A sunbeam. Get me one.
Tattoo And how am I supposed to do that?
Glitter Ask the Wizard.

Tattoo approaches Satchel.

Satchel So you wanna catch a –
Tattoo Ain't told you yet!
Satchel I'm a wizard, dickhead!

Slight pause.

I'll make you a giant flying seahorse.
Tattoo I don't wanna bloody –
Satchel You can ride this giant flying sea horse up to the sky. Catch a sunbeam. Then give it to the Prince.
Tattoo It's for the Princess.
Satchel Then no way.
Tattoo What d'you mean?
Satchel The Princess finds my stories boring. I wouldn't piddle on her if she was burning.
Tattoo You're banished.
Satchel Goodbye.
Tattoo Goodbye.

Slight pause.

I'll . . . I'll get someone else to help me – You're a witch, ain't ya?
Old Woman Thought everyone had forgotten about me.
Tattoo I need a giant flying sea horse.
Old Woman Why?

Tattoo You're a witch, you should know.

Old Woman You're right. Forget it!

Tattoo Make it or I'll have you . . . fed to piranhas.

Old Woman All right. But be careful. Catching a sunbeam is dangerous. Better men than you have been burnt to a crisp.

Tattoo Just make it.

Old Woman It's behind you.

Tattoo . . . Where?

Old Woman There!

Tattoo Where?

Old Woman Giant flying sea horses are invisible.

Tattoo Princess Glitter. I'm ready to catch the sunbeam.

Glitter Get a move on, then.

Tattoo A kiss before I go?

Glitter A kiss when you get back.

Slight pause.

Tattoo I'm sitting on the sea horse now.

Glitter Chop-chop!

Tattoo is unsure what to do.
Slight pause.

Glitter Ain't got all day, you know.

Tattoo is still unsure what to do.
Slight pause.

Suddenly, Child has an idea.
He runs round the house searching for something.
Finally, in an old cardboard box, he finds a mirrorball.
Light refracts everywhere.

Tattoo Sunbeam!

Tattoo starts chasing Child.

Child is laughing, enjoying every moment of it.
Others laugh and cheer.
Much joy and play.

Finally, Child is cornered.
Tattoo takes mirrorball from Child.

Tattoo Gotchya!

Takes mirrorball to Glitter.

Glitter Amazing!
Tattoo Kiss?
Glitter Later! I want to put my sunbeam in this shell.

Picks up shell.

My glowing crown!

Tattoo clutches his chest.

Tattoo Aaahhh! My heart!
Glitter Look at me wearing my crown.
Tattoo Ain't anyone gonna help me?
Old Woman You banished them all.
Tattoo (*at Old Woman*) Well, *you* ain't!

Old Woman helps Tattoo over to bed.

Old Woman Told you that sunbeam was a bad idea.
Tattoo That ain't *exactly* what you said.
Old Woman Don't split hairs.
Tattoo Is the Princess happy?
Old Woman Delirious.
Tattoo That's all that matters.

Settles on bed.

Old Woman Comfortable?
Tattoo Not really, no.
Old Woman Well, I can't help that.
Tattoo I don't want to die.

Old Woman Can't help that either.
Tattoo I want . . . a kiss.

Old Woman bends towards Tattoo.

Tattoo Not you! The Princess!
Old Woman Oi! Princess!
Glitter What?
Old Woman Fancy kissing the King?
Glitter Nah.
Old Woman Might save him.
Glitter I'm busy.
Old Woman Doing what?
Glitter Wearing the crown. Everyone falls to their knees when they see me.
Old Woman That's the sunbeam. Not you.
Glitter Shut up. Or I'll have you fed –
Old Woman Fed to piranhas, I know, I know. (*at Tattoo*) She won't come.
Tattoo I only want a bloody kiss.
Old Woman You're looking sicker by the second, I'm afraid.
Tattoo One bloody kiss.
Old Woman The King is dead.
Glitter Long live the Queen!
Others Long live the Queen!
Glitter OK. We've got to bury the poor old King. Let's do it at sea. Could do with a boat trip.

Gently sways from side to side.

Gradually, others join in.

Slight pause.

Glitter Look! A whale!
Satchel It's me! Wizard Satchel! I've changed myself into a whale. Splash, splash!
Old Woman Look! The water's put out your sunbeam.

Glitter My crown.
Old Woman Now everyone can see you for what you are.

Old Woman and Satchel close in on Glitter.
Others (except Child) join in.

Glitter No . . . no . . .

Backs away
Others get closer.
Closer . . .
Closer . . .
Then just as Glitter is about to scream –

Child Stop!

They all look at Child.
Slight pause.

Old Woman Stop?
Child The story can't end like this.
Old Woman Finish it for us, then.

Slight pause.

Child The whale . . . it splashes the boat.
Old Woman OK.
Child The shell – it rolls everywhere!
Satchel Good.
Child The Princess chases after it.

Slight pause.

Go on, then.
Glitter Do I catch it?
Child You fall overboard.
Glitter I drown?
Child No. The whale swallows you up.
Satchel Splash, splash.
Glitter I'm eaten?
Child No. Alive in its belly.

Glitter I'm in a whale's belly!
Child You'd be more scared than that.
Glitter I'm gonna die!
Child Are you sorry for what you did to the Prince?
Glitter Yes.
Child And for what you did to the Queen?
Glitter Yes.
Child So they ain't banished any more?
Glitter No.
Child (*at Quiff and Bruise*) Come back, you two.

Quiff and Bruise approach.

Child Now, all I need is a feather.
Old Woman Why?
Child To tickle the whale's nose.
Satchel I'm gonna sneeze.
Child Sneeze out the Princess.
Satchel Ah-tishoo!
Glitter I'm alive!
Child Now kiss the King!

Slight pause.

He ain't thrown overboard yet, is he?
Old Woman No, no.
Child Then give him that bloody kiss.

Glitter kisses Tattoo.
Tattoo sits up.

Tattoo I'm alive!
Glitter Oh, forgive me. Everyone. Please. Forgive.

Pause.

Child Last story, everyone.

Child sits by fire.
Others gather round him.

Child There was once a child – Me! He was very scared. And he met some people. And they told him stories about –

Old Woman Witches.

Satchel Wizards.

Bruise Queens.

Tattoo Kings.

Quiff Princes.

Glitter Princesses.

Child And now . . . I'm not so scared any more.

Blackout.

Putting Marks on the Blackboard of Memory

Philip Ridley interviewed by Jim Mulligan

Philip Ridley's play for *Connections 1997*, *Sparkleshark*, was a huge success. It was subsequently staged professionally at the National Theatre and taken on a major tour of the UK. The play has been in constant production somewhere in the world ever since.

> *Sparkleshark* is a bit of a phenomenon. It just touched a fuse-paper and flared into a life of its own. Everyone who has done the play tells me that it is a very empowering experience. It gives young people a new way of talking about their lives no matter who they are or where they come from.

Brokenville is the third part of a storytelling trilogy. *Fairytaleheart*, the first in the sequence, is about two people – a boy and a girl – who use the language of fairy tales to make tentative and flirtatious contact with each other. Then comes *Sparkleshark* with a group of young people exorcising their fears – about growing up, sexuality, responsibility, love and bullying – by speaking in the roles of prince, princess, king or wizard. This fairy-tale language is anything but twee or sentimental. It is hard-edged and streetwise, a way for young people to score points off each other and confess intimate feelings. *Brokenville*, however takes these themes and pushes them into a broader, somehow more global context. There is something breathtakingly epic about these stories.

The action takes place in a ruined, house. A young boy – only ever referred to as Child – is joined by six characters, all of them suffering collective amnesia. Everything about them is deeply buried, even their word-finding power. One of the most moving elements of the play is to see these people move from inarticulacy to oratory, from stilted narration to fully fledged drama, from isolation to community.

> We are only what our memories tell us we are. The characters' memories are like a blackboard that has been wiped clean. As they go on their journey through the play they start putting marks back on the blackboard by telling stories which touch on half-remembered things about who they are, what they might have been and felt and what might have happened.

Philip Ridley believes story-telling is the way we make sense of the world. It is what children like to hear before they go to sleep at night, what parents instinctively do for their children.

> *Brokenville* has changed significantly since I started the project five or six years ago. It started to come together in its present form soon after the war in Bosnia and everyone saw it as a child in a bombed-out Bosnian village. Since 9/11, however, people are seeing it in terms of a terrorist attack. It could just as easily be a natural disaster. It is up to every production to interpret the 'what has gone before' in its own way. This is part of the joy of the piece. It's not about a specific thing. It's about a universal truth. It's about what makes us human, what makes us humane.

One of the things the play does is to link the personal with the global. It shows how our actions have consequences. The old saying that 'no man is an island' is aptly demonstrated. Whatever one character does or says affects the whole group. We are all responsible for each other.

> As the people in the play act out their stories we see, for example, mass starvation caused by a prince not

wanting to look old. A whole kingdom is burnt to the ground because a queen wants to keep her son all to herself. Individual actions have a knock-on, domino effect. At first the Child encourages and relishes this destruction and carnage. He refuses to allow happy endings to the stories being told.

Central to *Brokenville* is the way the characters learn and discover their language (and thus their identities) through telling stories. There is one electrifying moment when Queen Bruise lets loose a shell-burst of poetry.

And the walls are decorated with gold leaf. Images of trees made of emeralds. Apples of rubies. You see? Across the ceiling a map of the heavens. A million diamonds make the stars. The moon is purest silver with craters of mother-of-pearl. The rising sun a swirling mix of gold and platinum. You see? And across the floor . . . a river made of crushed sapphires. The ripples are rarest crystal. See?

And this from the woman who at the start of the play has difficulty remembering the word 'lullaby'. By the end, though, such poetry has awoken the humane in all the characters. The Child takes control and restores broken relationships. He is willing at long last to allow a happy ending, willing to acknowledge a future.

The play is about one moment of grace. Everything outside the room is the same as it was when they went in, and even though Child might be less afraid at the end, they still have to go out of the building into the devastated world. The question is: what happens then? Do they revert to what they were or do they use some of the humanity they have discovered?

Brokenville is a concept play and Philip Ridley is confident young people can cope with the ideas because they understand the power of stories. He is optimistic about the power of young people to understand a world of poetry and magic and wondrous coincidence.

> I believe we are all poets. It's in our DNA. I've heard incredible things from young people. Breathtaking things. Images and words of purest magic. And this is what art does, what *Brokenville* tries to do. It prepares us for the perception of magic. We leave the theatre . . . and the world is transformed.

Production Notes

STAGING AND SETTING

Brokenville is set in the ruins of a house after a nameless catastrophe. There's no ceiling, the walls are nearly demolished, windows are smashed, there's a stairway, several piles of rubbish and a big puddle. Signs of family life are everywhere: framed photographs, toys, etc. There's also a bed, table and chairs.

The use of found objects should become ever more inventive and surprising. Some things are mentioned (the table leg as a sword, a mirrorball as a sunbeam) but the possibilities are endless.

Lighting effects include moonlight, and each character carries a torch. You'll need to produce a fire effect on stage.

CASTING

The names of the characters give visual clues to their appearance. There are seven roles, with five in their mid-teens: Satchel (m), Glitter (f), Quiff (m), Bruise (f) and Tattoo (m). The Child (who is written as male but could be female) should be younger than the others. The woman, who's around 80, needs to have an old soul, confidence and wisdom. The trick is to play her attitude rather than her age.

RESEARCH

Brokenville is the third play of a trilogy. The other works are *Fairytaleheart* and *Sparkleshark* (available in *Two*

Plays for Young People by Philip Ridley (Faber & Faber). All the plays deal with the redemptive power of story-telling. Look at all three plays and discover the reasons why the characters tell stories in the first place. Do they begin reluctantly and become more enthusiastic? Ask why the characters have been compelled to join in and whether they've been bullied or cajoled.

In *Brokenville* the dramatic engine that forces the group into story-telling is the Child. He is the one who stops the stories from having happy endings because his experience tells him otherwise. His relationship with the Old Woman is the catalyst for the drama of the play. Without the Child and the Old Woman nothing would happen. We need to see how the Child's rising hysteria, his whimpering and fear, and the Old Woman's forcing the others into calming him is what motivates each story. Never lose sight of the fact that, although a trauma has occurred, the characters in the play cannot remember it (except possibly the Child). Track how, gradually, the Child is led from his first spine-tingling utterance to the point where he can allow a happy ending.

Decide what the catastrophe was that ruined the house and made the Child hysterical. Why are there references to lost babies, piles of cut hair, or fear of being attacked by things from the sky? Scour the text to find moments that fit your decision.

As the play develops and the stories emerge, the characters stumble on fragments of memory or insights into their 'real' selves. For example, Bruise, as the Queen having a baby in the story, discovers its significance for herself when she announces: 'I know I'm young. But I'm going to be the best mum in the world. It's my body, my choice.' This is the real Bruise speaking, not the Queen in the play, and we glimpse fragments, flashes of what her life might have been like before, echoes of what makes her 'Queen character' the kind of queen she is.

Break down the way the stories develop. For example:

- A character finds an object.
- The child indicates that he wants a story.
- They tell the story.
- The object is put in the fire.

As soon as the ritual is established it is changed. Never let the audience get ahead of the play. Keep it moving. It must not feel repetitious. Discover how each story can move on a gear and have its own distinctive feel.

For contrast, the play has a static beginning, but as the characters get into the story-telling it becomes more theatrical. They get up, move about, start improvising in character, miming things, exhilarated by their own and others' invention. Look at how the characters learn how to use the stories to score points; how they find a way of saying things to each other that they would never otherwise dare say. You'll find some of these things have a nasty edge to them – there's sarcasm, especially at the beginning; but as the play progresses, real warmth appears, and they start to talk about friendship, affection and love.

EXERCISES

A good first session would be to listen to a piece of jazz together. Hear the different 'voices'. This is what is going on in the play. No one knows where the stories are going or how they will fit in. In a jazz group – particularly free, improvised jazz – everyone has to listen to the other instruments in order to develop the themes and appreciate each others' invention. In *Brokenville* characters may stop speaking, but they never stop playing.

Work out how objects in the house (apart from the ones used to start each story) are used as ever more inventive props for the stories being enacted. Every member of the company should throw ideas in. For example, an actor could say, 'If only I had an umbrella for this point it could be used as a ——— .' Well, get an umbrella and use it. It's a ruined house, almost anything, within reason, could be there.

Have each member of the cast find an everyday object. Have them pass the objects round the circle one at a time. Each person should change the object into something else – for example, the umbrella might become a child's humming top. Don't move on until everyone recognises what the 'new' object is.

Place an object in the middle of the room. Have the cast decide what it might be. For example, a small milk carton might become the head of a man buried in the sand, or a top hat, or a switch, etc. Encourage the group to enjoy a sense of collective invention.

Look at the description of the house. Decide what's in the pile of things. Why is the bed in the room? Has it fallen through the ceiling ? Did the family sleep in the same place? We know by the end of the play that this is the Child's house. Create his back history with help from the objects lying around; decide what's in the photographs. Create a back history for the other characters, improvise the defining moments that gave them their names and how they came to be in the ruined house.

Suzy Graham-Adriani
March 2003
based on a workshop facilitated by Lawrence Till

THE CROSSING PATH

Maya Chowdhry

Maya Chowdhry is an award-winning playwright and poet, an inTer-aCt-ive artist, and believes in writing from 'under the skin'. A winner of the BBC Radio Young Playwrights and the Cardiff International Poetry Competition, as well as having her play *Kaahini* nominated for Best Children's Theatre by the Writers' Guild, her plays include *Seeing*, workshopped at the Royal Court Theatre, and *An Appetite for Living*, at the West Yorkshire Playhouse. Maya is currently under commission by the National Theatre Studio and BBC Radio Drama, Glasgow.

Characters

Rhiannon Foy – the Fool
seventeen, a traveller

Gregory Rafferty – the Devil
nineteen, grew up in a wealthy family

Stella – the Star (female)
eighteen, Kendra's friend

Kendra – the Magician (female)
eighteen, Stella's friend

Hina – the High Priestess (female)

Freya – the Empress (female)

Alisha – the Sage (female)

Jiro – the Emperor (male)

Monisha – the Crone (female)

Nori – the Hanged One (female)

Tivona – the Lover (female)

Hubert – the Charioteer (male)

Oscar – the Strong One (male)

Zada – the Fortuneer (female*)

Euridice – Justice (female*)

Renee – the Reborn (female / male)

Levia – the Alchemist (female*)

Fordon – the Tower Dweller (male*)

Cindy – the Moon (female*)

Kira – the Sun (female*)

Elvira – the Judge (female*)

Ye Shen - the Universe (male*)

*it is possible to change the gender of these characters if required by the company.

Script Conventions

/ Indicates an interruption at this point in the dialogue by another character

. . . indicates that the character doesn't finish their line of dialogue

brackets ( ) are used to indicate dialogue that is not spoken due to the character either being interrupted or not finishing their dialogue

SCENE ONE

Music (Ascension, 'Someone', Paul Oakenfold – Tranceport 1): 'Sometimes I wonder if my dreams are wild, sometimes I know they'll all come true. I need somebody who can move my world . . .'

Noon. A young woman: Rhiannon (seventeen, wearing a short violet dress and red boots, carrying a purple bag, hair in long plaits – feather in her hair) stands in front of the railway tracks. She looks first in one direction and then the other.

Rhiannon I can't decide.

Rhiannon takes a pack of Tarot cards from her pocket and cradles them in her hands. She looks down, shuffles them through her fingers, draws one card and holds it up in the air, facing it away from her.

If it's the Fool Card I'll know what to do. (*Rhiannon turns the card to face her.*) A young person hovers over the edge of a cliff; they appear to be flying, arms outstretched towards the noon sun. In the distance a bird glides towards the plains. Numerous paths stretch out in different directions. (*Rhiannon puts the card into her pocket, looks in both directions and climbs across the railway tracks.*) A youthful journey. Stepping onto the path with no fear for the future.

Thunder rolls and the sky lights up: silver to black, silver to black.

The sky dreaming, watching me go.

Rain pelts down. Rhiannon runs along the railway lines and into the near distance.

SCENE TWO

Rhiannon rushes into the train carriage; she's soaked. She takes off her coat and tries to dry her hair with it. She rummages in her bag, makes a roly; lights it and inhales deeply. She squints as she stares at the fuzzed countryside through the window of the moving train.

Rhiannon Where am I going?

Gregory (nineteen, wearing indigo twisted Levi jeans, trainers and a gold designer shirt) flies through the carriage holding his mobile phone to his ear.

Gregory (*to Rhiannon*) Wake up, wake up, wake up!

Rhiannon ignores Gregory, takes out her Tarot cards and shuffles them; she fans them out on the seat and closes her eyes. Gregory reaches out a hand to shake with.

And smell, smell, smell.

Kendra (holding a glittery wand) and Stella (holding a silver vacuum flask) sit down opposite Rhiannon. Rhiannon opens her eyes but continues to stare at the cards.

Gregory A spell, spell, spell?
Kendra And dance, dance, dance!
Stella (*to Kendra*) Yeah, if we ever come up we will.
Gregory (*into phone and to Kendra*) Yeah? You going clubbing? Me too? Where? Good. Yeah.

Kendra leans round Gregory and holds out a light for Rhiannon's roly.

Gregory Come on, baby . . . (*light my fire*).
Kendra Who's your friend?
Rhiannon (*takes a drag*) No friend of mine.

Gregory I'm Gregory. Speak to me, here – (*Tries to pass phone to Rhiannon, who blows smoke in his face.*) She's not having any of it. / What? I'm on the train, place is full of losers. (*Pause.*) I've already left the coast.
Kendra What a total arse!

Rhiannon focuses on her Tarot cards.

Rhiannon Ignoring him's the best bet. Where you off to?
Stella Clubbing. What about you?
Gregory (*into phone*) There's girls, wanna speak to them, go on.

Rhiannon chooses a Tarot card and lays it in a Celtic Cross spread; she turns the card over.

Rhiannon (*to herself*) The Fool, the heart of the matter. (*to Stella*) I'm . . . I've . . . I'm going on the anti-globalisation demo. I've got this interview as well . . . for a college in London.
Stella Cool. We're at Southampton.
Rhiannon (*they shake hands*) I'm Rhiannon, have we met?
Kendra (*shakes head: no*) Kendra.
Rhiannon (*to Kendra*) The wand's cool.
Stella She's a bit of a magician. You read the Tarot cards?
Rhiannon My own.
Stella You a traveller?
Rhiannon Is it that obvious?
Stella No, just wondering.

Gregory pushes through them and tries to put the phone to Stella's ear.

Gregory Say hi.
Stella (*she brushes him off*) Get off, idiot!

Rhiannon chooses another Tarot card and lays it in the spread.

Rhiannon (*to herself*) That which crosses you.

The train stops abruptly; they lurch forward, Gregory falls onto Rhiannon's cards.

You're really bugging me.

Rhiannon pushes Gregory off and he falls onto the floor.

Kendra Who's steering the ship!

Rhiannon turns over the Tarot card.

Rhiannon The Collective Unconscious.

The carriage doors are opened and groups of young people, dressed up for a night out, flood in.

Kendra (*waves wand*) Yea, party in the house!

Gregory gets up and pushes through the crowd into the end of the carriage, grabbing some devil finger-puppets off Fordon (holding a laser light) as he goes.

Hubert (wearing a helmet and pads) flies into the carriage on his 'switchboard'. Jiro (holding a silver flight-case) and Nori (holding a climbing rope and crampon) saunter in and sit at one end of the carriage.

Levia dances (holding an MP3 player – pumping out dance music: 'Castles in the Sky'). Levia raves to the music, Kendra gets up and dances with her, pumping the air with her fist; Stella dances round her.

Glowsticks and laser lights flash and swirl, illuminating the journey. Rhiannon continues to draw her Tarot cards and lay them out; she's obscured by everyone – the music blasts out, their dance surrounds her.

Singers (*sing along with club track*)
You can set yourself free
If you dance with me

If you can see
A way to be.

Renee (wearing a white mask) raves with Oscar (leaning on a metal crutch). Cindy (wearing a bag in the shape of a crescent moon) looks for a seat. Hina (wearing an ankh around her neck) stands on the seat next to her.

Hina (*sings along with club track*)
Life circles life
Opens up a place in leaving
Hasn't got a place for grieving
Lift yourself beyond death
Carry love onto the path.

Zada puts down a bicycle wheel and sits down with Ye Shen (who holds a metallic balloon) and Tivona (holding a make-up mirror).

Singers (*sing along with 'Castles in the Sky' club track*)
You can set yourself free
If you dance with me
If you can see
A way to be.

Alisha (holding a philosophy book) spins around Elvira (wearing a bugle around her neck). Euridice puts down her dumb-bell set and dances with Freya (holding a small bottle of spring water).

Freya (*sings along with club track*)
Swirling high
Take the sky route
One step
Beyond journey
Glowing urban stars
Hanging down.

Monisha (holding a glowstick) dances with Kira (wearing a yellow neon band around her neck).

Singers (*sing along with club track*)
You can set yourself free
If you dance with me
If you can see
A way to be.

Gregory walks down the carriage; he eyes Rhiannon and pushes his way through the crowd of ravers; they part and Rhiannon is revealed. Rhiannon lays a Tarot card on her Celtic Cross spread. Gregory puts his hand down over the card. Rhiannon pulls the Tarot card from under his hand and turns it over.

Rhiannon The Past. What is passing out of influence.
Gregory Where you from then?

Rhiannon places another Tarot card and turns it over.

Rhiannon (*ignores him*) Your Higher Self or Guide. (*Rhiannon places another Tarot card and turns it over.*) That which is before you, the next turn of events.

Stella stands opposite Rhiannon; bites into an apple. Gregory snatches the apple from Stella's hands and then another two apples from Kendra; he juggles with them.

Kendra Calm it, *mate*.
Gregory (*to Rhiannon*) Want a dance or to see the sights?
Stella (*shaking with laughter*) He's mental.
Kendra Coming up?

Stella tries to grab the apples as they're thrown into the air; she misses. She dances round Gregory. Rhiannon gets up; leans over the Tarot card spread; one card falls to the floor.

Don't go.

Rhiannon Magic him away then, he's getting on my tits.
Gregory (*into phone*) Yeah, nice tits.
Rhiannon Get off. Waster!

Gregory gets the devil finger-puppets from his pocket, ducks behind the baggage racks and starts doing a puppet show.

Gregory The oracle speaks; can she foresee our destiny?

Rhiannon bends down and grabs a Tarot card from under Gregory's foot.

Gregory No, 'cause she's standing on it.
Kendra (*to Gregory*) What are you on?
Gregory Hey, what you got, can I have some?
Kendra Get lost.
Gregory Come on, mate, they (*points to ravers*) won't give me a drink; you got drugs, I know you have. I'll pay.

Gregory gets out his wallet, flicks some notes.

Stella (*to Kendra*) He's loaded.
Rhiannon Can't buy you / (*love*).
Gregory Name it, shame it, blame it!

Rhiannon sits back down; she places another Tarot card down and turns it over.

Rhiannon (*to herself*) Yourself as you see yourself. I don't know how I attract the loser types but I do.
Gregory (*into phone*) Agree. They're spinning out. The bad loser types.
Kendra We gotta move out, claim some space. Come on.

Stella and Kendra get up and go to move away from Gregory; start dancing together amidst the other ravers at the far end of the carriage.

Rhiannon Yeah.

Gregory stands directly opposite Rhiannon; blocks her way.

Gregory (*into phone*) Can you juggle, can you buggle, can you find your way home?
Rhiannon Get out my way, idiot.

Rhiannon shoves past Gregory and sits further up the carriage opposite Alisha, who's reading her book. Gregory follows and slumps down next to Alisha, who looks out of the window.

Gregory (*to Alisha*) Why won't she talk to me?
Alisha (*keeps reading*) Who?
Gregory Her, I've tried everything.
Alisha Maybe she doesn't want to.

Rhiannon re-lays her Tarot card spread.

Gregory Maybe she does and she's playing hard to get.
Alisha Guys like you don't get it. / She's not interested.
Gregory (*parodies her*) Guys like you don't get it. She's not interested.

Gregory bangs the back of her book. Alisha looks up.

Alisha And yer a tosser. (*Turns away.*) No wonder she's ignoring you.
Gregory Don't, don't, do. Wait, look at me. We can chat, never mind about her.
Alisha (*puts her hand out towards his face*) Whatever!

Gregory gets up and tries to sit down next to Rhiannon; she protects her Tarot cards.

Gregory So. What ya saying, Gypsy Rose? Wanna dance?
Rhiannon I'm not getting into this with you so you can get lost. What you on?
Gregory Wait! Wait a minute. I've got things to say. Listen!
Rhiannon Not interested.

Gregory You're gagging.
Rhiannon You're bugging me and if you don't get lost I'm gonna / . . . (*give you a slap*).
Gregory What? What you gonna do? Say it. You gonna get one of your *mates* to crack my head?
Rhiannon As if they could be bothered.
Gregory What you saying?
Rhiannon You need to get a life.
Gregory And you! (*Gregory knocks all the Tarot cards to the floor.*)
Rhiannon See!

Rhiannon picks up the Tarot cards and lays them out again. Kendra, Stella, Jiro and Nori move through the crowd of ravers, working their way towards Rhiannon and Gregory.

Stella He still bothering you?
Rhiannon What a prat. He's like glue.
Kendra Bigoted / glue at that.
Gregory (*gets on his phone*) Yeah, mate, cool, got other plans now.
Stella (*nods towards Gregory*) Does that exist?
Gregory (*listens*) Babe on the train. Yeah . . . gonna give her one / and these cute girls.
Rhiannon Can't believe *he* exists!
Stella Wish he'd do one, he's bringing me down.
Kendra Let's dance!
Stella Come on, Rhiannon!
Rhiannon Nah, I wanna finish this.

Music: Reality, Yahel (Tsunami) 'Creating a Bond with Reality'. Kendra and Stella continue to dance together. Nori and Jiro sit opposite and watch. Gregory sidles up to Rhiannon.

Gregory (*into phone*) Moving in on her. Yeah. Think she's biting.

Rhiannon places another Tarot card; she turns it over.

Rhiannon (*to herself*) Your environment. That which surrounds you.

Gregory goes to sit next to Rhiannon.

Rhiannon What is your problem?

Gregory Do these cards on me.

Rhiannon No way! You trashed them.

Gregory Who are you? Where you going? Talk to me.

Rhiannon You don't look my type; you're from another world.

Gregory Why does it matter who I am?

Rhiannon You're wearing flash clothes, you've got loads of money, think you can buy your way into the party and I *know* I've nothing to say to you.

Gregory Are you a student?

Rhiannon See, you've just made a big assumption about me based on how I look.

Gregory I w – (*as*) – am studying economics at York University . . . dabble in stocks when I get a chance.

Rhiannon (*gets up*) I've nothing to say to you, except you better not cross my path on the anti-globalisation demo tomorrow.

Gregory (*gets up*) Your type are a waste of space, smashing up other people's property. What gives you the right? Who d'you think you are?

Rhiannon And what gives you lot the right to dictate commodity prices based on your profit so that a farmer growing rice in India gets crap money and can't feed his family?

Gregory You know nothing about how it works, that's just socialist diatribe. / I bet you've not bought a train ticket.

Rhiannon And you know nothing about life and the earth and how humanity can exist.

Hubert appears on his switchboard from the midst of the crowd of ravers, followed by Oscar on his crutch.

Gregory (*into phone*) The mob's just moved in.
Hubert (*to Rhiannon*) Is he bothering you?
Gregory You know nothing about anything.

Rhiannon stands face to face with Gregory.

Rhiannon Get out of my face, idiot.
Gregory Can't admit you're wrong.

Hubert and Oscar stand behind Rhiannon.

Hubert Leave her alone.
Gregory What you gonna do about it?
Hubert Shut yer mouth for you.

Gregory goes to grab Hubert. Jiro and Nori rush over and grab Gregory. Rhiannon sits down; she places another Tarot card; she turns it over.

Rhiannon (*to herself*) Hopes and Fears of a Goal.

Jiro, Hubert, Elvira, Renee and Fordon grab Gregory. There's a scuffle and they hold him tight, lift him up towards the train door.

Gregory (*struggling*) Get off, losers.
Hubert We were gonna say jump but you wouldn't have the nerve.
Nori Leave it, he's not worth it.
Jiro I say bounce him.
Rhiannon He wants attention. You're winding him up even more.
Hubert Thought he was bugging you.
Rhiannon More than.
Jiro Come on.
Rhiannon Don't . . . (*get violent with him*). Just put him in the next carriage or something.

Jiro We can do better than that.

Gregory I'll get you for this.

Elvira and Renee hold open the carriage door; the others act like they're going to throw him out. The train lurches forward, sparks fly up from the tracks, Gregory falls out of the door. Kendra and Stella stop dancing.

Rhiannon You idiots, you could've . . . / (*killed him*).

Jiro He fell.

Hubert Deserved it.

Rhiannon No, no one does. (*Rhiannon holds her hands over her Tarot card spread.*) The outcome. (*Pause.*) I see it now; it's not about me.

Stella and Kendra stand over Rhiannon.

Kendra What?

Rhiannon The Tarot reading, it's not about my journey, there's a message about this train journey.

Stella What do you see?

Rhiannon (*points at the cards*) Six and Eight of Birds. The train's going in a different direction from the one it should.

Stella What does that mean?

Rhiannon I don't know.

Kendra Back there, when Gregory fell out, the jolt was from the train changing tracks.

Stella So?

Kendra Maybe it's on the wrong line.

Stella That's always happening, it doesn't mean anything.

Rhiannon takes her Tarot cards and shuffles them – she draws out three cards; holds one and passes the others to Kendra and Stella.

Rhiannon Body, Mind, Soul.

The train carriage jolts abruptly as it pulls into a station.

You should get off here.
Kendra Why?
Rhiannon I've seen it, you've got to tell everyone.
Kendra (*looks out the window*) This is the right station; the train can't be going in the wrong direction.

Rhiannon grabs her bag.

Stella Where you going?
Rhiannon I don't know. I feel like I should go and look for him.
Kendra Why?
Rhiannon The cards . . . (*said I should*). I have to know he's all right.
Kendra Watch out for him, he's full of crap.
Rhiannon I can look after myself, I'm a traveller. I know where I'm going.

Rhiannon leaps onto the platform and closes the door. Darkness.

SCENE THREE

Darkness. A torch cuts through the blackness and then plunges and tumbles as Rhiannon falls down the embankment dropping from the railway lines into a forest.

The moon slides from the clouds; it is full, and lights Rhiannon's path. Rhiannon stands in a forest clearing; the forest is dense all around her.

Hina (wearing a veil over her face) stands on the other side of the railway tracks bathed in moonlight; she whispers to the moon.

Hina exists beyond the Crossing Path, unseen, in a parallel universe to Rhiannon, so Rhiannon is unaware of her presence.

Hina (*whispers*) The knowledge that I seek is within myself awaiting my question. The knowledge that I seek is within myself awaiting my question. The knowledge that I seek is within myself awaiting my question.

Rhiannon gets up and starts to walk. Clouds obscure the moon; she stops and shines the torch up into the sky, illuminating her face.

Rhiannon (*shouts*) Gregory, you prat! Where are you? (*Rhiannon stops and takes her mobile phone out of her bag; she shines her torch on it and then puts it away.*) No signal, typical. (*Pause.*) Why am I here?

Rhiannon starts walking along the side of the railway tracks; spots Gregory lying ahead. Rhiannon rushes up to him and kneels down.

He's . . . (*dead*), they . . . (*killed him*)?

Gregory is lying face down; Rhiannon turns him over.

Is he . . . (*breathing*)?

The wind gushes through the forest, rustling the leaves on the trees. The full moon beams down into a small pool, throwing a shimmering light into the air. From this the Crossing Path appears in the forest. Hina crosses over the Crossing Path – the doorway into Rhiannon's world. Hina appears behind Rhiannon. Rhiannon jumps.

Who . . . (*is there*)? This is . . . (*creeping me out*).
Hina What are you doing?
Rhiannon Me? Weren't you / on the train with the others?
Hina A train?
Rhiannon Is there some rave going on in the forest?
Hina Your heart.
Rhiannon Help me. I don't know if he's breathing.

Hina You do.

Rhiannon OK, he is, I saw his chest move. (*Feels for her Tarot cards in her pocket.*) Why did I come looking?

Hina You know.

Rhiannon Don't do all this *you know* stuff, my community do that all the time and it's annoying.

Hina Ask yourself / questions.

Rhiannon Why do I have to?

Hina And wait for the answers.

Rhiannon What do I do? (*Pause.*) Bathe his wounds?

Hina nods yes. Rhiannon kneels over the pool, takes a water bottle from her bag and fills it. She bends over Gregory, pours out water and bathes his face.

Gregory (*stirs and opens his eyes*) What you doing here, you crazy bitch?

Rhiannon (*jumps*) You're the crazy one, jumping off the train.

Rhiannon looks around her; Hina has disappeared to her. Hina pulls her veil over her face and stands watching Rhiannon. Freya (*carrying a small silver watering can*) *appears from within the forest, unseen, beyond the Crossing Path and circles them, collecting herbs.*

Gregory I was pushed. (*Tries to get up.*) Oww!

Rhiannon Where does it hurt?

Rhiannon taps down Gregory's leg.

Gregory No, no, no, yes! (*Retches.*)

Rhiannon rummages in her bag and takes out a sheathed knife; she draws the knife.

Gregory Don't kill me, I was just messin' back there on the train. / I'm not really a capitalist.

Rhiannon Yes you are. I gotta cut your trainer off.

Gregory You can't, these were 150 quid!

Rhiannon If I don't do this the swelling will be confined. You wanna die or save your trainers?

Rhiannon cuts the laces on his trainer. Gregory cries out in agony.

Done. (*Shines torch.*) It's swollen and blue and there's a lump, definitely broken.

Gregory So you did fancy me, then.

Rhiannon Get real! I came back in case you were hurt.

Gregory I'm cool, help me up, I gotta get to London, got places to go, things to do.

Rhiannon I'd like to see you walk on that.

Rhiannon stands up and holds out her hand; Gregory tries to get up; he slumps down.

You're not going anywhere.

Gregory takes his mobile phone from his pocket, looks at it; it's smashed up.

Gregory lobs the phone into the pool.

You could've recycled that / it's worth a lot to charity.

Gregory You lot don't give up, do you?

Rhiannon Someone's gotta take care of the earth. You *lot* don't care.

Gregory I've got my priorities.

Rhiannon At any cost.

Gregory You don't know what you're talking about.

Rhiannon Neither do you. Curse you, you're a waste of space. (*Rhiannon turns to go.*)

Gregory Wait! I can't get up; you can't leave me here.

Rhiannon Yes I can. The others were right. Why should I care about scum like you?

Rhiannon strides off into the darkness of the forest.

Her torch illuminates a large oak tree; she walks around it and slumps at the base.

Gregory (*shouts after her*) Leave me a can, bitch.

Gregory tries to get up; he falls down. He gets up again and tries to hop; he rolls to the ground in agony.

Damn her!

Rhiannon (*puts her arms around the tree and whispers*) Why can't I walk away? Why've I gotta save every last one? (*Rhiannon gets her mobile out of her bag; looks at it, holds it up in the air, looks at it again and then puts it away.*)

Gregory (*shouts*) Rhiannon, don't leave me. I'm . . . scared.

Rhiannon takes her Tarot cards out and shuffles them. She turns over three cards.

Rhiannon Should I leave him? Ace of Discs, Ace of Trees, Ace of Rivers. Yes? (*Pause.*) Did I ask the right question?

Rhiannon gets up and walks back to Gregory.

Gregory Sorry.

Rhiannon The cards weren't in your favour.

Gregory Lucky me, then. (*Pause.*) I know I'm an arse, everyone says so. Help me and I'll pay you.

Rhiannon I don't want your stinking money, don't you get it?

Gregory No.

Rhiannon I'm not interested in your world, in the money economy, I've always lived on the outside.

Gregory That's crap! It's impossible to exist like that.

Rhiannon Who says?

Gregory You must have consumed, and if you consumed, then you are part of *my* world.

Rhiannon We consume what we produce.

Gregory I don't believe you're totally self-sufficient.

Freya and Hina continue to collect herbs in the unseen world of the Crossing Path.

Rhiannon Well we are, so get over it.

Freya (*to Hina*) I am a fertile garden in which creativity can be nurtured to fruition.

Freya holds up the watering can over the heads of Rhiannon and Gregory; she pours, glittery faery dust cascades over them. Hina leans against the oak tree.

Gregory So that's the answer then, back to the fields.

Rhiannon Not necessarily, but we can't carry on like this, the earth can't sustain us; we need to change the way we're living.

Gregory It's too late, might as well consume until we annihilate ourselves.

Rhiannon It's not too late, my mobile is carbon neutral.

Gregory Whatever that means.

Rhiannon It's recycled and I've planted trees to counter-balance any environmental damage.

Gregory Consuming makes you part of my world.

Rhiannon Never.

Gregory You and your grungies are living in a dream world, girl.

Rhiannon Living up your arse, *mate*. (*Pause.*) Look, I'll walk back to the station, tell them where you are.

Gregory Thanks for nothing.

Rhiannon grabs her bag and storms off; Hina shadows her. Rhiannon walks round and round in a circle; she changes direction and walks the opposite way.

Rhiannon stops, facing the oak tree; she stares up into its branches.

Rhiannon looks around, walks in the opposite direction, stops; walks back to Gregory.

Hina (*whispers*) 'Leave Setley Pond by joining the track running parallel to the track you came in on. It bears slightly away from the car park track to reach the minor road. Cross the road. Ahead of you there are two paths, one running fairly straight on, and on the left a few yards, another forking left. Take this one. Continue along this path in the same general direction across the heath until you see a station slightly below you. The path takes you past this station to a road.'

Gregory That was quick.
Rhiannon I haven't been, obviously. I can't find the embankment I came down.
Gregory Go the other way.
Rhiannon I've been in all directions and I'm telling you it's not there.
Gregory Are you off it?
Rhiannon Get lost. I've lived on the land all my life. I know how to find my way in the dark.
Gregory Are you messing? Trying to teach me a lesson?
Rhiannon Trust me, I don't want to have to spend one moment longer with you than is necessary.
Gregory What now?
Rhiannon We wait till it gets light and then I'll be able to find my way back. And till then you can keep your big mouth shut.

Gregory begins to shiver, throws up.

Have you double-dropped?
Gregory What's it to you?
Rhiannon Because if you haven't then you're in shock.
Gregory Maybe, maybe not.

Rhiannon kneels down and puts Gregory on his side.

Get off.
Rhiannon Be sick on yourself then.

Gregory rolls onto his side.

Have you?
Gregory No.

Gregory tries to get up again, sinks down. He lies on his back, staring up at the sky.

Rhiannon (*to herself*) Stay calm.

Rhiannon walks to the oak tree. Freya crosses over the Crossing Path; seems to appear from within the tree. Rhiannon jumps.

Rhiannon Where's the party?
Freya In your –
Rhiannon Heart.
Freya (*holds out a handful of herbs*) Herb of unity.

Rhiannon takes the herbs in her hands and raises them to her face; she inhales deeply.

Rhiannon Comfrey?
Freya Nurture him.

Rhiannon takes them, turns away and then looks back; Freya has crossed back and disappeared to her. Hina and Freya sit under the oak tree, watching. Rhiannon returns with the handful of herbs; she rubs them around Gregory's foot.

Gregory Oww! Get that muck off me.
Rhiannon I said keep your mouth shut. This will heal your foot.
Gregory A broken bone, I doubt it.
Rhiannon Did you see . . . / (*that girl*).
Gregory What?
Rhiannon Nothing. (*Rhiannon takes a bit of cloth from her bag and makes a poultice around Gregory's foot. She gets up and picks up a leafy branch and lays it*

over Gregory, then looks around.) This is stupid, I'm gonna miss the demo, my interview. What is this about?

Gregory Interview?

Rhiannon For college.

Jiro and Nori appear unseen, beyond the Crossing Path, under the oak tree; Jiro carries a sword and Nori a coiled rope. They start picking up branches and handing them to Rhiannon.

Nori (*skywards*) I am willing to suspend my personal comforts for the richness of the spirit.

Jiro (*to Nori*) I have the power and discipline to achieve my highest ambitions.

Rhiannon looks at Gregory and back at Nori and Jiro; it's obvious he can't see them. Rhiannon starts building a shelter with the branches, Nori and Jiro help, using the sword to cut and the rope to bind.

Gregory What you gonna do?

Rhiannon Build a shelter, it feels like it's gonna rain.

Gregory I mean at college.

Rhiannon Science foundation, Ecology.

Gregory More saving the whales.

Rhiannon Someone's gotta. (*Pause.*) Why's everyone in the forest?

Gregory (*looks around*) Who?

Rhiannon No one. I'm just tripping out on what I'm doing here with such an arsehole.

Gregory No one asked / (*you to stay*).

Rhiannon I know. (*Turns her head, listens.*) Did you hear that?

Gregory No.

Rhiannon There.

Gregory Probably a fox.

Rhiannon I'm going to see what's there.

Gregory (*looks all around*) Don't.

Jiro and Nori walk towards Rhiannon, Nori places a wand-like branch on the ground near Rhiannon; she picks it up and slides it into her belt. Freya stands over Gregory, showering him with faery dust from her watering can. It starts to rain; Rhiannon runs back to Gregory and pulls the branch off him.

Rhiannon Come on.
Gregory Not bothered. Leave me here.

Rhiannon grabs Gregory's arms and pulls him along the ground towards the shelter under the oak tree. Gregory pushes on the ground with his other leg. Rhiannon tries to push Gregory inside the shelter. Jiro and Nori stand watching.

Gregory It stinks in here.
Rhiannon It can't, it's freshly built.
Gregory . . . like smelly feet.
Rhiannon It's lobelia, I think.
Gregory Is it?

Rhiannon bundles Gregory inside the shelter; she grabs the branch and shoves it inside.

Gregory (*from inside the shelter*) Where you going?
Rhiannon Got to get you warm, build a fire, get kindling before it gets soaked.

Rhiannon scurries around grabbing branches from the ground; she drops her Tarot cards, they scatter on the ground. Alisha appears unseen from beyond the Crossing Path; she whispers in Rhiannon's ear.

(*to herself*) I commit my obedience only where and when my higher self directs.

Rhiannon gathers her Tarot cards. Stella and Kendra appear from the forest and run over to Rhiannon. Jiro and Nori cross over the Crossing Path and disappear behind the oak tree. The rain eases off.

Just in time.

Kendra For what?

Stella (*dances and sings*)

> You can set yourself free
> If you dance with me
> If you can see
> A way to be.

Rhiannon puts the Tarot cards in her pocket.

Rhiannon Explanations!

Kendra On what?

Rhiannon You're real, aren't you?

Stella I'd say you'd taken doves or more.

Rhiannon (*rummages in pocket*) Nothing. I forgot you gave me one on the train, it's here somewhere.

Kendra Is he OK?

Rhiannon Him? His foot's broken and he's in shock. I'm trying to (*heal*) . . . keep him warm. (*Points to the shelter.*) Did everyone get off at Ashurst?

Stella No, just us, we wanted to know you were all right. Your cards.

Rhiannon (*takes the cards*) The Ace of Trees, an opportunity. Place of Stones, using your knowledge.

Kendra goes over to the shelter, Stella dances behind her. Kendra crawls in and then crawls out.

Kendra He's not here.

Rhiannon scrabbles into the shelter and then out again.

Rhiannon Where the hell is he? He could hardly be dragged in there.

Stella (*points*) Cool bender. Will you teach me?

Rhiannon Later, I think we should / (*find him*).

Jiro and Nori saunter over.

Where did you appear from?

Kendra We didn't see you get off.

Nori Off?

Rhiannon I thought you said . . . (*the others didn't get off*).

Kendra wanders round collecting branches; Stella continues to dance.

Jiro They've got him then.

Rhiannon Who? The faeries!

Nori The others, on the Crossing Path.

Rhiannon What Crossing Path?

Kendra and Stella put down some branches.

Stella Something feels . . . (*strange about this*).

Kendra (*to Stella*) What?

Stella (*to Kendra*) The vibe.

Jiro Couldn't have taken him without him wanting to go.

Rhiannon Where?

Nori Must have wanted it.

Jiro Or, they tricked him.

Kendra kneels down and starts to build a fire.

Rhiannon Who?

Kendra Too many questions, let's chill.

Kendra lights the fire, smoke trickles up and then small yellow flames appear. They stand around the fire warming their hands.

Nori We can't . . . (*tell you*) – don't know.

Jiro It's . . . dangerous.

Alisha appears unseen, beyond the Crossing Path. She kneels at the fire; listens to them.

Rhiannon There must be someone . . . something going on in the forest. Earlier, I couldn't find my way out.

Jiro and Nori go over to the shelter, tighten the knots.

Stella Have you heard a sound, a . . . whispering . . . like trees rustling?

Kendra (*to Rhiannon*) When we started walking back along the tracks there was a shimmer of light coming from a clearing and suddenly the railway lines weren't there and we were here. We thought we were . . . (*off it*).

Rhiannon I keep hearing a strange music, kept thinking that there was a rave in the forest. I . . . feel uneasy.

Kendra and Stella lie down round the fire and stare up at the sky. Nori and Jiro walk back to the fire.

Rhiannon I saw a couple of girls from that party on the train.

Nori Hina and Freya.

Rhiannon How do you know about them? Are you all messing us around?

Jiro No.

Rhiannon I don't trust this.

Jiro You will.

Nori You must.

Rhiannon It's the sort of thing my community would do to me, some sort of 'Theatre of the Invisible' escapade to teach me one of life's lessons.

Nori We can't explain 'cause we don't exactly know what it is, just that something is and you got to be careful.

Rhiannon What's going on is your friends / threw that Gregory off the train for being an arse.

Nori They didn't. He jumped.

Rhiannon I went looking for him, found him here with a broken ankle, put him in that shelter when it rained and he disappeared. I've given up the whole purpose of my trip for this cheap magic trick? (*Rhiannon gets up, grabs her bag.*) Look, it was nice meeting you but . . . (*I gotta go*).

Jiro You want to leave, but you can't.
Rhiannon I suppose, before, it was straightforward. He was dumped, I found him, tried to sort him out. If I go now, then . . . what does that say about me?

Rhiannon takes her Tarot cards and looks at them. Alisha walks round Rhiannon.

I don't know what to do.
Stella (*sits up*) I believe in this three-choice way of deciding. You know, that if you just come up with one choice, then it's an ultimatum, two's a dilemma and three's some kind of choice.
Rhiannon I've only ever used my cards to decide; it doesn't seem right.
Kendra So?
Stella One – we go into the shelter and see if we can work out where he went. I know his foot was broken but I don't trust him.
Rhiannon I don't think he could've imagined I'd get off the train and follow. (*Rhiannon shuffles her Tarot cards, draws one; looks at it.*) The Speaker of Birds, who is trustworthy? I think we don't go into the shelter and sit here and wait for him.
Kendra Whatever you think you can do or believe you can do, begin it – for action has magic grace and power in it.
Stella Cool saying.
Kendra I say we do magic, bring him back.
Rhiannon / More tricks?
Stella / Magic. Wait till you see her spells.
Jiro Don't mess with it.
Rhiannon With what?
Nori Can't say, just leave it.
Rhiannon I need to know if . . . (*he's OK*).
Nori He's chosen.
Rhiannon What?

Kendra I know, we'll do a seeing spell. We need something to filter our energies.
Stella Build the fire up, use that.

Stella gets up and starts to collect branches.

Rhiannon I've got my Tarot cards.
Kendra Perfect.
Stella Magic!
Jiro Let's go, they don't know what they're playing with.
Rhiannon If you'd tell us.
Nori We can't, we don't really *know*.
Jiro Let's go.
Kendra Let's see the cards.

Jiro and Nori get up, Jiro puts his sword into the shelter; they walk beyond the Crossing Path and seem to disappear. Rhiannon fumbles in her bag; takes out the cards. Alisha gets up; goes over to Rhiannon and whispers in her ear.

Rhiannon I've never let anyone else use them. (*Listens.*) I was taught to obey the laws of the universe.
Kendra That's cool, I know this cleansing ritual.
Rhiannon You know when I asked you on the train if we'd met before, sure we haven't? Maybe at the Big Green Gathering?
Kendra I could have seen you, but I don't remember meeting you.
Stella Who knows if we've been this way before.

Alisha stands in front of the fire; she crosses over onto the Crossing Path so they can see her.

Alisha You have, all of you.
Rhiannon (*startled*) How do you know?
Stella Where did she appear from?
Kendra She was on the train, he was talking to her, maybe they're all tricking us.

The fire swishes up; they all pull back.

Kendra I think she's a witch.
Rhiannon What we gonna do?
Stella The spell, cast the spell.

Alisha walks around the fire. Stella gets up and blocks her way. Stella turns sharply and circles Rhiannon and Kendra, casting a sacred circle by drawing a circle with her hand in the air.

Alisha Can you find your way?

Rhiannon spreads her Tarot cards; she picks one up and hands it to Kendra.

Rhiannon Seven of Trees; defending yourself and your beliefs. Use this to symbolise Gregory.

Kendra takes the card. He grabs a handful of earth and throws it in the fire; sparks fly.

Kendra We can't cast without a wand.
Stella Use that branch, Rhiannon.

Rhiannon pulls the branch from her belt and waves it over the fire, casting a circle. Kendra holds the Tarot card over the flames.

Rhiannon
Hail, fair moon,
Ruler of the night;
Guard me and mine
Until the light.
Kendra Hail, guardians of the forest, of the journeys, show us the path of Gregory.

Gregory appears unseen, beyond the Crossing Path; they can't see him. He stands with Hina, Freya, Nori and Jiro.

Alisha So, you want to see your way through the Crossing Path.

Rhiannon No. We didn't say that; we want to see where Gregory is.

Hina and Jiro cross over onto the Crossing Path.

Hina Your spell did.

Jiro Come, the others are waiting for you?

Stella Look, we don't want to go.

Kendra Yes we do.

Rhiannon I thought I saw Gregory through the trees.

They turn, start walking in a circle into the deep forest.

Kendra Let's follow them.

Stella I don't want to.

Kendra You wait here then.

Stella Thanks!

Rhiannon I have to know . . . (*where he's gone*).

Kendra Only one way to find out.

Rhiannon kicks earth onto the fire; the flames fade, they disappear from sight.

SCENE FOUR

Rhiannon (wearing feathered wings), Stella (carrying a silver water carrier) and Kendra (carrying a magician's wand) appear beyond the Crossing Path; the forest appears to be in the distance. It's like they're superimposed. The trees hang from the moonlit sky.

Rhiannon What is this?

Kendra It's like all the worlds are layered together to make one spectacular world.

Rhiannon Where'd the others go?

Kendra I don't know.

Rhiannon Let's just find Gregory and go.
Stella How? He's not here.

They turn, noting their surroundings; see that all the characters from the train circle them, appear out of reach. They see beyond the Crossing Path into the Tarot Universe; these characters are the Tarot archetypes.

Rhiannon Did they just appear when I asked where the others were?
Stella It's so beautiful, the colours, it's like faeryland.
Kendra A world view beyond belief.

Stella goes to the pool and fills up her water carrier; she drinks from it.

Rhiannon Don't.

Kendra takes her wand and touches the fire with it; a flame ignites and burns.

This doesn't make sense. I thought the spell would lead us on a journey to some magical world, I mean it is magical and beautiful beyond imagination. (*to Stella and Kendra*) Are you two listening?

Alisha approaches; she carries an incense burner on a chain.

Alisha Welcome, you have decided to join us.
Rhiannon We're looking for Gregory.
Alisha He also has joined our community along with your friends.
Rhiannon I'm not joining your community. What is this?

Stella continues to fill her water carrier and empty it into the pool. Kendra stands over the fire.

Stella My inner being shines like a star, guiding my actions, renewing and cleansing me.

Kendra sprinkles earth on the fire, she waves her wand in the air.

Kendra I am a willing channel for the manifestation of spirit in the world.

Hina lifts her veil and approaches Rhiannon.

Hina Listen, we are being called upon.

Alisha and Hina stand silently.

Alisha The cards are shuffled. You are drawn. Take your place.
Rhiannon What you talking about?
Alisha You are the Significator of the reading, there is one other.

Gregory (wearing an antler) approaches and stands diagonally opposite Rhiannon.

Rhiannon What's going on?
Gregory You shouldn't have come.
Rhiannon It seemed like we had to.
Gregory You were / (*tricked*).
Alisha Silence.
Hina Meditate, let your energy flow from the source into the reading.
Rhiannon (*whispers*) What reading?

The Tarot archetypes shuffle themselves and then form themselves into a circle; Kendra and Stella join them. Tivona holds a mirror, Hubert a shield, Oscar a staff, Monisha a lantern, Zada a spoked wheel, Euridice a set of scales, Renee a kali mask, Levia a mortar and pestle, Fordon a burnt branch, Cindy a crescent moon, Elvira a golden bugle and Ye Shen a bubble-maker. The Tarot archetypes form the Celtic Cross spread, then back into a circle.

Alisha The question is chosen, what is your answer?

Rhiannon I don't know what the answer is without the question.

Alisha You must perform your duty for the universe, it is your destiny.

Rhiannon reaches behind her, she feels the feathered wings.

Rhiannon I can hear someone asking if they should leave home.

Gregory (*turns to face the other Tarot archetypes*) You are only looking at the surface, dig deeper for the answer.

Rhiannon Expect the unexpected.

Alisha The reading is closed.

Alisha walks into the circle of Tarot archetypes, Gregory follows; they fade back into the forest.

Rhiannon Gregory? Stella, Kendra where are you? I don't understand what's going on. (*Rhiannon walks around the fire and reaches out her hand; burns it on the flame.*) Oww!

Rhiannon places her hand into the water, scoops out some water and lets it trickle onto the earth; she reaches behind her, grabs the feathered wings and removes them. Rhiannon runs to the circle of Tarot archetypes and grabs the wand from Kendra, the water carrier from Stella.

Stella What happened?

Kendra Where did you get those from?

Rhiannon Come on, we got to get outta here, the energy feels wrong. I don't think we should have crossed over.

Stella Over?

Rhiannon lays the wand and water carrier by the fire, Kendra and Stella follow.

Rhiannon Don't touch them, don't think and don't try to make anything happen.

Stella Those people from the train, they weren't themselves, something's happened.

Kendra I don't understand.

Rhiannon I don't either; you seemed in a trance.

Stella I felt part of a journey; knew my place. I felt compelled to make wishes come true.

Kendra I felt like I knew something you didn't, Rhiannon. I needed to make things happen.

Rhiannon And I found myself listening to a voice, hearing a question and answering it from within against my will.

Stella Is that why we're here?

Rhiannon There's no time to find out. We must leave before it happens again.

Kendra What about Gregory?

Rhiannon He seems beyond our reach. I want to leave without him, but I . . . (*don't know if I can*).

Stella Come on, Kendra, magic us outta here.

Kendra I don't know if I can, I feel . . . powerless. I don't know where here is.

They wander around in a circle as if they're searching.

Rhiannon That's it! It's to do with the location. You know, I don't think we've gone anywhere, it's like we're right where we were standing a moment ago.

Kendra What's changed then?

Stella Us?

Rhiannon I don't know. Ask me another question.

Kendra Where are we now?

They change direction and circle the other way.

Rhiannon A forest, we're in a forest. (*Pause.*) Questions.

Kendra What's a forest for?

Stella Growing trees?

Kendra It's just a forest.
Stella How did we arrive?
Kendra By train.
Rhiannon What's a train for?
Stella It's just / a train.
Kendra Getting somewhere.
Rhiannon What happens if you put them together?

They stand still. Rhiannon uses her branch-wand to draw on the ground.

Kendra A train going through the forest?
Rhiannon A journey though the forest. That's what we're on. Except we've got off the train and are continuing the journey. Questions.
Kendra Why us?
Rhiannon Are we like the others? (*Pause.*) Who are you, Stella?
Stella I dunno, me?
Rhiannon But really.
Stella I'm from Cardiff, I'm doing Music at Southampton Uni.
Kendra Deeper.
Stella I play the lute, it's like water flowing, wheat growing, there are flowers at my feet. Music makes me feel like I'm growing.

Rhiannon rummages in her bag.

Rhiannon They're gone, my cards have disappeared, I can't check.
Kendra Maybe we are in an illusion and your cards are back in reality.
Stella Very funny.
Rhiannon (*to Stella*) I think you're the Star in the Tarot.
Stella Cool.
Kendra What about me?
Rhiannon Tell me about yourself.

Kendra I feel very present in the world, like I can really feel its elements. I juggle them.

Stella She's The Magician then.

Rhiannon And who am I?

Stella Easy, The Fool, the one with the innocent trust in the divine.

Rhiannon Thanks! (*Draws a circle on the ground.*) So Fool, Star, Magician and . . . who is Gregory?

Kendra An arsehole.

Rhiannon I know he's a total idiot, but he's why we came looking. We must ask him who he is.

Stella How?

Rhiannon Don't know, don't have the answer. It's like all my nightmares about rescuing whales, and children and trees. I try to save them to make an impact on change but it's not enough.

Stella It is enough. At least you're doing something, more than half the world isn't, and most of them are making it worse.

Rhiannon He's making it worse. It feels like we can't leave without Gregory, like he's the missing character. (*Pause.*) Maybe it's part of his nature to be evasive. He's keeping something from us.

Kendra What?

Rhiannon He disappeared from the shelter.

Stella Part of his nature too. Who'd do that?

Kendra A magician, but that's me.

Rhiannon We need to get to the heart of the matter. We need to find him, face him.

Stella But how exactly are we going to do that?

Rhiannon I don't know, maybe it doesn't matter how, we just have to go with what we feel. Hold hands with me around the fire.

They hold hands around the fire and start circling it.

Trust me.

Kendra She is the trustworthy type.

Rhiannon changes direction and starts spiralling off. She zigzags through the trees collecting the Tarot Archetypes from the Crossing Path. They form a large circle; they begin the Spiral Dance. Rhiannon breaks off and starts spiralling inwards, the others are dragged behind her until she's obscured in the centre.

Rhiannon (*shouts*) He's here.
Kendra Grab him then.

The spiral spirals outward like a coiling snake until Rhiannon is revealed holding Gregory, who is holding Kendra who is holding Stella. Gregory tries to pull free and they break off from the other Tarot characters. Stella reaches round to Rhiannon so they form a small circle round the fire. The Tarot archetypes fade into the forest. Gregory pulls his hand away from Rhiannon's. Kendra jumps back. Rhiannon takes a step towards him.

Rhiannon This is just like you, having the whole world chase after you. Where did you go?
Gregory Nowhere, I don't know, here, I think.
Rhiannon Where's here?
Gregory In a forest, I don't know.
Rhiannon Look around you, is this really where you are?
Gregory It's an illusion; if I don't believe it, it doesn't exist.
Rhiannon Didn't know that could apply to economists.
Gregory (*to Stella*) We're here because we're not here, because she spiked me, you.
Stella I did not. You were the one asking for beans.
Gregory Not like this.
Rhiannon Get real! You're not off it, none of us are, you don't, can't get it. It's about something else.
Gregory What?

Rhiannon Deep ecology.
Gregory What are you on about?
Rhiannon Our spiritual connection with the planet.
Gregory Like I have one.
Rhiannon (*to Stella*) What are we faced with here, now?
Stella Being somewhere that feels real but that isn't.
Gregory A fallacy.
Stella Like the devil.
Rhiannon That's it! (*to Gregory*) You're the devil.
Gregory Naff off! Just 'cause I've got money / doesn't mean I'm evil.
Rhiannon It's not about that, the devil is about fallacy, I think that's your character in this . . . illusion.

Stella and Kendra kneel at the fire.

Kendra The fire's exactly the same.
Stella So is it all an illusion?
Rhiannon It might be, and if it is, then we're all characters in it.
Kendra All got a part to play.
Gregory This is bollocks. I'm off.
Rhiannon Don't go . . . we need you.
Gregory Hole in the head.
Stella Circle's not complete without him.

Gregory walks off; he's limping and stumbling.

Kendra You won't get far.
Gregory As long as I get away from you fruitloops.

Gregory collapses at the trunk of the oak tree.

Rhiannon I'm tired of chasing him. Why? Why? Why did he cross my path? (*Rhiannon takes her branch-wand from her belt and waves it; the flames whoosh up. Rhiannon takes a step towards the flames.*) Are we lost? What should we do about him? (*Pause.*) What's the answer?

Kendra Dunno.
Rhiannon We've got to get him on our side.
Stella Go and talk to him, he wants you to.
Rhiannon I've tried.
Stella I know . . . / but (*there's more to say*).
Rhiannon I know, I know, I know I should talk to him but I don't want to, he's a lost cause as far as I'm concerned.
Stella It's up to you.

Rhiannon walks off to the oak tree; Gregory is slumped at the trunk.

Rhiannon How's your foot?
Gregory Killing me, the . . . (*herbs*) helped, though.
Rhiannon Shall I see if it's OK?
Gregory If you want.
Rhiannon I'll reapply the poultice. (*Rhiannon sits down next to him.*) We've got to leave, I can feel something. We can't be called to another Tarot reading.
Gregory What Tarot reading?
Rhiannon Don't you remember?
Gregory Maybe.
Rhiannon We haven't really worked it out, where we are, what's going on, but we think we shouldn't stay here.
Gregory Why not?
Rhiannon All this beauty and perfection of ideals, but it's not reality, our world.
Gregory Perfection sounds good to me. I like it here.
Rhiannon Do you? I thought you said it was illusion.
Gregory I don't want to go back to reality, if there's a 'back' to go to.

Rhiannon unties the poultice, takes a small bottle from her bag, sprinkles from it on the cloth and reties it around Gregory's foot.

Rhiannon Your life, though, being rich?

Gregory I don't really care about it. I wanted to be at university; it's just . . . I had this kind of breakdown thing and I felt . . . (*a failure*) like I'd let down my parents. Actually my dad told me I was a failure and to sort myself out, all that money they spent on boarding school had been wasted on me.

Rhiannon That's terrible, how could they say that to you when you needed them?

Gregory Do your . . . parents want you to go to college?

Rhiannon No.

Gregory Really?

Rhiannon In fact the whole community thinks it's a bad idea: 'How will I cope in the city, how will I manage for money, I'll just be buying into the whole globalisation thing and selling out.'

Gregory Ecology selling out? (*Pause.*) But it's what you want to do.

Rhiannon Try telling them that. I've been brought up to oppose the system, globalisation, but really I've got to do it on their terms.

Gregory They always think they know what's best. (*Pause.*) Children begin by loving their parents; after a time they judge them; rarely, if ever, do they forgive them.

Rhiannon Very profound.

Gregory Carl Jung.

Rhiannon I'm surprised.

Gregory Be surprised, I'm not all I seem.

Rhiannon I know, I judged you much more superficially than you judged me.

Gregory What you gonna do about college?

Rhiannon I don't know, I'm scared to go to the interview, scared of what it will mean for my life, how I'll cope away from the land, and I'm scared not to go.

Gregory Try it, go, you can always leave.

Rhiannon I didn't think about it like that. I'm afraid if I make a mistake they'll all say, 'Told you so.' (*Pause.*) Why don't you come back, you don't have to go back to your old life.

Gregory Still trying to convert me.

Rhiannon (*stands up*) No, it's not about that, about converting, it's about real life-choices. You can go back and change what you don't like about your life.

Gregory How do we get *back*, to the reality we were in before now?

Rhiannon (*holds out her arm*) I don't know, but we must leave now, before it's too late.

Gregory takes Rhiannon's arm and stumbles to his feet. They walk back to the fire.

Gregory Sorry, I just don't know how to be sometimes.

Stella Don't worry, mate.

Rhiannon How do we get out of here?

Kendra More magic? That's how we got to here in the first place.

Rhiannon I haven't got my Tarot cards though.

Stella But we have got all the Tarot characters now.

Rhiannon Have we?

Stella Look.

They look around and the Tarot archetypes become visible; circle them, cross onto the Crossing Path.

Stella It's like the power of action, if we want to see them we do.

Alisha walks over to the fire.

Alisha There is no going back, you cannot cross the Crossing Path.

Rhiannon Is that what this is, then? The Crossing Path between worlds?

Stella It feels dangerous.

Kendra Yes, it is; what you want happens, your fears and desires become reality.
Rhiannon Reach out, Gregory.

Gregory reaches out his hand; stands there with his hand outstretched.

Gregory Nothing's happening.
Stella Believe that you can make it happen.

The Tarot archetypes move in closer. Alisha reaches out her hand towards Gregory's; he takes her hand, Rhiannon breaks the connection. The Tarot archetypes all join hands in a circle round the fire.

Alisha We will not relinquish you.

Rhiannon waves her branch over the fire, casting a circle. Kendra holds Gregory's hands over the flames; throws the antlers in. The Tarot archetypes line up on the Crossing Path; the wall is impenetrable. Rhiannon, Stella and Kendra cast the feathered wings, silver water carrier and wand into the flames.

Rhiannon
Hail, fair moon,
Ruler of the night;
Guard me and mine
Until the light.
Kendra Hail, guardians of the forest, of the journeys, show us the path of Rhiannon.

Gregory, Rhiannon, Kendra and Stella weave in and out of the Tarot archetypes; they fade into the forest. Gregory, Rhiannon, Kendra and Stella remain standing around the fire.

Gregory Is this it?
Stella I don't know, how will we know? It all looks the same.

Kendra Rhiannon, check for your cards.

Rhiannon (*rummages in her bag for her cards and shuffles through them*) Got them, all here, one burnt.

Stella I don't understand about the others, why are they there and we're here?

Rhiannon It's like a . . . parallel world that we crossed into and back. I think the others are here in this world just like we are, only not at this precise place . . . moment in time.

Stella (*looks around her*) Daybreak.

Rhiannon Let's find our way back to the station.

Stella and Kendra link arms with Gregory and they walk off into the dawn. Rhiannon kicks earth into the fading fire; she looks up at the sky though the trees.

SCENE FIVE

Dawn. The train carriage is at the station; it is empty. Rhiannon, Kendra and Stella step inside, Gregory hovers in the doorway. Stella flops on a seat, Kendra looks around the carriage.

Rhiannon What you doing?

Kendra Checking.

Stella (*about Kendra*) She's working it all out, can't you see her brain whirring?

Rhiannon Working what out?

Stella Where we've been, where we're going.

Rhiannon What time do you think this train goes?

Kendra Dunno, six, seven? Are you going to the demo?

Rhiannon Of course.

Stella You're gonna be wasted.

Rhiannon It's important to me.

Gregory I thought college was.

Rhiannon I can do both.

Gregory If you're really serious, really wanna get in, you gotta rest, be focused.
Kendra He's right.
Rhiannon I'll try next year, or another college.
Stella But the moment's right, now.

Kendra sits next to Stella; they lean on each other and crash out.

Rhiannon I know, I'm scared, I'm just bumbling along letting destiny decide.
Gregory But you're not, 'cause you know if you're tired you might mess up the interview and not get in, so you're making a conscious decision.
Rhiannon I feel like I'm letting everyone down if I don't turn up on the demo.
Gregory What about you, about your life plans?
Rhiannon Never really had any.
Gregory You could get off this train now and not go, rest up and go to your interview tomorrow.
Rhiannon I know I could, but how do I know it's the right decision?

Rhiannon takes out her Tarot cards; looks at them, puts them away.

Gregory You don't, you just do it. (*Pause.*) That's what I don't get about you: you'd leap off a train and go and look for a stranger without thinking, but this you can't make sense of.
Rhiannon It's down to what I believe in, I suppose; making decisions about that's easy.
Gregory Go and see, you'll never find out otherwise. (*Pause.*) I believed in what you said; thought it was worth seeing.
Rhiannon What you gonna do now?
Gregory Dunno, sleep.
Rhiannon Here?

Gregory Maybe? (*Points to Kendra and Stella.*) They are.

Rhiannon So we just fall asleep on this train and wake up wherever it takes us. Cool.

Rhiannon sits down opposite Stella and Kendra. Gregory turns to go.

Aren't you sleeping?

Gregory Places to go, people to see.

Rhiannon I don't think you're a bad person.

Gregory The devil?

Rhiannon A Tarot character about experiences or like a function in life.

Gregory Traditionally it's not a great person to be.

Rhiannon It's not a person. You should read up on the Tarot, it's not what you think. Spell it backwards.

Gregory Wow, that's a trip.

Rhiannon (*holds out her hand*) Take care.

Gregory (*looks in his hand*) Apple pips. (*Pause.*) How do I plant them?

Rhiannon You'll find a way.

Gregory Good luck.

Gregory walks out through the train door; he trips. Rhiannon looks out of the window; all the characters from the train wait on the platform.

Rhiannon What if I never got on this train? Would I still be at this point in my life? (*Rhiannon puts her bag down on the seat and lies down with her head on her bag. Laughs.*) Let's see where my dreams take me.

Action Has Magic Grace and Power

Maya Chowdhry interviewed by Jim Mulligan

Maya Chowdhry is an award-winning playwright and poet. She writes lyrical drama for radio, the web and the theatre and has continually crossed boundaries to produce vibrant challenging work. In 2000 she received a Year of the Artist Award for *Destiny*, which she describes as a digital poetic tapestry. Maya Chowdhry started writing poetry when she was a teenager as a way to survive and then, when she went to Sheffield to work as a film-maker, she collaborated with three other writers to produce an anthology of their poems: 'This started a journey taking my intimate writing to the outside world.'

The Crossing Path takes place on a train journey into the New Forest and then with a magical shift moves to an enchanted forest. Rhiannon, who lives in a New Age travellers' community, is on her way for a college interview. There are some lively events on the train as Rhiannon seeks to avoid responsibility for her life-choices by consulting her Tarot cards.

> I believe in Tarot cards and I occasionally go to have my cards read. I believe there is a vibrational energy in the universe and the Tarot cards are a way to tap into it. That's the way the universe gives us messages on our day-to-day life. I sometimes use the cards in my writing to access ideas on a more symbolic level, so if I'm stuck with the plot of a play I might use the Tarot cards to ask questions and look for answers in unseen places.

On the train the young people are having a rave, but as the action whirls round and Rhiannon tries to consult the cards the seemingly obnoxious Gregory pesters her until her exasperated friends try to move him into the next carriage. Then, as the train lurches, Gregory falls. Rhiannon, defying the cards, leaves the train when it stops and goes in search of Gregory. It is in the forest that the Crossing Path allows the characters to move from one world to another.

> I believe that there is more than one world existing simultaneously and in our creativity we gain access to that world. Sometimes we know why we write things and sometimes we don't. And also in our day-to-day real lives sometimes we know why we do things and sometimes we don't. In *The Crossing Path* I have tried to create a world where you can make a decision and carry on with that journey while in another world your alter ego is making different decision and going on another journey.

Rhiannon finds Gregory possibly dead. 'The wind gushes through the forest rustling the leaves on the trees. The full moon beams down into a small pool, throwing a shimmering light into the air. From this the Crossing Path appears in the forest.' It is the doorway to and from Rhiannon's world.

> There's a spiritual journey in the play, but there is also a real physical journey. The play looks at life-decisions and how making one decision or another can change your life and affect your destiny. I'm not saying there are wrong decisions. If you make a decision you go with it and if you change your mind you go in a different direction.

The Crossing Path gives Rhiannon and Gregory, from very different worlds, the opportunity to meet. She lives in a close, unconventional community while he is from a private school, wears flash clothes and has loads of money. Although they are so different, Rhiannon cares enough to get off the train to look for Gregory. She does not want him to die.

Rhiannon is facing a tough situation. She has decided she wants to do some kind of formal education and she expected her open-minded community to support her, but she has found resistance from them. She feels disappointed in her community and she is searching for the reason why they have brought her up to be open to life and all its different directions and then are unsupportive. Gregory has had a breakdown and is hurt by his father's rejection.

The clash of their two philosophies appears irreconcilable: 'We can't carry on like this, the earth can't sustain us; we need to change the way we're living,' as opposed to: 'It's too late, might as well consume until we annihilate ourselves.' But it is possible to be optimistic if we follow Kendra's advice: 'Whatever you think you can do or believe you can do, begin it – for action has magic grace and power.'

> Often when people are trying to make a decision about something, they think there is only one way of acting so they have to do it. But if we can think of three choices we can unlock the mindset that this is the only thing I can do. Often people are unable to make a decision because they see it as a big weighty life-decision. But if you make a small move in the direction you want to go, then perhaps something will change.

As the characters slip back into reality at dawn on the railway station, Rhiannon and Gregory have reached a kind of respectful consensus and they part. In some ways Rhiannon still finds it difficult to choose between going on the demonstration or going for her college interview. She is still tempted to fall asleep on the train and let it take her where it will. She is still prepared to see where her dreams will take her.

I think young people will like the juxtaposition of the two worlds, the reality of clubbing with your mates and the enchantment of the forest. If they've got imagination I don't think it is a difficult play to put on. I described a set because I had an idea of something quite symbolic but I am open to all options. It's up to people to create the world that feels right for them. Once the director's decision is made that will be their production style.

Production Notes

STAGING AND SETTING

The play takes place on a train and in a forest. The writer suggests using four wooden benches radiating out with trees rising up from the corners to signify a train carriage and a forest. One tree should be slightly bigger to suggest an oak. A canopy could be pulled down from the tree to represent the shelter. A transparent bucket of water with an orange light over it might be placed in the centre of the benches to represent the pool and the fire. But these are only suggestions, and there's scope to be as inventive as you like with the set. Just use what is absolutely necessary, because locations shift and the action should be as fluid as possible.

Effects include rain pelting down, an intercity train passing by a level crossing, an arrow being fired high into the air. Lighting glowsticks and laser light-flash and swirl, sparks fly from the track, torchlight cuts through darkness, a full moon slides from the clouds and is obscured again. The moon beams down into a small pool throwing a shimmering light into the air. A fire is lit; smoke trickles up and a yellow flame appears; later the fire swishes up and earth is thrown onto it. A crossing path appears in the forest – the path could be a beam of light, represented by physical objects, or it could be imagined and represented by a chord of music. When Maya Chowdry wrote it she imagined two fairy lights that moved about the stage.

Lots of props are indicated – keep them to the minimum. Many are linked to the Tarot characters, and are quite specific. For example, Stella's mineral water becomes a silver water carrier, symbolic of her

Tarot archetype. When the characters are given their new props they pass over to the Tarot Universe. Maya has made strong indications of what the characters should look like, and you'll be able to consult the Tarot cards for ideas. Because the actors carry quite a lot of props it will be worth finding ways of concealing or carrying them within the costume design.

Sound includes dance music pumping out, wind gushing through the forest and rustling the leaves on the trees, and old-fashioned train doors slamming. There is scope to build a supernatural atmosphere through the use of 'found instruments', percussion and rainsticks.

CASTING

This is a large-cast play. The casting of the four central characters – Rhiannon, Gregory, Stella and Kendra – should keep to the gender indicated. Some of the other characters can be played by males or females. The characters are based on Tarot cards. There are seventy-eight cards in a set, of which twenty-two are characters which are said to represent all archetypes in life. There are twenty-two characters in the cast and the age range is fifteen to nineteen years.

EXERCISES

Pick out the moments in the play where the whole ensemble can be physically involved. As a whole group, start by creating the train stopping abruptly, lurching forward, changing direction, the characters being knocked off balance while dancing and raving. Add the effect of the door slamming and play with the characters entering and exiting. Discover how the arrival of a less likeable or more popular character affects the dynamic. See how Gregory's fall from the train can be achieved physically and how it affects the whole group. Experiment with exaggerating and speeding up the action or moving in slow motion.

There are two locations for the play: on a train (noisy and not a smooth ride) and, by contrast, in a forest (extremely quiet). Either visit a forest or use your imagination, and run the dialogue to see how the location affects the cast physically and vocally. Do the same exercise on a train.

Treat Rhiannon's Tarot cards as another character; they are at times helpful but they can be manipulative. Give the cards a personality and work through the script to find out how they influence or fail to influence Rhiannon. Create her back history and decide when she was first introduced to the Tarot and what prompted her to start using it. Look at the script to find at what points she goes to the Tarot for help. Look at the moments when the cards seem to be leading her (for instance the cards draw her to Gregory, and his Tarot archetype is the devil, which represents temptation). Decide how the other characters are influenced by the readings. Discover why most of the characters are drawn into the Tarot universe but Gregory isn't. Find out what this enables him to do. Decide why Rhiannon doesn't get caught in the Tarot universe for ever.

Take a pack of Tarot cards, distribute them among the actors but don't let them see what card they've been given. Have each actor place their card on their own forehead so the rest of the cast can see what card they've got but the actor can't. Get the actors to circulate and question each other to find out as much as they can about their own card's Tarot archetype. The idea is to learn not only through questions but from reactions; however, make it a rule that the actors can't give away the identity of the character, and can only answer yes or no to questions posed. Let the actors discuss what they've discovered and guess which card they've been carrying. At the end of the exercise the actors can look at the card they've been given.

RESEARCH

Tarot for Your Self: a Workbook for Personal Transformation by Mary K. Greer (New Page Books: 1-800-227337-1), newpagebooks.com

Suzy Graham-Adriani
March 2003

DUST

Sarah Daniels

Sarah Daniels lives and works in London as a writer for stage, radio and television. She has received the Most Promising Playwright Award from both London Theatre Critics and *Drama* magazine as well as the George Devine Award. With over fifteen plays to her credit, Sarah also writes for *East Enders* and *Grange Hill*, and for Radio Four.

Characters

Flavia
fifteen

Chloe
fifteen, previously Flavia's best friend

Claudia
also Roman Girlie Glad*

Tara
sixteen, leader of the pack

Achillia
also Roman Gladiator

Lisa
sixteen, Tara's sidekick

Trifosa
also Roman Girlie Glad

Robert
twenties, in charge of the group

Julius
also Roman Master of the Games

Julia
twenty-four, tube-train driver

Amazon
also Roman Gladiator

* Roman meaning 'in Roman times,' not nationality

Bo
woman in tube carriage with cigarettes

Boudicca
also Woman Warrior / Woman in Crowd

Faith
woman in tube carriage reading horoscope magazine.
Also Roman Fortune Teller

Hope
homeless Woman with Baby in tube carriage
Also Roman Woman with Baby, thrown to the lions

Octavia
woman on tube putting on make up.
Also Roman beautician

Vendor
man on tube train eating burger.
Also Roman vendor of stuffed mice and thrushes

Leopold
man on tube train taking cat in basket to the vet

Carpophorus
also Roman Bestiarii

Fireman
also Roman Centurion 2

Busker
busker on the tube. Also Busker under the stands
at the amphitheatre

Ticket Tout
Roman ticket seller under amphitheatre.
Also Roman Centurion 1

Curator
the Curator of the British Museum

Criminals 1/2/3
criminals under amphitheatre

and, if casting allows, non-speaking extras

Passengers in tube carriage
Roman musicians, jugglers, acrobats
Extra criminals under amphitheatre
Group of spectators under amphitheatre
Roman soldiers in/under amphitheatre
Extra Girlie Glads (non-speaking)
Extra Female Gladiators (non-speaking)

SCENE ONE

The front carriage of a packed London tube train travelling from High Barnet to Morden via Bank. Tara, Lisa and Chloe have to stand, squashed in the bit in between the middle doors. Flavia stands near them, but excluded from the group. The speed and occasional jolting of the train mean they're inclined to knock against a suitcase positioned to one side of them. Robert, having already got them on the wrong train, is obsessed with double-checking that they are now on the right train, and is standing a little way up the carriage, studying the tube map. Amongst the other passengers are: a big woman (Bo), who is fidgeting with a packet of cigarettes and matches (she obviously can't wait to get off and light up); a woman (Faith), who is reading a horoscope magazine; a man eating a burger (Vendor); a man on his way to the vet with a cat in a basket (Carpophorus); and Octavia, who's holding a small compact mirror up to her face with one hand and vigorously applying mascara with the other. (It can then be filled with as many or as few other characters as the director wishes, provided that these characters play an equivalent role under the amphitheatre.)

The train's automated announcement sometimes punctuates the dialogue and sometimes comes under it. (It is written in full for authenticity but I suggest that the wording in brackets is cut because it slows down the scene too much.)

Automated Announcement This station is Kentish Town. (*Change here for mainline and suburban rail services. This train terminates at Morden via Bank.*)

A couple of people get on, including a Busker. S/he plays on an instrument (or if this isn't possible, sings) M People's 'Search for the Hero'. (If it's sung, choose a bit which doesn't include the chorus or the actual line 'Search for the hero inside yourself'.) During the following dialogue the Busker then walks up the carriage holding out a hat which one or two passengers might drop a coin into but most of the others ignore.

Tara (*to Flavia*) I like your jeans, Flavia.
Flavia Mine?

Tara nods. Flavia falls for it and smiles. Lisa looks slightly puzzled. Chloe worried.

Tara Turn around.

Flavia turns.

And they look so much better from behind.
Lisa Or they would do if they had any sort of label.
Tara And they fitted properly.
Lisa Made them yourself, did you?

Flavia starts to turn back.

Tara No, stay like that. It's just about bearable on the retina.
Lisa Yeah, we're the eye candy. You're the eye cabbage.

They laugh. Flavia stays with her back turned to them.

Automated Announcement The next station is Camden Town, Bank branch.

Robert, who's been studying the map out of earshot, comes towards them, almost collides with the Busker and, embarrassed, fishes in his pocket and puts some change in the hat.

Chloe (*wanting to distract the others from picking on Flavia, to Robert, slightly sarky*) Ah, that's generous, Sir. Is that the sort of entertaining you did before they gave you a job as a drama teacher?

Robert I never had to do stuff like that. I was a classical performer.

Tara (*to others*) Classical plonker.

Robert Haven't I ever told you about the time I was in *The Cherry Orchard*?

Lisa What doing, nicking cherries?

Robert Chekhov!

Chloe Bless you.

Tara It's all this dust in here. You must be allergic.

Lisa Yeah, it's filthy.

Chloe I think we should be provided with pollution masks.

Robert Dust is merely bits of dead skin and other people –

Lisa Make it worse, why don't you?

Tara That is disgusting –

Robert You, as would-be actors, you should be wanting to embrace it, breathe it in, desperate to get into other people's skin –

Tara, Chloe and Lisa pull faces, put two fingers in their mouths and generally make derisory sounds. As does Flavia, desperate to join in.

Automated Announcement This station is Camden Town, Bank branch. (*Change here for southbound trains via Charing Cross and northbound services to Edgware. This train terminates at Morden via Bank.*)

Robert (*panicked*) Did it say Charing Cross? (*He darts to a door and puts his head out to check the indicator on the platform.*)

The Woman with a Baby gets on and immediately goes up the train approaching each passenger with something written on a small tatty piece of card and her hand held out. Everybody immediately looks down and completely ignores her as she comes up to them.

Lisa (*to Tara, about the woman*) Flavia didn't tell us her mum was coming on the trip.

Tara, Lisa and Chloe laugh but Chloe sounds a bit false.

Flavia 'Cept my mum doesn't have such good dress sense. (*Makes herself laugh.*)

Tara Ugh. She's coming near us.

The train jolts, causing Flavia accidentally to brush against Lisa.

Lisa Don't touch what you can't afford.

Flavia (*to impress the others, more awkward than aggressive*) Yeah, do one. Scrounger.

The Woman with the Baby looks at Flavia, then moves on.

Tara (*to Flavia*) Lisa meant you.

Lisa and Tara turn away.

Flavia I've got it.

Lisa What?

Flavia What you wanted. (*Pulls an expensive lipstick from her pocket.*) I was sure the assistant saw me but I got away with it.

She sees them looking at her and stops. She puts the lipstick in the palm of Tara's outstretched hand.

Faith looks up from her magazine, to see where the train is. Sees the business with the lipstick. Looks disapproving and then looks back down at her magazine again.

Lisa You were supposed to buy it, not nick it.
Flavia But it was twelve ninety-nine –
Tara (*opens it and looks at it*) It's the wrong colour.
Lisa (*looks at the end*) You didn't try it out, did you?
Tara Err . . . no . . . herpes. (*Tara gives it back.*)
Flavia But you said –

Robert comes back over to them.

Robert Everyone OK?
Tara We are now we're on the right train, Sir
Robert This line is very confusing. I just got on the wrong branch.
Automated Announcement The next station is –
Robert (*listening to the announcement*) Shush, shush.
Automated Announcement – Euston, Bank branch. (*Upon arrival the last set of doors will not open. Customers in the last carriage please move towards the front doors to leave the train.*)
Robert And I've told you. You don't have to call me 'Sir' on the trip. You can call me Robert, OK? (*then noticing Flavia has her back to them*) Are you all right, Flavia? Flavia?
Flavia (*turns round*) Yeah.
Robert That's better. Excited?

Flavia nods unconvincingly.

And so you should be. We're going to hear the Bard's words just as they would have been spoken in Elizabethan times.
Lisa What does Bard mean, anyway?
Chloe It's the Elizabethan name of one of the Simpsons.
Tara More like Elizabethan for Bored.
Lisa (*smirks at Tara. To Robert*) Robert, what would you do if one of us were caught shoplifting?

Flavia looks very uncomfortable.

Robert Put them in for the Strongest Woman in the World competition. You'd have to have some muscle to get a building off the ground.

Chloe laughs. Tara and Lisa look at her. She stops.

Tara That's funny, Sir. Not. (*She looks at Lisa then to Robert.*) Have you ever been in a French play, er, Robert?

Robert Some days I feel my whole life has been made up by Feydeau, Tara.

Lisa So you know some French then?

Robert Poss-cee-blur, poss-cee-blur, Lisa.

Tara Do you know what the French for Robert is, Robert?

Robert (*with relish*) Rob-bear. Why?

Tara Robber, eh?

Lisa That right? Do you know anyone, Flavia, who should be called Rob-bear?

Flavia looks down. Robert is again distracted, listening to the announcement.

Automated Announcement This station is Euston, Bank branch. (*Change here for northbound services via Charing Cross on Platform 2, for intercity and mainline rail services. This train terminates at Morden via Bank.*)

Tara (*during the announcement*) You still want to be one of my Girlz?

Flavia Why?

Tara Do you?

Flavia nods.

Tara OK. See that bag. Pick it up and put it on the platform before the doors close.

Flavia Then you'll be all right with me?

Tara You'll be one of us.

Flavia picks up the suitcase and is about to put it on the platform.

Automated Announcement This train is ready to depart. Please mind the closing doors.

Robert Flavia, what are you doing with that bag?

Flavia (*putting the bag back down*) Just admiring it –

Lisa Like attracts like.

Robert Flavia? What on earth possessed you? (*to the people around*) Sorry about that. (*Under the next couple of speeches he apologises to the passengers nearby.*) I do apologise. I am sorry.

Tara You are such a moose. (*She turns away from her.*)

Burger Man (*mouth full of burger, in response to Robert*) It's not mine.

Woman Mine neither.

General shaking of heads.

Robert (*nervous laugh*) Someone's going to be sorry when they reach the check-in desk.

Lisa You're supposed to report unattended bags and packages.

Robert It might belong to someone up the other end of the carriage.

Tara Hadn't you better ask?

Chloe (*whispers to Flavia*) If you keep standing here, they'll keep picking on you.

Tara (*having overheard, flicks Chloe*) I thought you said she wasn't your friend any more.

Chloe (*but lowers voice*) She's not. (*And then looks away.*)

Robert Well, I – OK, I'll take this side if you'll take –

Tara We can't go up the carriage talking to strangers.

Automated Announcement The next station is King's Cross St Pancras.

Faith (*stands up*) Does this case belong to anyone? (*No response. She pulls the alarm.*)

The driver, Julia, applies the breaks and the train screeches and jolts to an abrupt halt. She gets out of her cab and comes into the carriage.

Julia Who pulled the emergency handle?

Faith Me. No one seems to own that suitcase.

Julia (*going over to it*) Any idea what's in it?

Lisa (*sarcastic*) Hang on, I'll get out my X-ray specs.

Tara Duh, like we're psychic or something.

Faith Oddly enough, I have been told I've got the gift but I'm not getting a negative aura from it. Nothing at all.

Julia (*can't help but roll her eyes, weary*) OK. Nobody touch it. I'm going to pull in to the next station and evacuate the train. (*She goes back to her cab.*)

Tara (*pulls a face, about Julia*) N.O.T.

Lisa (*agreeing*) N.B.

Flavia (*to Chloe*) Not? Not what?

Chloe N.O.T. Not – Our – Type. N.B. Never Be.

Flavia Meaning me?

Chloe (*checking to make sure that Tara and Lisa can't see her talking to Flavia*) No, they're talking about the driver.

Flavia But they might as well be talking about me.

Julia (*over PA system*) Ladies and gentlemen, we shall shortly be arriving at King's Cross, where this train will terminate.

Some shushing and muttering from the other passengers in the carriage as they strain to hear the announcement.

Please make sure you have all your belongings with you as you leave the train. It is very important that you all alight as quickly as you can from the carriage and follow the signs to the exit. We have received information that there is an unattended package on this train.

There is a pause, then a big rush, scramble and crush to get to the doors. The sound of brakes. The train stops.

The sound of the doors opening. Everyone piles out. Julia, her radio in one hand, comes out of the driver's cab into the carriage.

Robert (*to Julia*) The thing is, we've got to get to London Bridge.

Julia Everyone leave the train as calmly as possible, please.

But her words are drowned in the rush of people making their exit. Then to Robert:

There'll be someone to help you when you get off, Sir. (*She then walks into the next carriage. Voice-over:*) That's it. Quick as you can, please. (*The sound of her shutting the doors manually.*)

Tara (*as they get off, about the driver*) No job for a woman.

Lisa Not one with a brain.

Chloe Definitely N.O.T. N.B.

Tara Maybe it's the sort of thing Flavia could aspire to, eh, Chloe?

Chloe (*reluctant*) Yeah.

Lisa Probably one of the few jobs where she could get away with wearing her own clothes.

Robert looks round, believing all the girls are off, and gets off. Flavia has positioned herself out of view and hangs back. The gang are making their way out after the other passengers. A fireman supervises the evacuation.

Lisa This is what I call drama.

Tara Better than the boring geezer Julius Caesar.

Chloe Hooray, we'll get out of seeing the crappy play.

Tara Barred from the Bard. That's what I call a real tragedy. Not.

Lisa (*about the fireman*) Ohh, look at him in his big trousers.

Tara Things are looking up in the eye-candy department.
Chloe Where's Flavia?
Tara You care?
Chloe It's just that I can't see her.
Lisa Probably pushed her way ahead.
Tara Yeah, so she can pick some pockets.
Robert (*pushing his way amongst them*) Everyone here?
Fireman Stop pushing there, Sir. You're nearly out.
Robert Flavia? Has anyone seen Flavia? Tall, slight, dark hair, about fifteen (*or whatever description fits the actor*)?
Fireman Keep moving. This area has to be fully evacuated. We haven't been given the all-clear.
Robert But I've lost one of our group.
Fireman She'll be up on the surface, Sir. There's no one left down there except the driver. Move along now.

As they go:

Lisa (*delighted about the fireman*) He touched me.

SCENE TWO

Julia, believing the train is empty, is at the controls facing out. The train jolts into life and starts moving very fast. She then becomes aware Flavia is also in the cab.

Julia (*turns, frightened, barks*) Who are you?

But Julia has to turn back to keep her eye on the controls and Flavia is too scared to respond.

Does that bag have anything to do with you?
Flavia No, no. I'm nothing to do with anything. I was on a trip to the Globe with my drama group.
Julia Come and stand next to me then where I can see you, and tell me what you're doing here.

Flavia gets up and stands next to Julia. All the time the train jolts and swerves erratically, making sparks. Lights flash on and off. They are both facing out, looking in front of them.

Flavia I didn't . . . I didn't want to get off the train.
Julia Today, right, I don't think they'll be that bothered about fare-dodgers.
Flavia I've got a ticket. I just wanted to lose the friends I was with.
Julia At this rate you could lose your life as well. (*Looks at her.*)

Flavia shrugs.

(*turning back*) Friends, you say? These are your friends?
Flavia Everyone wants to be in their posse. They're really cool. They recruited my best friend Chloe but they don't want anything to do with me. And now she doesn't either.
Julia Listen, I don't want to be patronising or nothing, but out of the things which might feel like the end of the world today, that's no longer top of the list.
Flavia Not for you, maybe.
Julia You know what. This isn't a hoax. That bag's for real. They've had a coded message.
Flavia What are you still doing on the train, then? I thought they sent in bomb-disposal experts.
Julia Usually, but they think there could be enough Semtex in that case to turn everything in a five-mile radius of the Angel to dust. Someone has to divert it to where it won't do so much harm. And now I'm cursing myself, believe me, for insisting to my centurion that I'd do it.
Flavia Your what?
Julia My line manager. That's what they're called on the Underground 'cos they're in charge of a hundred

people. He'd got blokes lined up to do it. I should have just let them.

Flavia Where are you taking it?

Julia To a disused track under the Regent's Canal. But first it looks like I'm going to have to drop you off at an abandoned tunnel under the main line of King's Cross station –

Flavia I don't want to take you out of your way.

Julia (*laughs in spite of herself*) It's on the way. Get ready, you'll have to get out just round the next bend.

Flavia But what about the power? I'll be electrocuted.

Julia You'll be walking along a very ancient sewer.

Flavia What?

Julia Don't worry. It might be dusty and derelict but at least it's no longer used and there is no power.

Flavia How will I be able to see?

Julia (*gives her a torch*) Here. Hold on.

She then applies the brakes. The train shudders and screeches to a halt.

Flavia (*about the torch*) You sure?

Julia (*nods*) That little ledge there, step onto it and follow the tunnel.

Flavia But –

Julia Just get off and keep going. Now.

Flavia See you then. (*Steps off.*)

Julia (*calls after her*) I hope so. Go, go, go. And good luck.

Flavia And you.

Julia nods. Sound of the train starting. Flashing lights, and sparks as it rattles and screeches on its way.

SCENE THREE

Flavia is alone in the dark. She switches the torch on and stares after the train.

Then the sound of a very loud explosion followed by the sound of falling masonry and rubble and dust. Flavia screams and moves to one side. Sound of falling rubble to the other side of her.

Flavia Help! (*She cowers, sound of more rubble falling.*) Hello? Hello? (*Nothing. She realises that she is hemmed in.*) That's it then, finished.

She makes no attempt to move and closes her eyes. Bo (Boudicca), an extremely large woman with very big red hair and a loud, booming voice, looms towards her.

Bo Someone looking for me?
Flavia (*opening her eyes*) My luck. A freak on the line and she's seen me.
Bo Never fear, Boudicca's here.

No response.

Boadicea? (*Flavia merely continues to gape at her.*) Never mind, Petal. You can call me Big Bo.
Flavia (*closing her eyes again*) Just let it be over.
Bo (*pulling Flavia to her feet*) Stand up. That's it. Don't let them see they've won. I said don't let –
Flavia I'm just trying to find a way out.
Bo Of course.
Flavia Do you know where it is?
Bo Yes.
Flavia And?
Bo I found it, didn't I? Now what's that thing you've got there?

Flavia A torch.

Bo (*delighted*) A torch. (*holding out her hand*) Put it there, Sister. (*She shakes Flavia's free hand vigorously.*) At last, a woman after my own heart. Most of them these days wouldn't know how to make a spark in a firework factory if you put paraffin in one hand and a Roman candle in the other. Do you know what I'm saying?

Flavia (*not really. Uneasy*) So where is it?

Bo What?

Flavia The way out.

Bo Right here.

Flavia To the light?

Bo The light? (*then warming to her theme*) Yes, yes, the light. You find the brightness. Go on, child, with my blessing. My flaming temper raised the temperature all right, all night and set 'em alight. I burnt them in their beds. I turned their pets to biscuits and baked the ground they marched on. They were no match for my blistering attacks. I doused and scorched them and lit up their lives until they were so fired up they decided to do some comeback cooking of their own. But I wasn't going to end up branded as their charred trophy. They thought that they'd be having the last laugh but I saw to it that I got that. Ha ha. And I'm still laughing about it. See. (*then*) So, you want to stay with me, do you?

Flavia Don't take this the wrong way. You seem very nice, but I think you might be an arsonist.

Bo (*laughs with delight*) What a compliment! (*putting her arm around Flavia, squeezing vigorously*) I said what a kind word. A long overdue tribute and accolade to be savoured. (*Still squeezing, she winks.*) One person's terrorist is another's freedom fighter. (*She unpins her large cloak and takes it off.*) Go on. Off you go now and give them a roasting from me.

(*putting her cloak around Flavia and pinning it together with the brooch*) This brooch represents me. It was shaped and beaten on a boiling forge. (*Taps the brooch.*) In here is the spirit of a woman bowed but not cowed, whose memory is still alive although she's long since been buried.

Flavia (*turning the brooch over in her hand*) It's quite lush.

Bo It's not a trinket. It's a symbol of courage. Show it to the world.

Flavia nods.

And memorise the motto. It's always better to be the hammer than the anvil.

Flavia You mean you get a choice?

Bo Always, always. In return you must tell them you found me and that I want to be restored to my rightful place.

Flavia (*unsure*) Yeah, right. (*then*) Actually, would you mind if I stayed here and hung out with you?

Bo Afraid?

Flavia nods.

(*softer*) Remember this. There's only one of you.

Flavia doesn't respond.

Who are you? Eh? I said who are you, to deprive the world of your uniqueness?

Flavia It's so lonely.

Bo Strictly speaking you can stay with me but –

Flavia – I should really try and find another way out?

Bo nods. Flavia smiles but doesn't look convinced. The faint sounds of a fair and music (M People: 'Search for the Hero') *can be heard.*

Flavia What's that?

Bo Your other way out.

Flavia A sort of fair?

Bo That's the one thing you can't put money on. It's not always fair but it can't be all bad or no one else would stick it out, would they?

Flavia seems tempted by the music fairground-type sounds, but then she looks back at Bo.

Go on. I said go on.

Flavia puts the torch inside a pocket in the cloak and goes towards the music.

SCENE FOUR

Bo (*to the audience*) If she thinks it's lonely there, it's much worse here. Are you listening? I said it's much worse here. Oh I know I've got some great company. Virginia Woolf, Sylvia Plath, Marilyn M., Del Shannon, Kurt Cobain. Music? If music be the food of love, no wonder I'm on my own. The racket I've had to get used to. I don't like to judge but some of the stuff those people call tunes sounds worse than when Caligula's horse got its head trapped under the wheel of a chariot. Lovely people though, most of them. The artists anyway. Got a couple of weirdos. One with a small moustache who quite frankly was lucky to have got off so lightly, dying by his own hand. I put him in a room of his own straight away. You can imagine how Virginia kicked off about that. Then there's a lovely monk who set himself alight. I've got a few of those actually. I said right out to their faces. I said, 'Nice action but wrong target, babes.' How we all ended up may have taken more courage than most could muster in a lifetime, but whichever way you look at it we still finished it off with an act of cowardice. Oh yes. Taken me centuries to come to terms with that. Me! Me, who rode around fearlessly wreaking revenge, wrecking their cosy lifestyles. But when they turned and came looking for me, I could see the way it was going. And I knew, this was it. My chickens were coming home to roast. So I said to myself, 'OK Big Bo, time to go.' I took such last-resort pleasure in picturing their disappointment when they found I'd got myself rather than let them get me. But hey, they got over it. It took them all of a morning, and then they got on with their conquering and forgot all about me. When life doesn't go on, when it stops – then that is it. It really is. The end of all possibilities. I should know. If I could have my life again the one thing I'd do is not kill myself. And it's not just me. We all think that here.

SCENE FIVE

As Bo goes, the music increases in volume but becomes more Roman (drums, cymbals, trumpets, horns, fifes and flutes) and fairground-sounding. The lights come up on the fairground atmosphere underneath and around the stands of the amphitheatre. Flavia looks around and sees as many or as few of the following as it's possible to create: musicians, jugglers, acrobats, food and drink sellers, ticket touts, souvenir sellers, kite sellers, a sword sharpener, a mask seller and a cushion seller.

A man, Vendor, selling stuffed mice and baby thrushes is talking to the Fortune Teller. Two young women (Claudia and Trifosa – the 'Girlie Glads') are buying make up from Octavia's stall. (The make-up consists of chalk to whiten the neck, ochre, a reddish earth, to redden the lips, and ashes to darken the eyebrows.)

Claudia and Trifosa are glamorously rather than functionally dressed. Their gladiatorial costume is customised to maximise the visual effect (e.g. ripped T-shirts, short tunics, thigh-high boots with gold leg irons, etc.).

A Ticket Tout (the tickets are made from wood with the entrance number and seat number on) makes his way amongst them, trying to sell his tickets.

Tout (*aware that he shouldn't be overheard by the wrong people*) Tickets for the games still available. Even the big ones. Anyone want to buy a ticket? Good seats. Do you a good price.

Trifosa What do you think you're doing?

Tout Don't give me a hard time, girls.

Claudia Making an easy profit out of our hard-earned sweat.

Tout Like I have the monopoly on easy.

Trifosa Meaning?

Tout You just have to prance around pouting and looking pretty.

Claudia We risk our lives in that dirty arena.

Trifosa And our nails.

Tout And the rest. The only thing you risk is your reputation, but that's long since gone.

Claudia Don't let the centurion catch you, or you'll risk being flayed alive.

Trifosa Then it won't matter how good the seat you've wangled for yourself is, you won't be able to sit in it.

Tout He's not going to find out though, is he? (*He gives them a couple of tickets.*)

Claudia Not now he isn't.

Trifosa Don't forget to tell your customers to come and cheer for us.

Tout You'll be lucky if I don't put a word in our leader's ear to give you the thumbs-down.

Claudia He wouldn't dare.
Trifosa The crowd would tear him to pieces.

The Ticket Tout goes, accidentally bumping into the Fortune Teller, causing her lucky charm, a small leather heart hung around her neck, to fall on the ground.

Tout Get out of my way, you decrepit old crock.
Fortune Teller Watch where you're going, you cheating young crook.
Claudia Takes one to know one.
Fortune Teller (*looking around*) Will someone help me?
Trifosa (*to Claudia*) Here we go –
Fortune Teller (*to Flavia*) Did you see where it went?
Flavia (*still trying to take it all in*) What is this – some sort of theme park?
Fortune Teller I've lost my lucky charm. My lucky charm.
Trifosa (*turning away from the make-up woman*) If you were any good, you'd be able to see it with your third eye.
Claudia No use to you, anyway. It's not brought you any luck, has it?
Flavia (*picking up the charm*) Is this it?
Fortune Teller (*takes it*) Thank you. May you always know the climate which produces fair-weather friends. (*She moves away.*)

Trifosa and Claudia laugh at her.

Flavia What?
Claudia Take no notice. She's three ravens short of a stew.
Trifosa Pathetic old rooster.
Flavia What was that thing, anyway?
Trifosa Haven't you got one?
Flavia No.
Claudia (*in response to Flavia's blank look*) You foreign?

Flavia I'm beginning to think so.

Claudia (*to Trifosa*) There's more and more of them.

Trifosa (*to Flavia*) Weren't you given a charm to protect you when you were born?

Flavia From what?

Claudia From the world. 'Cos you don't have a man to protect you –

Flavia I'm lost, you see. I need –

Trifosa (*talking over her*) We all get one but when we get married we give them up.

Claudia The Fortune Teller's too old to still have hers.

Trifosa She's too ugly not to.

Claudia We'll go the same way if Octavia doesn't get some better stuff for her stall.

Octavia If you can find better in the whole city I'll refund the difference.

Trifosa That antimony I got off of you last week, Octavia, made me look like I hadn't slept for a week.

Octavia Some improvement, then.

Claudia She's a beautician, not a magician.

Trifosa Very funny.

Octavia Girls, girls, no need to bicker. I did manage to get your hair remover in.

Trifosa At last. My legs look like they belong to a dog.

Octavia Just your legs? (*She quickly continues measuring out and putting in a bowl the hair-removing concoction.*) Blood of she goat, mix this with some sea-palm and a dash of powdered viper.

Flavia You don't have a policy about not using animal products, then?

Trifosa (*to Claudia about Flavia*) Definitely foreign.

Octavia Then rub with this until all the hair falls off. (*Gives them a very rough stone.*)

Flavia Does it hurt?

Claudia Is the Emperor mad?

Trifosa (*about the large bowl of ochre*) Haven't you got a better colour than this? I'm not putting that anywhere near my mouth.

Octavia I'm not sure I've got enough of it to cover the whole area, anyway.

Flavia It looks very dry.

Claudia You're an expert now, are you?

Flavia Hang on. (*She produces the lipstick from her pocket.*) Do you want to try this?

The other two take a step back as if she's produced a weapon.

No – look. (*She puts some on.*)

They look amazed. She offers it to them. They put it on.

Trifosa (*pleased*) This will get them shouting out our names in their sleep.

Claudia What do you want for it?

Flavia Keep it. I hope it gets you a husband. I just need to . . . (*find out where I am and how to get back*).

Claudia You think we can't get one without this?

Trifosa We can have any man we want.

Claudia Yeah, we're the Girlie Glads.

Flavia The what?

Octavia The Gladiator Girls.

Trifosa Come and watch us perform. (*Gives Flavia the two tickets.*)

Flavia Where are you going?

Claudia Routines to learn.

Trifosa Money to earn.

Flavia Can I come with you?

Claudia Sorry, but you're not really one of us, are you?

Trifosa And we've got important work to do.

Flavia watches as Trifosa and Claudia go.

Flavia How do I get to be one of them?

Octavia (*laughs*) You know what your problem is. You haven't got any ambition at all.

The Vendor of Snacks comes up to her.

Vendor (*holding out the tray*) You look like you need some sustenance.

Flavia (*looking at the items*) I don't have any . . . (*money*).

Vendor You can have the whole lot for those tickets.

Fortune Teller (*to the man*) Those tickets are worth more than you are. (*to Flavia*) I'll treat you. Which one would you like?

Flavia points at one. The man hands it to her and the Fortune Teller pays for it. Flavia takes a bite and puts it back.

Vendor What's the matter – never had stuffed dormouse before?

Fortune Teller Bit of an acquired taste. Here, try one of these.

Flavia Why, what are they?

Vendor Baby thrush. Boiled.

Fortune Teller Might be more to your liking. They're not stuffed.

Vendor Yes, lovely and crunchy.

Flavia No, you're all right. I'm a vegetarian.

Vendor I hope that's not contagious.

Fortune Teller Some sort of foreigner. That's right, isn't it? What's the matter?

Flavia I'm lost.

Vendor No, you're not. You're under the Londinium Amphitheatre.

Flavia The what?

Vendor Amphitheatre.

Fortune Teller I think no matter how many times you told her where she was, she'd still feel lost.

Flavia Look, I just want to get out of here.
Fortune Teller I can help you.
Flavia Can you?
Fortune Teller Of course. Give me your hand.
Flavia (*looks unsure*) Why?
Fortune Teller Don't look so concerned – I'm not one of those old-fashioned soothsayers who still insist on poking through the innards of animals to predict the future.
Flavia I tell you who should be concerned: animal rights people. There is some weird stuff going on here. I just want to know how I can get home.
Fortune Teller Your hand will tell us.
Flavia How can it?
Fortune Teller Everything you need to know is right here. Let me show you –
Flavia (*eagerly holds out her hand*) Go on then.

The Fortune Teller looks at Flavia's hand and then drops it as if it were hot.

Flavia What's the matter?
Fortune Teller I'm sorry.
Flavia Why, what's it say?
Fortune Teller I don't know.
Flavia No?
Fortune Teller I can't read it.
Flavia Why not?
Fortune Teller Because it's the hand of a thief.
Vendor (*overhearing*) Thief? (*to Octavia*) D'you hear that? She's a thief.
Octavia That would explain it. I knew something wasn't right. I thought she looked shifty, right from the off. I was just saying to the Girlie Glads you've got to watch her. (*pointing*) Her over there – she's a thief.
Crowd (*one or two start, growing louder*) Thief, thief, thief.

Centurion 1 Take her down.
Fortune Teller Take this.

The Fortune Teller hurriedly presses her lucky charm into Flavia's hand and looks upset as two Roman soldiers flank Flavia on either side and escort her off. Claudia and Trifosa look on, enjoying the show.

Trifosa And she said she wanted to be one of us.
Claudia Like we need to be dragged down with her.
Centurion 1 Like you've got time to stand there pointing the finger. Games Master said to come and tell you you're on after Carpophorus and the bears with the beehives.
Trifosa Beehives?
Centurion 1 Did you hear me?
Trifosa Yes, yes. You can tell him we're standing by.

The Centurion goes.

(*to Claudia*) What is all this about bees?
Claudia Apparently the crowd gets a buzz out of it.
Trifosa Today maybe but what will they want tomorrow?
Claudia As long as we're getting paid and having a laugh, who cares? Shall we run though it again?
Trifosa Have we got time?
Claudia Loads. As long as Carpophorus hasn't had a pig's bladder full and decided to try and make the bear kiss the bees.

They start to go through their 'Girlie Glad' dance/cheerleader/pom-pom-type routine to music.

Centurion 1 Stop tapping and twirling around under here. You're on.
Claudia Why, what's happened now?
Centurion 1 The queen got in a rage, flew at him and got trapped up his tunic.

Trifosa If he will work with bees . . .
Claudia . . . it won't be the last time.
Centurion 1 But this time it's left its sting in a place where no one will offer to suck it out for him.
Trifosa Like that's our problem.
Centurion 1 It will be if you don't get out there before the crowd decides to come looking for you.

Trifosa and Claudia go.

SCENE SIX

Flavia is pushed into a communal prison cell under the amphitheatre. Centurion 2 is in charge of a rabble of very poorly dressed, cowed people. The Woman with Baby, looking exactly like the Woman with Baby on the tube is amongst them. Flavia stares at her.

Woman with Baby What are you looking at?
Flavia Nothing.
Woman with Baby Don't look down your nose at me. I might be a beggar but at least I'm not a thief.
Centurion 1 Stand up. Stand up.

Flavia stands.

Centurion 2 Up straight and look up there and repeat after me, 'We who are about to die, salute you.'
Flavia (*bursts out laughing. Everyone looks at her*) You have got to be joking, right?
Centurion 2 What's so funny?
Flavia It just sounds so corny.
Criminal 1 You have something to eat?
Criminal 2 You heard her. She has corn.
Criminal 3 I could use a loaf.
Criminal 1 If you'd known how to do that, you wouldn't have ended up in here.

Centurion 2 (*threatening them with his sword*) Get back or you'll end up as sliced dead. (*When order has resumed, he turns to Flavia.*) It's up to you. You're going to die. We all are, for that matter. I can help you do it with dignity and courage or you can go your own way and shamefully disgrace yourself. (*to the Criminals*) OK, now get back, stand and face me as if I were Caesar and show her how it's done –

Criminals (*facing in slightly different directions, each one a beat behind, drone*) We who are about to die, salute you.

Centurion 2 Mithras, give me strength!

Flavia Excuse me, but I don't want to go out there.

Centurion 2 You don't have any choice.

Flavia There's been a mistake. You don't understand – I have to get out of here.

Centurion 2 No, *you* don't understand. That is the way out. The only way out. Will someone explain to her?

Woman with Baby We all have to take our chances in the arena.

Flavia What are they, though? Our chances?

Centurion 2 You want a tip from me? Don't bet on yourself or anything with two legs for that matter. Now again.

As they try again, Carpophorus, the Bestiarii, comes in.

Carpophorus (*in some physical discomfort from the bee sting*) You told them yet?

Centurion 2 Give me a chance. Getting them to stand up, turn to the Emperor and say a few words is like trying to build Hadrian's Wall out of seaweed. I heard your big bee mistook your bum for a buttercup.

Carpophorus You'd do well to keep your nose out.

Centurion 2 No worries on that score.

Carpophorus (*to the rabble*) Now, you lot, listen up. Don't ask me how but they've managed to bring a couple more of those exotic cats over here.

Flavia Cats?

Criminal 2 With claws that can kill you outright with one swipe.

Flavia (*to Carpophorus*) I'm sorry but I really do have to go. Please can you help me get out of here?

Carpophorus 'Course I can. That's what I like to see – an eager volunteer.

Centurion 2 Don't get too excited. (*indicating with his forefinger against the side of his head*) She's not right in the Celtic trophy department.

Carpophorus As if I haven't got enough on my plate with dogs, bears and bees and now lions, tigers and leopards without having to find a way of coaxing these miserable two-legged creatures to perform in this damp, windswept and desolate country.

Criminal 1 That' s what you're paid for, isn't it?

Centurion 2 Right, you, Maximus Mouth. You just talked yourself into being top of the bill.

Carpophorus My job is to train the beasts to attack you –

Criminal 3 They need classes?

Criminal 2 Now I've heard everything.

Carpophorus For your information, chariot chops, it does not come naturally to them. It takes hard work. It's a two-way thing. Between the hunter and the prey. I've got to teach you, the prey, to play your part too.

Criminal 1 That is our part – praying.

Criminal 2 That's right. And you don't have to teach us how to do that. It comes natural to even the most hardbitten non-believer once they've had a limb or two chewed off.

The Games Master comes in.

Games Master What's going on here? Get on with it. Get them up and training.

Centurion 2 Motivation-wise we've hit a bit of a Hadrian's.

Games Master We need some volunteers. Who's going to go into the arena with the lion? (*Silence.*) This is a one-off, once-in-a-lifetime offer. Those of you who willingly put themselves forward, I will personally guarantee that your children will not have to go into the arena and perish with you but will be sold as slaves instead.

Pause. Then the Woman with the Baby steps forward.

Woman with Baby What do you want me to do?

Carpophorus Wise decision, dear. Someone take that baby from her and arrange for it to be sold.

Centurion 2 A few more of you would do well to take this opportunity. You'll only meet a worse end if you don't.

Carpophorus (*to Woman*) If you just stand still, the lion won't pay any attention to you because you don't have a smell –

Games Master Then you can't be standing close enough.

Centurion 2 Yeah, you sure that bee didn't fly up your nose?

Carpophorus She doesn't smell like their natural prey, so it won't even know that she'd be good to eat. Would you get on with your job and let me get on with mine?

Games Master All right. All right. (*to Woman*) Give it here.

The Woman kisses the baby and gives it to the Games Master, who takes it and goes.

Carpophorus (*to Woman*) I can help you out by putting a fresh deer or moose skin on you, but you mustn't start running around or yelling or screaming or you'll scare it.

Woman So what do you want me to do? Dance for it?

Carpophorus More or less. (*He stands close behind her and shows her, perhaps enjoying it slightly more than necessary.*) Move your hands just a little and sway your body slightly so it knows you're alive. Once it realises that you're alive but not dangerous it'll charge.

Centurion 2 So you get into the arena and then what do you do?

The Woman shows him.

Carpophorus Good, good. Lovely. I'll just go and find you a skin that's still warm.

He goes. The rabble shuffles and mutters.

Centurion 2 Come on. It's not as if you've got to learn any complicated moves or anything. Get an animal skin and line up.

Flavia goes over to the Woman and offers her the charm.

Woman Is it yours to give?

Flavia Yes.

Woman It's of no use to me now.

Flavia For the baby?

Woman (*shakes her head*) Nor her. (*Turns away.*)

Flavia (*remembering the torch*) Wait. (*holding out the torch*) What about this? (*Pause.*) Take it.

Woman Why, what is it, poison?

Flavia No. (*Shows her how it works.*) Look.

Woman It's magic?

Flavia Not really, but I think if you shine it in the animal's face, right in its eyes, you might temporarily blind it or at least scare it.

Woman You're giving it to me?

Flavia Yes.

Woman Because you feel sorry for me?

Flavia Sort of.
Woman I see. You still feel superior to me.
Flavia No. I wish I were as brave as you.

Bell rings.

Games Master Stop jawing. It's the lion's turn to do that. Up you go. Carpophorus will have your skin waiting at entrance five.

The Woman goes.

Centurion 2 The rest of you line up.
Criminal 1 Why aren't we allowed to see what's happening?
Games Master Because they don't let us have enough sponges on sticks down here for the clear-up job. (*He goes.*)
Centurion 2 Like everything in life, the longer you have to think about it the worse it gets. So I'll do you a favour and let you go next. Try this for size. (*Throws a skin at Criminal 1.*)
Flavia If we can't have a look, how will we know what to expect?
Centurion 2 (*chucks her a skin*) You're so eager to find out, you can be second.

Amazon comes in. She is a gladiator who happens to be female and very proud of it. All heads turn at her entrance.

Centurion 2 Morning, Mam. To what do we owe this pleasure?
Amazon (*nodding in Flavia's direction*) I want to speak with her.
Centurion 2 Don't go upsetting her, she's next but one up into the arena.
Amazon (*going over to Flavia*) Did you mean it?
Flavia What?

Amazon I was training next door and I heard you.
Flavia What have I done now?
Amazon When you said to that poor vagrant that you wished you were as brave as her.
Flavia Why wouldn't I?
Amazon You can be, you know.
Flavia Yeah?
Amazon By becoming one of us.
Flavia (*goes over to her*) Who are you?
Amazon You don't know who I am?
Flavia No.
Amazon You haven't seen my picture?
Flavia No.
Amazon Nor heard of me?
Flavia Sorry.
Amazon They call me Amazon. I'm one of the most famous female gladiators that ever lived.
Flavia You don't look like the others.
Amazon You've met others?
Flavia The Girlie Glads.
Amazon Those stupid, air-headed, idiots. Their very existence discredits everything we've worked for. We fight with dexterity and ingenuity. They merely flit and jig about like the empty baubles they are. We look death in the eye and face it with courage and dignity. The only thing they have to face with courage is their reflection. They run from life by preening and screaming, whereas there is no situation we can't confront.
Flavia But can you get me out of here?
Amazon Only if you agree to be one of us.
Centurion 2 Hold on. She's not going anywhere. Not without the Master of the Games's permission.
Amazon I'll go and get his permission then. (*She goes.*)
Centurion 2 (*calls after her*) Better hurry – I've got them in order now. There'll be a riot if I try and change it.

The crowd can be heard shouting and cheering.

Centurion 2 (*to Flavia*) Sounds like your friend has reached the arena.

Claudia stands at one side and shouts down her commentary to the crowd. Carpophorus stands at the other side, shouting his.

Carpophorus You should see this. You should see this. The cat is out of the trap and it's massive.

Claudia She is so small. She can barely stand up under the weight of the deerskin.

Carpophorus This creature could pull the Emperor's chariot with half a legion in the back seat. Look at that magnificent beauty.

Claudia From here she looks thinner and shorter than its hind leg. All the odds are against her. In fact they've stopped taking bets. The bookmakers are refusing to take bets.

The crowd falls silent.

Carpophorus Listen to that. The crowd's holding its breath. Such is its majestic authority and power.

Claudia She looks so ill. She's about to collapse –

Carpophorus Stand up, you stupid cow, like I told you.

Claudia Now – now she's started to sway like somehow there's a tune only she can hear –

Carpophorus That's it. That's it. Lovely. Just like I taught you. Well done. No, keep moving, don't stop. OK, OK, here it comes, let my lovely big brute do its work.

A roar from the beast and a collective gasp from the crowd.

Claudia It's charging towards her.

Carpophorus Yes, yes.

Claudia She's stopped swaying. What's she doing?

Carpophorus What's the matter? Go on, go on.
Claudia She's pointing something at it. Would you look at that? It's stopped in front of her. It's like she's hypnotised it. She has. She has. It's turning away. It's starting to sway. It's trying to get out only it can't see.

The crowd roar with excitement.

Carpophorus My cat. I can't believe it. It's bumping into the side of the stands. It can't see where it is or where it's going.

Crowd starts laughing.

Oh my lovely big beast.

The Games Master comes running in.

Games Master Someone tell the Girlie Glads not to get changed yet.
Flavia Is she still alive?
Games Master Can't you hear them? They're calling her the female Androcles.

Carpophorus comes running in.

Flavia What will happen to her?
Carpophorus She's only blinded the best cat. The money and effort. I could weep. By rights she should be stoned to death.
Games Master You'll be lucky. Looks like she'll get the thumbs-up.

The sound of the crowd clapping and cheering and shouting 'Mitte'.

Centurion 2 She has. She has. The crowd's going mad. He's gone and given her the thumbs-up. She's been spared.
Carpophorus It's criminal. What an atrocity.
Flavia What will happen to her now?

Centurion 2 Go back to her begging ways, I shouldn't wonder, and end up in my charge again soon enough.
Flavia But wasn't Androcles given special privileges?
Centurion 2 She's a woman. If she's spared she'll be allowed to go back to her begging ways but outside the city walls.
Flavia Will she get her baby back?
Games Master That's now an offering to the gods.
Flavia But you said –
Games Master It was dead before she ever handed it over. Don't look at me like that. We all knew it. She knew it. She knew we knew it but she just didn't want to admit it.

Sound of the crowd starting to grow bored and restless.

Carpophorus The crowd are throwing things at my poor, poor creature. Get the Girlie Glads. Where in the name of Caesar are they?

Claudia and Trifosa come in.

Claudia What d'you want now? We've done our act.
Games Master You're on again.
Trifosa Who's paying?
Games Master We'll talk about that after.
Claudia Call your animals in then and we'll do another routine.
Games Master You'll do one with the beasts.
Trifosa But we haven't rehearsed anything.
Centurion 2 I'm sure you'll be able to improvise.
Carpophorus If not, they certainly will. (*Laughs.*)
Games Master What are you still doing here? They need you to get that sightless lumbering thing back in before they can re-sand the ring.
Centurion 2 Talking of which, how's your sting?
Carpophorus Will there be no end to today's humiliation? (*He goes.*)

Claudia (*to the Master of the Games*) Julius, surely you don't mean us to –

Trifosa I'm sure we could come to some arrangement that suits us all.

Games Master We just have. Good luck.

Centurion 2 You'll need it.

Trifosa and Claudia look at one another.

Trifosa (*looks in Flavia's direction and nudges Claudia*) What d'you think?

Claudia Worth a try.

They go towards Flavia.

Centurion 2 Wrong way. You need to be –

Trifosa We won't be long.

Claudia The dust hasn't even settled up there.

Trifosa And we've got an idea of how to improve the act.

Claudia Do you remember us?

Flavia Yes –

Claudia You gave us that lip stuff. Flavia, isn't it?

Flavia That's right.

Trifosa Do you still want to be one of us?

Flavia Well, I –

Claudia It's your lucky day.

Trifosa Actually, we've been looking for you since we met you –

Claudia I can't tell you how pleased we are to have found you now. You're just right, you know.

Flavia Yeah?

Trifosa We could have our pick of anyone but –

Claudia Not anyone will do. You have to be special.

Trifosa And have the looks.

Claudia And the figure.

Trifosa And the style. (*to Claudia*) With the right clothes?

Claudia Perfect.
Flavia But I don't have the right clothes.
Claudia You can have ours.
Trifosa Yes, mine. (*meaning the cloak*) Take that thing off and put these on. (*Starts to take her clothes off.*)

Flavia starts to try and undo the brooch.

Claudia (*to Trifosa*) Yours? What about me?
Trifosa (*taking her to one side*) We'll find someone else to replace you. It was my idea. Besides, as long as there's one victim the crowd will be appeased.

Amazon comes back.

Amazon What are you two doing here?
Trifosa We don't answer to you.
Claudia We're just going anyway. Come on, Flavia.
Amazon (*to Flavia*) I thought you wanted to be one of us?
Claudia One of you? No one would choose to be like that.
Trifosa (*to Flavia*) Well, what's it to be?
Flavia I just want to get out of here.
Amazon What, as a woman warrior or – (*looking disdainfully at the other two*) – a woman worrier?
Trifosa We're warriors too.
Amazon All you worry about is if your eyelashes are long enough, if you lips are red enough –
Claudia That is our war paint.
Amazon That is your mask to hide your cowardice.
Trifosa Oh ple–ease. Just 'cos you wish you were born as a man there's no need to take it out on the rest of us.
Carpophorus (*shouts off*) Get the Glads. We're ready for them.
Trifosa This is your chance.
Flavia (*looks at Amazon*)

Amazon I can't choose for you.
Flavia (*to Trifosa and Claudia*) You didn't want anything to do with me earlier. You walked away. You laughed when I was locked up.
Claudia That was then. This is now. We thought you wanted to be one of us.
Trifosa You won't get this opportunity again. If you don't join us now you can forget it.

The Games Master comes in with two soldiers to find the Girlie Glads.

Flavia (*to Trifosa and Claudia*) You can forget about me then. I've decided I want to be a real gladiator.
Centurion 2 Sure you don't want to throw your lot in with them?
Games Master Wise decision.

The soldiers grab Claudia and Trifosa and march them off towards the arena.

Claudia (*squealing as she goes*) Leave me alone.
Trifosa Take your hands off me.
Claudia Stop it.
Trifosa Let go.

They go.

Amazon (*to Flavia*) We start training right away.
Centurion 2 No, I've told you she's next in line for when Carpophorus gets his cat's act together.
Amazon The Master of the Games said it was all right.
Centurion 2 I think you'll find he said it was all right if it was OK with me.
Amazon I don't get paid until I've performed.
Centurion 2 Not my problem.
Flavia (*gives him the tickets*) There, it's all I have.
Centurion 2 That'll do nicely.

Amazon (*to Flavia*) Come on. Let's get started.
Centurion 2 Sure you've got the right one? Look at her. She doesn't talk, she squeaks and she can hardly stand up under the skin of a tomcat.
Amazon Don't judge everyone by your own standards. (*giving her sword to Flavia*) Here, grab hold of that.

Flavia grabs the sword but it's so heavy it almost pulls her over.

Centurion 2 (*laughs*) She can't even lift it.

As Flavia and Amazon go.

Amazon What sort of things have you lifted before?
Flavia I'm sorry. The only real lifting I've ever done is shoplifting.
Amazon Then you have a lot to learn. Firstly, we never say sorry. And secondly we make sure we never do anything we have to say sorry for. This way.

They go.

SCENE SEVEN

Woman with Baby, although she obviously no longer has the baby.

Woman (*directly to the audience*) I was the girl whose panties stank of poverty, who grew to be a woman who smelt of stale breast milk, who gave birth then turned her face to the wall, who gave her baby away, whose kid died for lack of food, out of neglect, who used her dead baby to smuggle drugs, who abandoned her child on the train to Auschwitz, who murdered her offspring in a fit of jealous rage at its innocent lack of anxiety.

You look at me like I'm the shit on your shoes but you cannot shake my dust from your feet. You've drawn me into your lungs but you want to suffocate me 'cos I'm now part of you. I have always been with you.

You have always revelled in reviling me but you have no room to breathe because after two thousand years of your civilisation I am still alive and thriving amongst you and you are more concerned with making sure animals don't become extinct than with trying to eradicate me.

SCENE EIGHT

Flavia is practising her new-found skills using a wooden sword against either a wooden post or a straw-filled dummy.

Amazon (*shouting instructions to Flavia*) A bit higher. Don't leave yourself undefended. Good, good. You've come a long way.

Flavia I'm still here, though.

Amazon I think you're ready to try out on the real thing. Keep practising and I'll see if I can find you a sparring partner.

Amazon goes. Flavia continues to practise. Achillia comes in, and watches Flavia.

Achillia Amazon around?

Flavia Somewhere. She's gone to find someone for me to spar with.

Achillia You think you're ready for that?

Flavia She does.

Achillia Do you know how to defend yourself if you're attacked from behind?

Flavia We haven't done that yet.

Achillia Give me the sword and I'll show you. (*Flavia hesitates.*) Don't give me the sword then, just turn around. (*Flavia doesn't respond.*) Go on.

Flavia (*turns on her, brandishing the sword*) Who are you, eh? Who are you to order me around? Turn around yourself. (*going towards her*) Go on, you turn around –

Achillia (*backing away*) There's no need –

Amazon comes back.

Flavia Yes, there is. Turn around and kneel down or I'll have your guts for a bit of old-fashioned fortune telling.

Amazon Flavia?

Flavia stops.

Achillia Whatever you've been teaching her, you seem to have missed the dignity part out.

Flavia I know. I know. 'The only way to prove you have real power is never to abuse it.' But you were really winding me up. (*to Amazon*) She was getting at me.

Amazon and Achillia look at her, eyebrows raised.

Flavia (*throwing her sword down*) I'm going to be stuck here for ever.

Amazon You will if you give up. Pick it up and carry on.

Flavia Do I have to?

Amazon No. It's completely up to you.

Flavia thinks about it. Then picks up the sword and continues practising.

Achillia (*to Amazon, about Flavia*) What are you wasting your time for?

Amazon She'll be fine.

Achillia By the time she is, she'll need a stick to walk with and she'll have turned your hair grey in the process.

Amazon (*laughs*) That was what you used to say about yourself. Now look at you. One of the biggest crowd-pullers in Londinium –

Achillia But for how long?

Amazon You're not jealous, are you? You don't think she'll replace you?

Achillia What is the matter with you? Can't you see what's happening? The crowd don't gasp at the sight of women fighting any more. Now they want bigger and better and bloodier spectacles.

Amazon So we give them something more. You should see what I've been practising with the net and –

Achillia They don't want to see that any more. They only want to see human bodies becoming corpses.

Amazon But we'll be spared because we have skills –

Achillia They don't give a stuffed dormouse about that. When was the last time you actually went out there? Because you know, they no longer take bets on who's going to win but on how long it will take them to die. For Christ's sake.

Amazon Who?

Achillia You are just so out of touch you're a liability.

Amazon I think I might be. That's why I've been thinking more and more about retiring.

Achillia Really?

Amazon Yes, I think these games should be our last.

Achillia You do? (*then*) But what will we live on?

Amazon I know you haven't seen much to convince you but I haven't done such a bad job with Flavia there. We could set up a training school.

Achillia You mean it?

Amazon (*nods*) I thought you'd be pleased.

Achillia Just relieved. Really relieved.

Achillia goes. Amazon goes over to Flavia.

Flavia I'm so –

Amazon I don't need an apology, I need an explanation.
Flavia She reminded me of someone.
Amazon Ah.
Flavia You see –
Amazon No, you see. You will never move forward if you try and use your past to punish others.
Flavia Are you still going to get me out of here?
Amazon I am teaching you to get yourself out of here. You're the only person holding you back.

SCENE NINE

Trifosa (*doing, or fiddling with, her nails*) I didn't quite know what to expect when I reached the other side. Well, of course, I wasn't expecting to reach the other side so suddenly. And I wasn't expecting it to be like this. Trifosa is a pet name given to me by my parents. It means delicious. Well, the big cat back there certainly thought so. I know you've got my number. I always thought of myself as special, better than the rest. The fat, the hopeless and the weedy kid right from the time we all had to play in the sandpit together always got on my nerves. I couldn't stand their humourless, lifeless miserable whining. I got pleasure baiting them. The more I did it the more I wanted to and the better I became at it. And I could barely conceal my smile when, because of me, they cried. Sometimes, even on my own, I would laugh out loud, the memory was so pleasurable. I never touched them, much less hit or assaulted them, but here I've been given a worse room than a whole heap of mass murderers. What's more, they're allowed to sleep whereas I haven't been allowed so much as a catnap. Someone out the back just told me that I'll probably have to start again and for every horrible thing I said or did back then, I'll have to do a good one. How long will that take? It makes me exhausted just thinking about it.

SCENE TEN

Flavia is with three other female gladiators.

Amazon (*to Flavia*) Now show us what you can do.
Flavia (*turns to the imaginary Emperor*) We who are about to –
Amazon (*stops her*) No, no, no. We never say that until the real thing. It's bad luck.
Flavia Right.
Amazon When I lower my hand. (*She lowers her hand.*)

Flavia then turns and with a wooden sword fights every other female gladiator in turn. Amazon then leads the others in clapping and cheering. Flavia goes over to her.

(*to the others*) Thank you. You can go.

They go.

What's the matter now? You would have just got the thumbs-up for every bout.
Flavia This is just pretend.
Amazon But it's shown you that you've now got the skills to go out there and win.
Flavia I know –
Amazon And?
Flavia I don't want to. I don't want to die.
Amazon You won't. You've just proved that.
Flavia But I don't want to have to kill anyone, either.

Pause. Amazon looks at her.

Amazon (*making sure that they're not overheard*) Nor will you have to do that.

Flavia What?

Amazon Shush, keep your voice down.

Flavia Well, what do you mean, I won't have –

Amazon Just that –

Flavia Why have you spent so much time teaching me everything if –

Amazon (*confides*) We have to put on a convincing show and make it look like we've fought with every fibre of our being to the very brink of death. Then, weary and exhausted, we both take off our helmets or lay down our weapons to signal a truce. The crowd is so pleased with us and our performance that they applaud and cheer their approval and we are allowed to live another day.

Flavia But how do you know that the other gladiators will go along with it?

Amazon It's prearranged of course. Trust me. Achillia and I have done this many times.

Flavia When it comes to it, though, how do you know you can really trust them?

Amazon How do you ever really know who you can trust? You have to take a risk sometimes.

Flavia What? With your whole life?

Amazon It can seem like that. But don't worry, you won't be. I've arranged the programme so you'll be fighting me.

Flavia And then I'll be able to find my way out?

Amazon Yes. If you truly commit to all I've taught you, then you'll be free, just like me, to do whatever you want.

SCENE ELEVEN

Everyone is now assembled below the podium. The musicians. acrobats, Vendor of Snacks, the Fortune Teller and the Ticket Tout. The atmosphere is full of tension and excitement.

Ticket Tout Tickets still available. Last few. Standing room only for the fight of the decade between Amazon and Achillia. Come on, people, it'll cost you, but I can still get you in.

Vendor Snacks. Get your stuffed dormice and baby thrushes here. Three for the price of two. (*Offers them to audience, one of whom takes and eats one.*) Lovely and crunchy, aren't they? It's their tiny little bones.

Music starts, trumpets fanfare and the Centurion(s) leads the Criminals out under the stands.

Octavia How come they get to watch?

Centurion 2 Got to do something to get their blood-lust up. Besides, I'm not missing this.

Games Master (*from the arena, to the crowd*) My Lord, ladies, vestal virgins, rabble and barbarians, what you have all been waiting for. The fight between the cream of the fairer gladiators. Please put your hands together for Achillia and Amazon.

Thunderous applause. Achillia and Amazon come out and nod to each other in greeting. The bell goes.

Amazon (*in unison*) We who are about to die salute you.

Achillia (*in unison*) We who are about to die salute you.

They start to fight. Each of them uses skilful moves and tricks which earn them the crowd's approval. Flavia stands below, looking up, waiting her turn.

The Fortune Teller, Claudia, Octavia, Carpophorus, the Centurion(s) and the Criminals stand with her, all reacting to the amazing fight.

Amazon and Achillia have one last exhausted swipe at each other, then take their helmets off or put down their weapons, and kneel down to signal a truce. The little group starts clapping but the crowd starts booing.

The chant goes up: 'Iugula, iugula.'

Games Master The crowd chants, 'Iugula.' They must fight to the death.

Flavia gasps. Amazon and Achillia look at each other. Achillia stands up. Amazon doesn't move. Achillia picks up her sword. Amazon stands. Achillia indicates that she too should pick up her sword. Amazon does so reluctantly but doesn't raise it. Achillia runs up and shoves the sword into Amazon, who offers no resistance. The crowd cheers their approval. Achillia then has to ensure Amazon is dead by cutting her throat.

The Master of the Games comes on with two soldiers, who drag Amazon's body off. Achillia turns away as the crowd scream for more. Flavia is terrified.

Centurion 2 Oi, Flavia. It really is your turn. Get out there.

As Flavia makes her way to the arena everyone in turn offers his or her advice.

Carpophorus You better hope that the fight's gone out of her.

Claudia (*giving her a sexy garment*) Put this on. It's your only chance to wow them.

Octavia I've got a new supply of antimony. Have some, go on –

Carpophorus If she's going to have any chance at all she's got to fight like a man.

Woman (*giving her a weapon shaped like a hammer*) Take this.

Criminal 1 Put an animal skin on and fight like an animal. That's your only hope of surviving.

Criminal 2 Don't matter what she does – if she don't please the crowd she's dead meat.

Man (*giving her a mask*) Put this on. Don't let anyone see what you're feeling.

Carpophorus (*giving her a spear*) Take this.

Claudia (*giving her a gold breastplate*) Put this on.

Octavia (*giving the make-up*) Put this on.

Fortune Teller Take this lucky charm.

Weighed down by everything she's been given, Flavia goes into the ring.

Criminal 3 Never mind dignity. Give up now.

Centurion 2 Any more talk like that and you'll go straight back to your cell.

Flavia is now facing Achillia.

Achillia Do you think you can frighten me? Nothing can frighten me now. I am the most deadly of all opponents because I have nothing to lose. Come on, fight me.

Flavia (*putting down each item she's been given as she speaks*) I don't want to fight you. I don't even want to frighten you. I don't want to be something I'm not. I don't need your approval and I'm not going to pretend so I can get it. If I'm going to do this, and it looks like I have to, I'm going to do it as me.

She steps forward into the arena. Great applause, cheering, roar of the crowd and ringing of the bell. Achillia runs towards her, as the crowd chants for Flavia –

SCENE TWELVE

The crowd can be heard chanting 'Flavia, Flavia', which is mixed with the sound of a radio news bulletin. The crowd's cheering fades as the radio announces:

Radio Finally, it has been confirmed today that the young woman who was pulled alive from the rubble following the terrorist attack on London Underground did in fact find Bouddica's grave. Archaeologists can confirm that the final resting place of the great warrior queen, which has been the subject of much curiosity over the past two millennia, is indeed under Platform 8 at King's Cross Station. The curator of the British Museum is understandably delighted at the find and told this programme that it couldn't have come at a better time. The new Roman Wing is due to be officially opened later this week.

Flavia is sitting in a chair in her bedroom. There is a knock. She switches off the radio. Julia comes in.

Julia Hi . . .
Flavia Hello?
Julia Your mum said it was OK to come up.
Flavia Did she tell you that I can't remember much?
Julia Yes. She thought seeing me might help.
Flavia I'm sorry but I don't . . . (*remember you*).
Julia We only met once . . .

Beat.

Flavia (*remembering*) You were the train driver?
Julia That's right.
Flavia And because I didn't get off the train when I should, you nearly lost your life –
Julia We both nearly did. But now we're both heroes.

Flavia You might be. (*Nods towards the brooch.*) I only found that brooch and I can't remember how I did that.

Julia And you managed to crawl your way out. Loads of people would have given up.

Flavia I can't remember anything much about it.

Julia They've invited me – to the special do, opening thing at the British Museum. (*picking up the brooch*) They said they'd asked you so you could present it officially.

Chloe comes in.

Chloe Sorry, I didn't realise you had a visitor – your mum said it was OK.

Flavia (*pleased to see her*) Hi. Do you remember the tube driver?

Julia Julia.

Chloe Hi.

Flavia This is Chloe – my best friend.

Julia The one you told me about?

Flavia Did I?

Chloe So you've got your memory back?

Flavia Bits. Just now. I remembered who Julia was.

Julia Are you going to go to the ceremony at the British Museum?

Flavia I don't know. What about you?

Julia (*giving Flavia back the brooch*) I don't fancy going on my own. I'll leave my number with your mum. Will you let me know what you decide?

Flavia Yeah. Thanks.

Julia goes.

Chloe You going to take her up on that?

Flavia I dunno – why?

Chloe N.O.T.

Flavia (*laughs*) N? O? (*remembering*) Oh, not – our – type. I'd forgotten all about that. How are Tara and Lisa?

Chloe The same.

Flavia Hasn't it made any difference to them then?

Chloe If it did they're too cool to admit it. I told them I had to see my gran today.

Flavia You didn't tell them you were coming here?

Chloe So you remember what they're like.

Flavia I do, yeah.

Chloe I knew you'd understand.

Flavia (*turning the brooch over in her hand*) Chloe, do you still want to be my friend?

Chloe Look, it's not me –

Flavia Then who is it?

Chloe It's them.

Flavia If you don't like me for who I am –

Chloe I didn't say that –

Flavia – then I don't need a friend like you.

Chloe What are you saying?

Flavia Just that. You go and tell Lisa and Tara that they're free of me, because I don't want to steal, lie, or humiliate myself any more just so as I can hang out with you.

SCENE THIRTEEN

The new Roman Room of the British Museum. The Curator, Flavia and Julia stand together. Behind them the characters from the amphitheatre, or as many as possible, are now statues or exhibits behind gauze and if possible not revealed until Flavia declares the room open.

Curator Ladies and gentlemen, it gives me enormous pleasure to be standing here in one of the newly refurbished Roman Rooms of the British Museum. Little did I know when the work started over two years ago that the centrepiece would, thanks to the brave young woman who found it, in fact be Boudicca's long-lost brooch. So without further ado I would like to ask Flavia to say a few words and officially open the wing.

Flavia Thank you, but I feel a bit of a fraud standing here. I always thought history was boring. I didn't know anything about Boudicca and to be honest I don't really recall much about that day either except when we got on the train I remember thinking, 'Today can't get any worse.' Which shows just how much I know.

I do know I owe my life to Julia the tube driver, who kept calm and put my safety before hers, and the firemen who later rescued me from the rubble. Somewhere in between those two events, when I thought I was going to be stuck for ever alone in the darkness, I remember feeling only fear and really wanting to give up. Then something happened, something which seemed more powerful than myself was urging me on. And I do now know something about Boudicca. She was a woman who wasn't afraid to do what she thought was right, who stood up for what she believed in, and whose courage I've found truly inspiring. I still think a lot of history's boring but what I know now has made me realise that I am just a part of a much bigger picture. And so I'm delighted to be able to present this brooch to the Museum and declare this room well and truly open.

She cuts the ribbon or pulls a cord or simply gestures to reveal the tableau behind them.

Music: 'Search for the Hero'.

The End.

Journey to the Centre of Yourself

Sarah Daniels interviewed by Jim Mulligan

Dust is the second play Sarah Daniels has had in *Connections*, the first one having been *Taking Breath*. Her 1983 play *Masterpieces* has been produced around the world and was selected by the National Theatre as one of the hundred best plays of the twentieth century.

The idea of writing a play about female gladiators came from a newspaper cutting sent by at least three people to Sarah Daniels with the message, 'This could be the play for you.' The article described how the grave of a female gladiator had been found near the site of the London Amphitheatre in Southwark.

> The fact that these people, who knew my work and my desire to put women characters centre stage, thought it was a project for me seemed like an omen. For the next few months when anyone asked me what I was doing I would tell them about the idea, my research trips to the Museum of London, the British Museum, the Guildhall, hidden bits of Roman London, the baths at Bath and even the Coliseum in Rome. They too thought it was a great idea. This enabled me to delude myself into thinking that when I did sit down to start work the play would write itself. Of course it was at that point I became stuck – or do I mean unstuck? When I really started to think about it, I didn't want to do it. I don't like the idea of women boxing (I don't like the idea of anyone boxing, which is probably the nearest sport we have left over from gladiatorial combat). And I certainly didn't like the idea of women killing each other for entertainment.

So I decided to write about something else. But what? And what of Suzy Graham-Adriani, who'd commissioned the play, and the people who were so excited about the idea of women gladiators? I then began thinking about approval. How much it meant to me. What was I prepared to do to get it? How it's difficult at any age but much more painful to go against the flow when you're a teenager. And so the gladiatorial idea became a metaphor for a young woman, so desperate to be part of the group she tries to buy their friendship and ultimately betrays herself in the attempt. Her 'fight' becomes a journey during which she finds the courage to be true to herself.

Dust starts with a group of young women and their teacher on the Underground going to see a Shakespeare play at the Globe in Southwark. Lisa, the leader of the gang, is goading Flavia, trying to come between her and Chloe, who is torn between maintaining her friendship with Flavia and being accepted by the other girls. At this point an unattended bag is found and the train is evacuated, leaving the driver and Flavia on board. There is an explosion and Flavia finds herself in a disused tunnel under King's Cross Station with Boudicca. (Boudicca's body is thought to be under Platform 8.) Before they part, Bo addresses the audience with one of three pivotal monologues in the play. This one is a reflection on suicide. It is light-hearted but deadly serious.

I don't necessarily agree that 'It's better to be a hammer than an anvil', but it is the sort of thing Bo would have said. She is very fiery, but she is also giving some serious advice: if you think it's lonely out there it's much worse here. I am concerned about the rate of suicide among young people and she is saying, 'Don't go there. It's not better.'

Under the arena Flavia encounters the Woman with the Baby, the alter ego of the woman begging on the tube. Her baby is already dead when it is taken from her. She is the girl who stinks of poverty, whose kid died for lack of food, who used her dead baby to smuggle drugs, who abandoned her child, who murdered her child. She sears the audience. 'You look at me like I'm shit on your shoes but you cannot shake my dust from your feet. You have always revelled in reviling me. You are more concerned with making sure animals don't become extinct than with trying to eradicate me.' Maybe we will think twice next time about ignoring the mother begging on the tube.

> When I set a play in the past I like to be able to connect it to today so that it really feels relevant. What's important is that young people doing the play, wherever they come from, can identify with it and don't think this was all yesterday. We still haven't eradicated poverty, yet we think we're so civilised.

The third monologue is delivered by Trifosa, the posse leader on the tube train. Under the arena she and Claudia are practising their glam-glad act with their long eyelashes and red lips, the mask to hide their cowardice. But their glamour does not save them when they have to go in against wild animals. Trifosa tries to beguile Flavia into taking her place, but she stands up against her and they go to their deaths. She confesses to the audience,
'I always thought of myself as special, better than the rest. I couldn't stand their humourless, lifeless, miserable whining. I got pleasure baiting them. The more I did it the more I wanted to and the better I became at it.'

> Morally I don't agree with retribution but in the Roman part of the story Trifosa and Claudia think they are so glamorous and sexy that it will save them and their lives will never be put at risk. Basically they

are living in a fool's paradise. What Trifosa does is evil in this sense. I think an evil act is when somebody does something nasty or hurtful and enjoys it. We all have the potential to do that.

Dust is intended to put women centre stage but it is not a comment on men or boys or the male gender. Indeed, there are some good, funny parts for boys. The staging can be simple. For example, the announcer at the beginning sets the stage and the audience knows precisely where they are.

Dust is not about creating some amazing spectacle. That can only be done on film. Keep it as simple as possible . . . The central thing about *Dust* is: try to be yourself and do not betray yourself. That affects everybody so I hope those involved in the play will be able to identify with Flavia. I don't think theatre can change the world, but it can change an individual's perception of some aspects of life.

Production Notes

STAGING AND SETTING

Dust is set in two eras: modern-day and Roman London around AD 70. It begins on a packed London Northern Line tube train. A group of students are on a trip to Shakespeare's Globe when an unattended, and ultimately explosive, package is discovered. Desperate to escape the so-called friends she is with, Flavia hides on the train while everyone else is evacuated to safety. Finding herself trapped beneath the rubble of an explosion, she wants to give up, but then finds that the only way out is along a disused tunnel. From under King's Cross station, where Boudicca is reputedly buried, Flavia finds herself in Roman London, specifically in the amphitheatre under the Guildhall, where the mob's lust for blood is paralleled by the cruelty of the so-called friends who left her behind in the present day. Forced to confront her fears in the gladiatorial arena, she seeks the courage to face life anew. The play ends where it began, in modern-day London, when Flavia is transported back to her bedroom and then to an exhibition in the Roman Room of the British Museum. As Flavia opens the exhibition by cutting a ribbon or pulling a cord, a tableau is revealed where characters from the amphitheatre are now statues or exhibits behind gauze.

The shift from location to location should be achieved as simply as possible. The tube can be suggested through the movement of the actors and by lighting and sound. The tube announcements can be used variously and may also be under the dialogue at moments. It does not matter if the audience do not hear the cue for Robert's 'Charing Cross', for instance, the reaction of the other passengers will make this clear. Keep sound effects to a minimum. The audience might see the tube scene from different angles. You might have the action shift from the profile of the carriage to the driver's perspective of the vehicle. There is no need to create sparks and the like, but you can give the impression of speed through the knocking of bodies together and through the swaying which comes from unsteadiness. The tunnel might be suggested through sound and lighting; the arena might be indicated with a round floor cloth. This would define the space nicely for the actors involved in the more physical scenes. There is much activity from the actors, and scene changes can be easily covered and become part of the action. Try your best to avoid blackouts and let the action flow from scene to scene as seamlessly as possible. For instance, the cheering of the crowd at the end of Scene Eleven might cut into the end of Flavia's speech, taking us directly into Scene Twelve. But there are stiller moments – the monologues, for instance. Think carefully about where to place the actors here: a monologue might easily cover a scene change. Sarah has suggested some music tracks and it's important to keep to those indicated, or at least to use contemporary music carrying similar sentiments.

Costume detail should be simple. It will help make the shift from modern to Roman times clearer. The armoury design could borrow from the protective wear of skateboarders and cyclists. Contemporary garb such as bumbags might be adapted, and there are some great synthetic animal fabrics around. If you choose helmets for the actors, these should not obscure their faces – the audience needs to recognise individuals.

Avoid using stage blood. It rarely works as an effect and you'll have real wardrobe issues. If you manage a realistic effect from blood you'll probably leave the audience behind in terms of plot as they wonder how you achieved it.

There are weapon-hire firms. But you might choose a non-naturalistic approach to the fight sequences without the use of swords. Wooden, painted weapons are an option but steel is better because you get that lovely clashing sound.

The cast could be around seventeen in size, 12 f and 5 m (Sarah has suggested where doubling might be used); however, you can make it as big as you like. There is endless scope for non-speaking extras who, at various times, can help to create the passengers on the tube and the onstage and offstage characters in the amphitheatre. Remember that although the play is set in London, the students on the trip can be from anywhere in the world.

EXERCISES

Fight Direction The key is to aim for maximum effect with the greatest safety. If you're using swords always make sure the actors move with the hardware pointing down and don't allow running. Remember when choreographing a fight that parrying (the defensive action of deflecting or blocking an attacking weapon with your own weapon) should not be a matter of necessity; the actor making the attack should direct it in such a way that if the actor defending makes the wrong parry or block, the attack will not hit them. If the actor's safety is dependant upon making the correct parry, then in all probability the fight is unsafe and risks genuine injury.

Explore some basic handling exercises working on a star pattern that moves through the vertical, horizontal and diagonal. The weapons should cleave on the diagonal whilst the handgrip is a little like that of a handshake. The free hand should be kept close to the body. In exploring the star pattern exercise, develop it to include the body in the swing.

Using a figure of eight, look for variations to build on the pattern, such as the use of both hands with the weapon blade in a flat plane as if slicing between ribs. Pay attention to breathing. Bending the legs and aiming for a compact physique will give a more assured appearance. Experiment with lowering the physical centre by splaying the legs.

Try this series of lunges:

- A leg lunge where one foot moves away.
- A cross step where the leg moves across the front of your own centre.
- A slip step where the leg moves across and behind your own centre.

Try a series of blocking movements using the body as quartered areas. Define the imaginary body as waist-high, waist-low, and through the vertical centre of the body. When parrying an attack above the waist, it is better to hold the point of a weapon high.

Be aware that in the articulation of stage fights, larger movements read better and if there is constant movement the actors look faster. They allow more time for the actor to adjust to the new focus of the fight. The movements need to be seen and there needs to be a consciously scripted story.

Fights should be conducted with frequent eye-to-eye contact so that the participants can check in with each other before each move. After every move, there needs to be a rechecking through eye contact. You need to do this as a general rule, but there will be specific places where this checking in, this eye contact, is essential before continuing with the fight.

It is important to keep movements to the edge of the body. If there is a shift from one side to the other, this needs to be achieved through vertical (not horizontal) carrying of the weapon. It's also important that this occurs within your half of the space.

When working out the fight sequence, structure a series of five to seven set moves. The set moves should vary in number from section to section. For example: section one, three moves; section two, five moves; section three, four moves; and so on. You can also work in the idea of the fight coming to a momentary standstill and involve the adversaries offering conspicuous acknowledgement. You might include a ceremonial adoption of armory, or the taking off of a helmet to signal a truce.

Headline each sequence. For instance, a sequence could be labelled Titanic Fight/Equally Matched.

Discover how silence can help to heighten audience unease and noise can signal aggression.

Within the fight there should be shifts of power and position and around twenty moves within the sequence. An attack and a block constitute one movement. Ideal the fight sequences should last between thirty and forty-four seconds.

Changes in the lighting state can be used to cheat the passage of time. The fight pace may move between slow motion and real time and the use of circling can heighten the menace of the fight.

Moves can be repeated and the angles of view for the audience varied.

It is very important to avoid giving in to real aggression. The most successful stage antagonists are the most caring and considerate of working partners.

Focus on a fight sequence involving Flavia. Use a mixture of real time and slow motion. Engineer Flavia's growth in power by having her do less and become slower in her movement. See how having her command the space more helps create the impression she's got the upper hand. When casting this part you might consider giving this role to a small actress and pit her against a bulkier opponent. Make it clear Flavia is capable of killing but doesn't want to exercise this power. The fight should not be about her power but more about her choices and the recognition of herself as an individual.

Discover how some characters might resort to foul tactics such as biting, face-kicking and hair-pulling. In contrast, some characters might show mercy.

Look at the fight between Amazon and Achillia in Scene Eleven. Look at the sequence which begins with the submission which can be signalled by the sword or dagger being turned down (see page 192). See how many different ways you can stage the throat-cutting. It could be done with Amazon's back to the audience. The throat-cutting could be a tender and emotional response, making the fight personal.

RESEARCH

Much is written about the Roman Era, and the London Underground. Sarah Daniels consulted a number of these books when writing *Dust*:

Roman Life by John Guy (Snapping Turtle Guide: 1-86007-072-8)
A Visitors' Guide to Ancient Rome (Osborne Timetours: 0-7460-306-409)
Roman London by Dominic Perring (Seaby: 1-85264-039-1)

Emperors and Gladiators: All in a Day's Work by Anita Gavers (Heinemann: 0-431-05578-2)
The Northern Line: an Illustrated History by Mike Horne and Bob Bayman (1-854-14-208-9)
The Roman World: a Source Book by David Cherry (Blackwell: 0-631-21784-3)
Interfact Romans (Toucan: 0-85434-903-1)
London under London: a Subterranean Guide by Richard French and Ellis Hillman (John Murray: 0-7195-5288-5)
Roman Britain by John Wacher (Sutton: 0-7509-2766-6)
History of Ancient Rome by Nathaniel Harris (Chancellor Press: 0-7537-0547-8)
Gladiators at the Guildhall by Nick Bateman (Museum of London Archaeology Service: 1-901992-19-5)
London's Disused Underground Stations by J. E. Connor (0-947699-29-5)
The Roman Record by Paul Dodswell (Osborne: 0-7460-2753-2)
Londinium: London in the Roman Empire by John Morris (Rhocinc Giants: 0-75380-660-6)
Gladiators: the Bloody Truth (0-14-029934-3)

Suzy Graham-Adriani
March 2003
based on a workshop facilitated
by Suzi Graham-Adriani with Richard Ryan

THE ICE PALACE

Lucinda Coxon

adapted from *Is-Slottet*,
a novel by Tarjei Vesaas,
translated from the Norwegian
by Elizabeth Rokkan

Lucinda Coxon works extensively as a film and theatre writer in the UK and US. Her other works for the stage include *Waiting at the Water's Edge*, *Three Graces*, *Wishbones*, *Nostalgia* and *I Am Angela Brazil by Angela Brazil*. Her most recent film release is *The Heart of Me*, starring Helena Bonham-Carter and Paul Bettany. She is currently under commission by the Royal Court Theatre, the National Theatre and South Coast Repertory Theater.

Characters

Siss, eleven years (female)
Unn, eleven years (female)
Mother (Siss's)
Father (Siss's)
Auntie (Unn's)
Teacher (male or female)
Torill, eleven years (female)
Helle, eleven years (female)
Inge, eleven years (female)
Selma, eleven years (female)
Erik, eleven years (male)
Klaus, eleven years (male)
Mats, teenager (male)
Searchers, minimum five (male/female)
Shadows, three (male/female)
Echo (female)

Stage directions are suggestions to help provide a picture for the reader. They should be deemed optional in rehearsal/production.

In the text, the scenes are clearly divided. I would not expect those divisions to be anything like as distinct in production.

Staging

I have assumed an upper and lower stage level and also an area dominated by verticals to represent the dredging poles, the Forest and the Ice Palace.

On the stage, a model village with little squares of orange, glowing from within, to mark the windows. The model should stay onstage throughout.

ONE

The Forest.

Afternoon. It's dark, but there's a moon that casts long shadows.

Siss starts to walk on the spot, facing front, full of purpose.

Siss The most important thing to remember when making your way through the woods in the dark–

Shadow 1 – especially on a very very cold afternoon in late autumn –

Shadow 2 – afternoon but already dark –

Shadow 3 – bundled up against the frost –

Siss – is never, never, never, never . . . to run. You can walk very fast, but it must be a walk. One foot on the ground at all times. Otherwise the things at the sides of the road can get you. Likewise, you must not look round if you hear a suspicious noise . . .

Shadow 1 A young white forehead, boring through the darkness –

Siss – but keep your eyes focused on the path ahead . . .

Shadow 2 an eleven-year-old girl –

Siss – and your mind fixed on your destination . . .

Shadow 3 Siss!

Then Siss's Mother calls:

Mother Siss! Why, Siss!

Siss is irritated. Keeps walking.

Siss Yes, what is it now?
Mother You're so excited you forgot your mittens! (*Siss's Mother flaps a pair of mittens.*)
Siss Oh . . .
Mother Your little hands'll freeze right off!

Siss keeps walking on the spot. Her Mother pushes the mittens onto her hands.
Siss's Father appears.

Father She'd forget her head if it were loose!
Mother She's just excited.
Father And maybe a little afraid!
Siss Am not.
Mother Afraid of what?
Father Of the dark.
Siss I'm not a baby.

There is a loud crack from the lake. Siss flinches.

Father It's only the ice on the lake.
Siss I know that.
Mother Should one of us go with you? I could fetch my coat and . . .
Siss No! I'm going by myself. I'll be all right.
Mother But . . .
Father It's the main road most of the way.
Siss See.
Mother So long as you're sure . . .
Father What's this new girl's name again?
Shadows (*whisper*) Unn, Unn, Unn!
Siss Oh! Stop it, you're making me late!

Siss flaps her parents away in a rage of impatience.

They disappear. She resumes:

Yes . . . keep your mind fixed on your destination. And stick to the path, because on either side is the forest and the undergrowth . . . deathly still with everything that might be alive and shivering in there at the moment . . .

But while she's talking a group of schoolchildren emerge slowly, from the darkness of the forest. Siss senses something, stops, listens hard, afraid.

Do you ever get the feeling . . . that you're being watched?

The children start to whisper noisily.

All What's the time, Mr Wolf?

Siss spins round, terrified, screams out, her heart racing. The children complain.

Inge You're not supposed to look round.

Siss laughs with relief that it's just her schoolmates.

Siss It's just you!
Torill Who else would it be?
Siss I don't know.
Helle Now turn back.
Erik And cover your eyes.

Siss does so. The children whisper again and steal towards Siss, all except one, Unn, who remains silent and still. Siss strains to hear the footsteps. The breath that approaches . . .

All What's the time, Mr Wolf? (*They stop.*)
Siss One o'clock.

They move again.

All What's the time, Mr Wolf?
Siss Two o'clock . . .
All What's the time, Mr Wolf?
Siss . . . Dinnertime!

She turns on the others and they scatter away, squealing with excitement. She tries to catch a couple of them but fails. Then she sees Unn. Stops in her tracks.

Siss You're not running.
Unn I'm not afraid.

Siss is nonplussed.

Siss You have to be, it's the whole point of the game.
Unn I'm not playing.
Siss Oh. Are you going to play later?
Unn No.
Siss Why?
Unn I can't?
Siss Why not?
Unn Why ask?
Siss It might be fun . . .
Unn I don't want to talk about it. And I don't want you to ask me again.

Siss is taken aback.

Siss Sure.
Unn I have to go now. My aunt will worry if I'm late.

Unn leaves. Siss watches her go, then realises that she has forgotten about her journey. Resumes walking, slightly shaken.

Siss Yes . . . your mind fixed . . . on your . . .

Unn appears in the orange-lighted window of her home. Looks out for Siss. Siss senses it.

your destination . . .

Siss closes her eyes, breathes in the sensation of being watched, keeps walking. The schoolchildren run in, passing a note from hand to hand, teasing. Siss suddenly opens her eyes.

Give me that!

Helle 'I must meet you, Siss,' signed Unn!

Siss chases the girl and catches the note off her, but immediately another one calls out.

Klaus 'When can I meet you, Unn?', signed Siss!

She chases him and again retrieves the note. But immediately:

Torill 'Whenever you like, Unn! You can meet me today!'

They toss the crumpled note to one another, making Siss jump after it, then throw it high in the air and run away. Siss grabs the note.

Siss Today.

Siss makes a secret promise sign to the invisible sender.

After all this time of waiting and watching . . . of hide-and-seeking . . . of imagining the day when . . .

A voice cuts through the air.

Unn Hello, Siss.

Siss sees Unn standing in the lighted doorway. She savours the sight. Beat.

Siss Hello, Unn.

They stand apart, tense for a moment. Then Unn laughs and the atmosphere is playful.

Unn At last.
Siss Yes.
Unn Must've been dark.
Siss Doesn't bother me.
Unn Freezing cold too.
Siss Doesn't bother me either.
Unn You've been here before. A long time ago.
Siss Before I knew about you.

Auntie appears behind Unn:

Auntie Siss! Come along in quickly! It's too cold to stand out there. Come into the warm.
Unn Come into the warm.

They follow her in.

Auntie Now take off your things.

Siss starts to undo her boots, watching Unn all the while.

Do you remember how it looked when you came here before? A long time ago, now. I've seen you since then, around and about. But there was nothing to bring you back here till now. Till Unn came to live with me. I'm lucky to have her . . .
Unn Auntie . . .
Auntie I know, I know! I'm carrying on! Now Siss must have a hot drink to warm her up . . .

Siss looks to Unn; Unn shakes her head.

Siss I'm really not cold, thank you.
Unn I have my own room. We'll go there.
Auntie Are you sure?
Unn Are you coming?

Siss smiles.
Unn guides Siss into the room.
Siss looks around – she's dreamt of this.

Unn Is your room bigger?
Siss About the same.
Unn There's no need for anything bigger.
Siss I agree.
Unn Please.

She points to a chair. Siss sits. Unn sits on the bed. A long uncomfortable silence, then Unn gets up and locks the door.

Siss Why did you do that?
Unn She might come in. I wanted us to be alone together.
Siss Oh. Yes. Of course. At last!

Unn sits down again.

Unn How old are you?
Siss Eleven and a bit.
Unn And me.
Siss We're the same height too.
Unn Yes. (*Beat.*)
Siss Do you like it here?
Unn My aunt's kind.
Siss No – I meant . . . at school . . .
Unn I don't mind it.
Siss You get good marks!
Unn I study hard.
Siss Why don't you join in more?
Unn I told you not to ask.
Siss Sorry. I didn't mean to . . .
Unn Don't go on about it . . .
Siss No. (*Beat.*) Are you going to stay here now?

Unn fixes her with a stare. Considers.

Unn I've nowhere else to go. (*Beat.*) Why don't you ask about my mother?
Siss I . . . I don't know.

Unn No?

Siss Because I heard she died, I suppose.

Unn She wasn't married. In case you heard that too.

Siss Oh. No. I mean, yes.

Unn Last spring she fell ill. She was sick for just a week, then –

Unn draws her finger across her throat with some relish, unsettling Siss.

Siss Sorry.

Unn Do you know anything about my father?

Siss shakes her head.

Nor me. Some things mother told me. I've never seen him. He had a car.

Siss That's nice.

Unn Do you think?

Siss Better than not.

Unn I shall stay with Auntie for ever now.

Siss is happy again.

Siss Yes. Stay here.

Unn Do you have brothers and sisters?

Siss No.

Unn smiles.

Unn That works out well then, doesn't it?

Siss It means we can meet often.

Unn We meet every day at school as it is. (*Unn laughs.*) Come over here.

Siss hesitates.

Unn Come on!

Siss goes to sit right next to Unn.

I want to show you something.

Unn slides out something from under the bed, lays it across both their laps. It has a scarf wrapped around it. As Siss watches, Unn removes the scarf.

Siss A mirror . . .
Unn Look into it with me . . .

Unn holds up the mirror, looks into it. Siss joins in.

Their attention is drawn further and further into the glass. The light flickers and a dislocated sound of girls' laughter fills the room, echoes louder and louder and louder until it is no longer laughter but the sound of someone crying out . . .

Siss and Unn start to cry out too . . .

The ice cracks on the lake, breaking the trance. Unn and Siss push the mirror away, shaken. A moment.

Siss Did you know . . . about this?
Unn Did you see it too? (*Beat.*)
Siss I don't suppose it was anything.
Unn No.
Siss But it was strange. Cover it over.

Unn does so, puts the mirror back under the bed.

Unn It's gone now.

More silence, until:

Unn I think we should take our clothes off.
Siss Take our . . .?
Unn All of them. It would be fun, wouldn't it?
Siss Would it?

Siss isn't sure, but Unn pulls off her shirt.

Waits. Siss copies. Then Unn pulls off her trousers. Siss hesitates, then joins in. Unn quickly pulls off her underwear and Siss is only moments behind. They stand naked. Look at one another. An extraordinary moment. The signal could be as complicated or as simple as you want to make it. The most important thing is that the two girls consider it grave and binding.

We look the same.

There is a moment of terrible intimacy, vulnerability. Then suddenly Unn is upset.

Unn It's too cold after all. (*She picks up her clothes, starts to pull them back on.*)
Siss No! Not if we jump about! (*Siss jumps up and down on the bed.*)
Unn There's a draught. Can't you feel it?
Siss But it's quite warm here . . .
Unn Put your clothes on, Siss . . . Now! I mean it.

Siss is bewildered, stops bouncing. Suddenly embarrassed, Siss pulls her clothes on again. Unn looks away. When Siss is dressed:

Siss I don't understand.
Unn I don't want to talk about it.
Siss So what will we do now?
Unn We'll think of something.
Siss I hope so, otherwise I might have to go home.

Unn looks round, makes eye contact again.

Unn No – don't do that . . . not yet.
Siss I don't want to.

It's clear that Unn's got to think of something to make Siss stay: suddenly she has an idea.

Unn Do you want to see pictures of where I lived before?
Siss Yeah!
Unn OK . . . (*Unn brightens, takes out a small folder.*) Look! This is my mother.

Siss looks.

Siss She looks nice.

Unn smiles.

Unn And my father. That's his car.
Siss It's a good one.
Unn Is it?
Siss Where is he now?

Unn shrugs.

Unn If they knew that I don't suppose I'd have come to live here.
Siss No.

They turn a page. Siss laughs.

Ha! That's you!
Unn Yes.
Siss When you were a little baby.
Unn Can I see?

She takes the folder from Siss. Looks at the picture of herself. Is quiet, until:

Siss?
Siss Yes?
Unn There's something I want to . . .
Siss What?
Unn Tell you.
Siss Oh?
Unn Something I've never told anyone.
Siss No one?
Unn Not another living soul.
Siss Not even your mother?
Unn Oh no! Never.

Siss thinks. It seems a bit scary.

Siss All right then.
Unn And if I tell you, you must swear you'll never tell.
Siss I won't.
Unn Are you sure you want to know?
Siss I think so.
Unn Swear it on our friendship, Siss.

Siss thinks a moment, then very seriously makes the promise signal.

Unn repeats it back to her, tries to summon the courage to speak.

Siss waits, nervous now of what Unn might be about to say. But Unn says nothing.

Siss Are you going to say it now?

Unn draws breath, then:

Unn No.

Siss is confused.

Siss I'd like to go now.
Unn Siss?
Siss Yes.
Unn It's something serious – I'm not sure I'll go to heaven.

Siss is shocked, scared. She's got to get out . . .

Siss What?
Unn You heard.
Siss I have to go now.
Unn Not yet . . .
Siss I have to be back before my parents go to bed.
Unn They won't go to bed yet . . .

Siss stands up. Unn bars her way.

Siss I have to go.
Unn Why?

Siss I told you. Let me go. (*Beat.*)

Unn unlocks the door without a word.
Siss goes through, starts pulling on her boots and coat. Auntie appears.

Auntie Are you leaving us so soon, Siss?
Siss Yes.
Auntie No secrets left?

The girls look at one another.

Siss Not this evening.
Auntie Is anything the matter?
Unn Of course not.
Auntie Won't you stay and have something to eat?
Unn She has to go home.
Siss Yes – thank you for having me.
Auntie Will you be all right going home?
Siss I'll be fine.
Auntie You must run all the way. It's getting colder and colder. Pitch-dark too.
Siss Yes, I will.

Siss moves to the doorway, but Unn is already there, facing her.

Auntie Unn . . .? You'll be seeing each other at school tomorrow . . .

Unn moves away.

Unn Of course.
Siss Yes.

Unn looks at Auntie. Auntie leaves the two girls alone.

Siss Unn . . .?
Unn Yes?

It's hard to know what to say now.

Siss Tomorrow.

Siss slips out of the house, leaving Unn in the lighted doorway. Siss starts to run towards the forest, but stops, turns, raises her hand in the secret-promise sign, which Unn gratefully returns.

Then, into the forest.

As Siss runs among the trunks, the light on Unn fades and hands slips out of the darkness snatching at her feet and legs.

Shadows Run, Sissy, run Sissy, run, run, run!!

Siss emerges suddenly into a lighted area where Mother and Father stand, surprised to see the state she's in.

Mother What on earth, Siss?
Siss Didn't you . . .?
Father What?

Siss looks behind her. Nothing there.

Mother What's wrong?
Siss Nothing – I was just running.
Mother How hot you are, as if you've been running for your life!
Siss I had to come home before you went to bed, that's all.
Father You knew we wouldn't be in bed for a long time yet . . .
Mother Now, now, it doesn't matter. What was it like at Unn's?
Siss It was nice.
Father I'd never have thought so!
Siss Why do you say that?
Father Your long face.

Siss Why are you picking on me tonight?
Father Siss. We were just joking!
Siss Well, it's not funny.
Mother Have we said anything?
Father No.

Siss pulls off her boots.

Mother Go and have a wash, Siss, it'll make you feel better.

Siss picks up her boots.

And I'll finish supper.
Siss I've already eaten.
Mother At Unn's?

Siss nods, leaves the room.

(*to Father*) I hope *you* still have an appetite.

Father folds up his newspaper.

Father Loss of appetite is strictly for the young.

The parents move off.

In her bedroom, Siss has taken off her shirt. She sits in her vest before a bowl of water, fastens her hair out of her face, looks down into the bowl, still breathing hard.

The light comes up again on Unn gazing out. Siss stares down into the water.

Unn (*to the water*) And we're the same height too.
Siss Yes. Yes. Yes.

Siss splashes the water over her face happily as Unn's light fades and Siss's comes down to blackout.

TWO

Unn's house and Siss's house.
The ice cracks and the lights come up on the two homes.
Both Siss and Unn pull on their coats and pick up schoolbags.

Auntie You're early this morning.
Unn Really?
Auntie I'd say so.
Unn I want to meet Siss.
Auntie I thought as much. Unn – slow down!
Unn What?
Auntie You fasten your coat well first – it's bitter out.
Unn OK, OK.
Auntie And you take an extra pair of mittens.

Unn takes them from her.

Now.

Auntie opens her arms, they embrace.
Siss dashes out of her house. Mother appears in the doorway, calls:

Mother I can't see why you have to go so early . . .
Siss Usually you complain I'm so late!
Mother Take care!

Siss heads into the forest.
Unn breaks away from Auntie, heads into the forest. They walk in determined circles through the trees, crossing one another's paths but oblivious to the fact.
The ice cracks again. They stop dead. Siss shouts loud in reply.

Siss I am going to meet Unn!

Unn I am going to meet Siss!

Then they begin hurrying along again. The sound of birds suddenly leaving the trees. The two girls stop, look up. Then:

Siss But what if she's embarrassed after last night?
Unn But what if she's frightened after last night?

They scurry along again, stopping only when they speak.

Unn I can't meet her today. Only think about her.
Siss But surely it won't matter . . .
Unn I won't think of anything bad today, not at all. Only think of Siss, now that I've found her.
Siss After all, we are friends now.
Unn But what should I do all day if not go to school . . .?

They resume walking again, until Siss rushes round a corner and comes face to face with another running child. The two frighten one another – Siss is particularly startled, cries out. But it's only Inge.

Inge Sorry!
Siss It's OK, I thought you were . . .
Inge Who?

Siss stops herself.

Siss I can't say.
Inge The bogeyman!
Siss (*lying*) Yes!
Inge I knew it!
Siss Are you always so early?
Inge I'm running an errand for my mum before school. How about you?
Siss Couldn't sleep!
Inge Hey, d'you want to go skating after school? There's a few of us getting together . . .

Siss Maybe . . .

Inge The ice was never better!

Siss Have you been to the frozen waterfall yet?

Unn (*offstage*) The ice palace!

Inge The ice palace? No.

Siss My father says it's more than ten years since it last froze up. I was a baby then – we all were!

Unn (*offstage*) That's where I'll go!

Inge Everyone's talking about it.

Unn (*offstage*) But I wanted to see it with Siss . . .

Siss Maybe we'll go at the weekend!

Inge Brilliant! I have to run, now. D'you want to run with me?

Siss No, it's OK. See you later.

Inge Bye!

Inge races off through the woods, disappears. Unn's head appears round a tree. Siss resumes walking.

Unn I'll see it the second time with Siss – even better!

Siss stops, looks round. Unn hides again.

Siss Do you ever get the feeling . . .?

Siss sees nothing, hurries on. Unn watches her until she is out of sight. Whispers:

Unn See you tomorrow, Siss. Tomorrow will be the real beginning of everything.

Unn disappears back into the forest.

THREE

School.

Siss arrives at school. The Teacher is just setting out the chairs.

Teacher Siss. Isn't this a little early for you!
Siss I'm turning over a new leaf.
Teacher We'll see if you can manage it again tomorrow before we jump to any conclusions. Would you finish this?
Siss Of course.

The Teacher leaves Siss setting out the chairs in rows. When she has finished, she sits in her own chair, near the front, and closes her eyes. Enjoys the sensation of imagining what's behind her.

Do you ever get the feeling you're being watched?

She flicks her head round suddenly, but, of course, there's nobody there.

Overhead, on the banks of the river, Unn walks by, her arms outstretched like wings, balancing as she goes.

A schoolbell rings offstage. The Teacher walks in swinging it in his/her hand. The children enter in talkative gaggles. Siss waits by the door.

Torill What's up, Siss?
Siss Why?
Torill I don't know – you seem . . .
Siss I'm fine.

All the seats except Unn's and Siss's are filled. Siss looks out of the door.

Teacher Siss?

She looks round.

Let's not spoil that new leaf.
Siss Oh – no.

Reluctantly, Siss takes her place.

Teacher Unn is missing today, I see. Does anyone know why?

Some of the class look at Siss.

No. Oh well. Now, who has not finished their assignment?

The class looks round. No one.

Good. A volunteer to read?

No one volunteers.

Siss, perhaps, to consolidate her promising start to the day?

Siss grimaces. Stands.

Which of our opening phrases did you choose?

Siss starts to read out her story.

Siss 'The ice on the lake shone bright as polished steel.'

Unn appears overhead again. Looks out over the 'lake'. The sound of the river faint in the background.
Siss looks to the Teacher for approval. S/he nods.

Teacher Good. A simile. What's a simile?
Torill When we say a thing is like another thing.
Teacher Yes. So what's a metaphor? Siss?
Siss When we say it is the other thing.
Teacher Very good.

S/he nods for Siss to continue. As she speaks, Unn inspects the ice at the edge of the lake.

Siss Inside the ice were leaves, reeds, seeds and twigs from the trees. A brown ant was trapped among the bubbles, which looked like beads when the sun caught them.

Unn lies down, slides forward a little way onto the ice. Peers through it.

The girl lay flat on the ice not yet feeling the cold. Her body was a shadow for a stranger one down below. She slid forward over the ice –

Unn does so.

– to the place where the lake falls away and you must be careful if you're not a good swimmer. The shadow followed her, fell down into the lake and disappeared. The girl was scared. But then she saw it again. It looked as if she were lying down below in the clear water. She felt dizzy. How lucky she was lying safe on top of thick thick ice!

Unn pulls back from the ice. Gets up and moves away.

Teacher Very good, Siss. Thank you.

Siss sits down.

And what do we think the girl might do next?

Hands shoot up.
Unn appears on the lower level, runs through the schoolroom, weaving in and out of her classmates, following the course of the river.

Yes? (*S/he points to a boy.*)
Erik She might fetch her skates and go out on the ice.
Teacher Good. Yes. She might.

The Teacher points to a girl whose hand is up.
Unn starts to climb back up to the higher level, still following the river, but there's a new sound now, a roaring in the distance, getting louder as she approaches the top.

Torill She might go home and have some hot chocolate.
Teacher Yes. (*S/he points to another girl.*)

Helle She might go and skim stones in the river.
Teacher Good. (*Points to another.*)
Klaus She might follow the river down to the frozen waterfall.
Teacher And then?
Klaus She might know it was a special place because it only comes in the coldest winters, and it vanishes again in the spring.

Unn has reached the top.

Teacher Good! See how so many different stories can follow from this simple beginning?

The students address themselves to their work.
The roaring of the water becomes deafening. Unn puts her hands over her ears, looks down over the partly frozen fall.
As Unn gets closer to the edge the 'fall' shines blue and green below, puffs of mist rise into the air. Unn is ecstatic, shouts for joy:

Unn Hello!

But the sound is lost. She tries to get closer to the fall, finds a place to climb down and squeeze inside. Inside is dark and spooky. She calls out:

Hey!

An echo answers.

Echo Hey!

Unn is surprised, scared. Tentatively investigates, moving towards the echo, squeezing between columns of ice into another area.

Unn Hey . . .?
Echo Hey . . .?

Unn presses on into the next room, which seems to be a kind of ice forest. She's intimidated by the strangely human structures that form it. Calls out:

Unn Hey . . .?

She waits for the reply. There's no answer. Unn senses danger, starts to panic, looks for a way out. Then the echo calls:

Echo Hey!

Unn calls back, relieved:

Unn Hey!

Unn finds that she is at a doorway, squeezes through into another room, distinguished by a constant dripping sound. A drop of water lands on the back of Unn's neck, then her nose, then onto her outstretched hands. But the dripping sound is slowly overtaken by another. Someone is crying.

As the sound of the crying increases, Unn finds that she too is crying. Then the other crying stops and Unn's cries echo alone. She is afraid again, tries to find a way out – tries to wriggle through a gap, but it's too narrow.

She takes off her satchel and coat and tries again – this time she slips through into a bright watery green room. A much happier place, filled with the roaring of the water.

Unn looks around, calls out:

Unn Hello!

A string of echoes from different directions calls back:

Echo Hello! Hello! Hello!
Unn Hello, Siss!
Echo Hello, Siss! Hello, Siss! Hello, Siss!

In the classroom below Siss looks round to Unn's desk, disturbed by something.

Unn Mother!
Echo Mother! Mother! Mother!
Unn Siss!
Echo Siss! Siss! Siss!

Unn is happier now, finds a dry place and sits down. Rubs her arms against the cold.
The Teacher taps on the top of the desk.

Teacher Siss?

Siss faces front.

Are you listening?
Siss Sorry.

Siss goes back to her work.
The Teacher looks up and down the class.

Teacher Isn't there anybody who's friends with Unn and knows if she might be ill?

The class look round at one another, at Siss. Beat.

Is she so lonely?
Siss No, she's not.
Teacher Siss?
Siss Yes.
Teacher Do you know what's wrong with Unn today?
Siss I haven't seen her today.
Teacher But you are her friend?
Siss Yes.
Helle No she's not!
Siss What do you know?
Teacher There's no need for that!
Siss I was with Unn at her house last night.
Teacher And she was all right then?

Siss Yes, she was.

Teacher Good. Well in that case perhaps you'd call in on the way home and find out what's the matter. You don't mind the extra walk, do you?

Siss No.

Teacher Thank you. So now we've established that, perhaps you could all continue with your work.

The children put their heads down again, but all secretly watch Siss after her outburst. The Teacher watches her too. Siss is aware of it, and keeps her face close to her book.

In the ice palace, Unn sits sleepily. Then a red glow seems to penetrate the ice, burn towards her. As the red light of the winter sun starts to fill the palace, the sound of the dripping water starts to play a strange insistent tune, a child's lullaby.

Unn Did you ever get the feeling . . .

The red beam gets stronger. Shines hard into Unn's face. She stares hard back.

. . . you were being watched?

She becomes transfixed, at first as though she's afraid of the light, but then as though it's someone she recognises . . . someone she's been waiting for . . . She smiles.

What are you looking for? Here I am. I've been here all the time.

Unn laughs to herself, delighted.

Siss looks up at all the faces around her.

Unn I'm not afraid. I haven't done anything . . .

Unn stretches out her arms in the warmth.

You won't go away, will you . . .? No. No, not this time.

Unn curls towards the wall, and goes to sleep.
In the classroom:

Teacher Now before you leave . . . the weather report indicates a change this afternoon. It seems the cold spell is coming to an end and the lake will no longer be safe for skating.

Groans of disappointment.

On the other hand, it also means that there is an increased possibility of . . .

A ripple of excitement runs around the class.

Helle Is it . . .?
Erik Will it?
Teacher Snow.

Klaus is already out of his seat and out of the door. As the others hurriedly pack up:

Torill Shall I walk with you to Unn's house, Siss?
Siss There's no need.
Torill Suit yourself.

Klaus rushes back in, plunges his hand into his satchel and pulls out a handful of 'snow'. Tosses it over his head.

Klaus It's started!

The others follow suit, cheering. As the snow is thrown we are out of the classroom and on the way home. As Siss fights her way through the crowd of schoolmates they toss the 'snow' over her. She keeps struggling to the front of the over-excited group, then getting pushed to the back,
Finally she breaks away and gets ahead of them in the forest. Siss runs now, runs and runs until she

emerges near Unn's. There is a covering of snow over everything.

Auntie carries a pile of wood back towards the house. Siss sees her, calls:

Siss Auntie?

Auntie looks round, is suprised.

Auntie Oh, it's you, Siss.

Then:

Has something happened to Unn?
Siss What?
Auntie Why have you come and not Unn?
Siss But surely, Unn's at home . . . ?
Auntie Didn't she come to school this morning?

Siss shakes her head, suddenly starts to feel afraid.

Oh no . . . oh no . . .

Auntie runs around to the side of the house. Siss follows a little way, but Auntie reappears and runs to the other side.

Siss Where is she?
Auntie Run home, Siss, run home and raise the alarm, quick before it gets dark. Run home and raise the alarm. Go!

Auntie hurries off in the opposite direction. After a moment, Siss dashes back into the forest, her father appears almost immediately, catches her in his arms, lifts her up. Siss cries out:

Siss Unn has gone! She's disappeared!

As Siss turns high in the air, the forest starts to fill with orange lanterns, swinging in the darkness as the search begins.

FOUR

The Forest.

The low tones of the adults calling out:

Searchers Unn!

The search party swarms about, converging and dispersing.

Searcher 1 If only the snow had come yesterday!
Searcher 2 Then there would have been tracks.
Searcher 1 Now it's come too late and made matters worse.
Searcher 3 After this we'll search up near the lake.
Searcher 2 What would she be doing up there?
Searcher 4 What would she be doing anywhere?
Searcher 1 Sh!! Quiet now!

They stop suddenly, listen hard. Nothing.

Searcher 1 Sorry. I thought . . .
Searcher 3 Just a bird.
Searcher 2 Let's keep moving.

In the darkness, Siss's voice calls out too as her Father drags her towards home.

Siss Unn! Unn!
Father Siss, listen to me . . . we can't have you running about in the night and the storm.
Siss I'm going. I have to . . .

Mother arrives.

Father There are other ways of helping, Siss.
Siss No . . .
Father Sh, quiet down now and tell me: what happened when you were with Unn last night? Was there anything special?

Siss hesitates.

Siss No.
Father Are you sure?
Mother Did she say anything?
Siss No.
Mother You were upset when you got home, Siss.
Siss I can't tell you.
Father For God's sake, Siss, if you know anything about this . . .
Siss I don't! But I must come with you . . .
Father No.
Siss Yes!
Mother Maybe she should . . . I mean, look how upset she is . . . We don't know what this is all about. Perhaps she can help . . .
Siss Father, please!
Father OK, only stay close by. No wandering off, understood?
Siss Yes.
Mother We mean it.

Siss and her Father head off and join up with the other Searchers.

Father Any luck?
Searcher 1 Not so far, but we'll search all night if we have to.
Searcher 2 She'll never survive out of doors.
Searcher 1 I can't help thinking of the road . . . the cars driven by all sorts of people.
Father Strangers.
Searcher 1 Exactly. It's Siss, isn't it?
Father That's right.
Searcher 1 Inge said you were with Unn last night?
Siss I don't know anything. I'm going to look down the hill.

Father Don't lose sight of us for a second.
Siss I won't . . .

Siss makes her way through the trees to lower down the hill. Crouches down. Looks out, scanning the night with quiet determination.

One of the Searchers makes their way to Auntie's. She waits outside the front door with Siss's mother, exhausted, impassive.

Searcher 5 Anything?

Auntie shakes her head.

Mother We've been telephoning all over, but there's no news.
Searcher 5 Well . . . no news is good news, I suppose.

Auntie seems unconvinced.

We had another idea.

Auntie nods.

What about the frozen waterfall?
Auntie The ice palace?
Searcher 5 There's supposed to have been some talk of a school trip to it. The young ones've never seen it before. Could Unn have gone there on her own and got lost?
Auntie To play truant from school, it's not like her.
Searcher 5 What would be like her then?
Auntie I don't know. She is simply like herself.
Searcher 5 Has she any friends?
Auntie Yesterday one of the girls from school was here – for the first time since Unn came to live with me.
Searcher 5 Who was that?
Mother My daughter, Siss.
Auntie But she can't tell you anything. She's as shocked as anyone about all this.

Mother There was something she didn't want to say.
Searcher 5 What?
Auntie Something they were giggling about, I expect. Siss is a good girl, and she is Unn's friend. She would help us if she could.
Searcher 5 Why did the snow have to come now?
Mother It's always the way.

Auntie turns away from them and heads inside. Mother and Searcher 5 whisper to one another so that Auntie can't hear.
On the hillside, Siss repeats over and over:

Siss Nothing must happen to Unn, nothing must happen to Unn, nothing must happen to Unn, nothing must happen to . . .

An exuberant cry comes out of nowhere:

Mats She's here – she's here! I see her!

An older boy, Mats, scrambles down the hill towards Siss. She jumps up, looking for Unn, but he grabs her.

Oh no you don't! (*His arms are around her.*) I knew I'd find you! I knew you'd be all right.
Siss But it's not me!
Mats Of course it's you.
Siss No, I'm looking for Unn too.
Mats You're not Unn?
Siss No. I'm Siss.

He pushes her away from him, despondent.

Mats What are you playing at down here?
Siss I'm looking.

The other Searchers appear. He calls out to them.

Mats It's not her – it's the other one. I'm sorry . . .

The Searchers shake their heads, move away.

(*to Siss*) You should be at home.
Siss I'm the only one who knows her.

He walks away to rejoin the others. Siss shouts after him:

And I'm staying till she's found!

A man breaks away from the group.

Searcher 2 Come over here, Siss.
Siss I'm busy searching.
Searcher 2 Just come here.

The man grabs Siss by the arm.

I'm surprised you're allowed out so late.

The others approach.

Siss It's none of your business.
Searcher 2 You said you know something about Unn.
Searcher 3 You were with her yesterday evening . . .
Searcher 2 What did you talk about?
Searcher 3 Was there anything she told you?
Searcher 4 She said something, didn't she?
Searcher 2 You must tell us.
Searcher 3 It might save Unn's life!
Siss She didn't say anything about this.
Searcher 2 What do you mean?
Siss About going anywhere.
Searcher 3 Was it something that could help us look for her?
Siss No.
Searcher 4 What did Unn tell you?
Siss Nothing.
Searcher 2 We can see you know something, now what did Unn say?

Siss I can't tell you.
Searcher 2 Why not?
Siss It wasn't like that.
Searcher 3 Siss . . .

Siss shouts out.

Siss No, I can't stand it!

The Searchers are shocked. They back off a little.

Searcher 2 She's exhausted.
Searcher 3 We're wasting our time.

The men start to move away.

Searcher 4 It's a shame you won't tell us. You might have helped find her.

They all move off back into the woods, their lanterns still visible among the trees.
Searcher 1 arrives, preoccupied.

Searcher 1 Ah, Siss. Did Unn want to go and see the big pile of ice . . . ?
Siss I don't know.
Searcher 1 Weren't there plans for the whole school to go?
Siss I suppose . . .
Searcher 1 Could she have gone by herself? After all, she'd no friends.
Siss That's not true! She had me!

Siss becomes hysterical, hits out at Searcher 1.

She had me, she had me . . .

Searcher 1 tries to hold Siss still.
Siss struggles, calls out:

Father! Father!

A voice out of the night.

Father (*offstage*) Siss? (*Father starts towards them.*) What's this?

Searcher 1 releases Siss and she rushes to her Father.

Siss She had me.
Searcher 1 She's soaked through . . . exhausted . . .
Father I'm taking you home.
Siss But you promised.
Father I thought it would be over by now.
Siss I'm just as good a walker as any of them.
Searcher 1 We're following the river to the waterfall. Unn may have taken it into her head to go there and then got lost.

Searcher 1 sets off without them.

Siss Father, please!
Father OK, OK. But keep close by, I don't want to have to keep looking for you when I should be looking for Unn.

Siss holds out her hand. Father takes it and she leads him after Searcher 1 into the night.
Ahead of them, a search party thrashes at the riverbank with sticks. In the distance, voices cry out Unn's name.

Searcher 2 How can you see anything with the river like a mirror?
Searcher 3 Anything could be hidden and sucked away down there.
Searcher 4 Don't think about it.
Searcher 3 No, you're right.
Searcher 2 Still, it doesn't look good.
Searcher 4 We're falling behind. Look at the lanterns on the other side. They're much further ahead. They'll be at the ice fall before us.

They pick up speed, still searching in the undergrowth.
Up above, Searcher 1 appears, tailed by Siss and her Father. Siss is calling out, combing the land with her tired eyes. The sound of the waterfall comes up – they have reached it. Siss is amazed by it, overwhelmed.

Searcher 1 I'll try and cut down, get a better look.

S/he struggles further down. Lifts the lantern. The palace flickers. Siss is afraid.

Bring your lanterns!

They move closer. Siss's Father calls to the rest of the search party:

Father Bring your lights!

As the lanterns mass, some of the splendour of the ice palace is glimpsed.
The crowd stand dumbstruck at the sight of it. After a moment . . .

Searcher 1 I'll see if I can find a way in.

They watch as he struggles to negotiate the structure, finding gaps in it which turn out to be dead ends, until:

There's something here . . . a gap, I mean.

S/he squeezes in a little further.

No. Someone smaller might do it though . . .

Everyone's attention turns to Siss, but Father pulls her close to him, shakes his head. A voice in the crowd:

Mats Shall I try?

He clambers down and tries to force his way in. Gets a bit further but not much.

It's no good. There may have been an opening earlier but it's frozen up now.

The Searchers stand helpless, considering the implications of this. In Siss's head, a sound starts to echo: the dislocated sound of girls' laughter . . .

Searcher 4 calls to Siss, making her the focus of all eyes.

Searcher 4 You're sure Unn didn't say anything about coming here?

Siss is distracted, distant . . .

Siss No . . .
Father That's enough, now. Siss is not to be questioned any more.
Searcher 1 She's told us what she knows.
Searcher 4 I'm sorry . . . I . . . I meant no harm, it's only . . .
Searcher 2 There are so many chasms she could have fallen into.
Searcher 1 If she came here.
Searcher 3 If.

Siss watches as the Searchers swing their lanterns around the structure. Their sticks strike at it sporadically, then stop.

The girls' laughter in her head echoes louder and louder and louder until it is no longer laughter but the sound of someone crying out . . .

Siss cries out too – a terrible long scream. The Searchers stop dead still.

Father Siss?

She shrieks at them, hysterical.

Siss Why are you just standing here? As if you'd given up. Unn is not dead! She's not . . .

The Searchers look at one another, embarrassed.

We have to find her! (*Siss starts to run away from the ice palace.*)
Father I'll catch you up . . .

He races after her. The Searchers look on.

FIVE

Siss's bedroom.
A figure lies under a white sheet on Siss's bed. Siss runs into the room, pulling off her clothes, throwing her coat and sweater onto the floor. She kicks her trousers off.
Siss finally notices the bed, stops. The figure sits up in bed, peeps over the sheet.

Unn Hello, Siss.

Siss is astonished, overjoyed.

Siss Unn? Is it you?
Unn Well who else would I be if not myself?
Siss I'm not myself at the moment.
Unn Oh. Who are you instead?
Siss I don't know.
Unn Are we still friends?
Siss Oh yes. More than ever.
Unn Then you are Siss. Because she is my only friend.
Here, you're the one supposed to be in bed.

Unn gets out of the bed.

Siss Am I?
Unn Oh yes! Doctor's orders!

They laugh. Siss gets into the bed.

Now I'll take care of you.
Siss Unn?
Unn Yes.
Siss I didn't tell anyone.
Unn Tell them what?
Siss Anything.
Unn But what was there to tell?

Mother comes in, smiling.

Mother Siss!
Siss Isn't it wonderful?
Mother I know, I thought I was lost for ever!

Siss is baffled.

Siss You?
Mother What is it, Siss?
Unn What is it, Siss?
Mother Lie down again.
Unn Here, lie down again.
Siss (*to Mother*) But can't you see Unn?
Mother Only if I look in the mirror!

Mother looks at Unn, they both laugh. They talk while they straighten Siss's bed, with her in it.
Dialogue is now split between Mother and Unn.

Mother You're not
Unn well . . .
Mother Siss . . .
Unn You
Mother have a
Unn high
Mother fever.

Siss looks from one to the other.

Mother It was too
Unn much for you

Mother out in the
Unn woods last
Mother night.
Unn You
Mother came home
Unn ill.
Siss But Unn . . .
Mother *and* **Unn** Unn hasn't been found.

Siss can't bear the confusion any longer.

Siss She was here. Just now.
Mother No, Siss. You're dreaming.
Unn Feel how hot you are.
Siss No, I'm cold. I'm freezing cold.

Siss is distressed.

Mother Sh . . . (*Mother hugs her.*) It's all right, Siss.
Siss I was out with the men.
Mother It was too much for you . . .
Siss We were at the big pile of ice.
Unn Your father brought you back.
Mother You managed to walk, I don't know how. The doctor says . . .
Siss What time is it?
Mother It's evening now.
Siss Where's Father?
Mother Out with the search party still.
Siss They *are* still searching?
Unn Of course.
Siss It was so like Unn in here earlier. She can't be far away.
Mother I hope not.
Unn I'm sure.

Siss looks at them both.

Siss I need to sleep now.

Siss pulls the covers over her head.

Go away now. Go out of the room.

Mother and Unn hesitate . . .

Go on . . .

Then give in and leave Siss alone. Slowly and silently the room fills with her schoolmates. They whisper:

All Siss . . . Siss . . . Siss . . . Siss . . . Siss . . . Siss . . . Siss . . . Siss . . .

Siss stays buried under the covers.

Siss I need to sleep now.

They gather up the sheet and Siss inside it, swing it between them, singing:

All Rockabye baby on the tree top . . .

Siss struggles against them.

Siss No . . . Put me down.
All Secret, secret, who's got a secret?

Unn enters.
The crowd pull the sheet taut and start to give Siss the 'bumps'.

Unn Tom-tale tit! Your tongue will split, and all the little birdies will have a little bit!!
Siss I'll never tell.
Unn Remember your promise!
Siss I do . . .
Unn Goodbye.

Unn waves goodbye and starts to walk away. Siss calls after her:

Siss But where . . .? When . . .? Unn, don't go away . . . I've only just found you . . .

But the bouncing continues and she can't follow.

Unn!!
All And one for luck!

There's a high bounce and then the sheet is lowered back onto the bed, Siss covered over with it, before the schoolchildren melt away.

Siss lies under the sheet. Her Mother comes in. Touches her through the sheet.

Siss sits upright suddenly, woken from a deep sleep. Looks around her.

Mother Feeling any better?

Siss eyes her with suspicion, tries to get her bearings.

You've had a good rest.
Siss Has anyone been in here?
Mother Father came in just now. He wanted to ask you about something, but you were asleep.

She feels Siss's forehead – cooler now. Siss collects herself a little. Mother continues:

He said it was important.
Siss Is there news?
Mother No.
Siss Oh.
Mother Siss . . . you must try and remember what you and Unn really did talk about . . .
Siss Oh, no!
Mother . . . what she said to you. That's what Father has to know . . . if only you can give them some hint.
Siss I told you it was nothing.
Mother But are you sure, Siss?
Siss Of course.
Mother While you were feverish you talked about the strangest things.

Siss starts to panic.

Siss What did I say?
Mother This is all for Unn's sake, Siss . . . Just tell us!

Suddenly Siss is furious.

Siss She didn't say it, I tell you! She didn't tell me anything, why don't you believe me, why doesn't anyone believe me? (*Siss collapses into hysterical tears.*) I am Unn's friend . . . I don't want my tongue to split . . .

Mother is shocked.

Mother Siss, Siss, it's all right.
Siss No it's not . . . No it's not . . .

Mother rocks the sobbing Siss in her arms.

Siss Nothing will ever be right again . . .

SIX

Auntie's house / Siss's house.
Outside Auntie's house a man sweeps a path free of snow. Auntie watches.

Auntie You're kind.
Man It's the least I can do.
Auntie All the same.

The man nods, continues. After a while:

Man I drove into town this morning.
Auntie Yes?
Man The picture of her is everywhere. In all the shops. Everyone's talking about it.
Auntie What're they saying?
Man Well, there's no news, of course.

Auntie Of course.
Man Or you'd have heard.

Auntie nods.

I asked around for an hour or so, but . . .
Auntie I see.
Man Nothing.
Auntie Thank you. It can't be helped. (*Beat.*)
Man She isn't forgotten.
Auntie No.

Auntie looks out, ending the conversation. The man goes back to clearing the path.

Siss appears in her dressing gown. She looks out towards Auntie's house, stretches out her arms.

Siss I promise to think about no one but you. To think about everything I know about you. To think about you at home and at school, and on the way to school. To think about you all day long, and if I wake up at night. I promise.

Siss makes the secret-promise signal.

Outside Auntie's, two Searchers approach carrying tall poles. They dig them into the snow with the others.

Man You've been dragging the river?

They nod.

Searcher 1 I don't know what hope there is.
Searcher 2 There comes a time when even bad news would be welcome.

Auntie approaches.

Searcher 1 Nothing to tell, I'm afraid.
Auntie I see. Oh well.
Searcher 1 I didn't know Unn myself.

Auntie No? (*Beat.*) I was very fond of her.

The Searchers make their way off again.

Man I'm more or less finished now.

Auntie nods. The man shuffles uncomfortably away.
At Siss's, Siss is in bed. She examines her palms.

Siss I feel you are so close I could touch you, but I daren't. I feel you looking at me when I lie here in the dark. I remember it all and I promise only to think about that, at school tomorrow. I shall do so every day, as long as you are gone. There is no one else.

At Auntie's, a woman approaches.

Woman I thought you might want this.

Auntie takes it. A picture.

We made it bigger.
Auntie I heard they were all round town.
Woman It's a good likeness.
Auntie Taken last summer.
Woman She looks so enquiring, don't you think?
Auntie She lost her mother in the spring. Everything she had. So she had something to enquire about, don't you think?
Woman Of course. I'm sorry. Yes. Well, I should probably . . .
Auntie Yes.

The Woman leaves.
Siss pulls on her clothes. Stops halfway.

Siss I feel you standing in the passage, waiting for me when I go out. What are you thinking about? There's still no one but you. No one else. You must believe me when I tell you so, Unn.
I shall never forget my promise as long as you are gone.

Siss makes the promise sign.
She walks over to Auntie's.
Auntie has her back to Siss.

Siss Hello?

Auntie stiffens. Turns slowly to face Siss. She's obviously happy but also disappointed to see Siss.

Auntie Oh, it's you, Siss.
Siss I'm sorry . . .
Auntie Not at all, not at all. No, no. How nice of you to come. Are you well again? I heard you were ill after that trip to the river.

Siss nods.

Siss I'm to go back to school tomorrow.
Auntie I knew that was why you didn't come. Because you couldn't. Perhaps you'd like to ask me about Unn?

Siss is a little surprised.

You must ask if you want to.
Siss Ask what?
Auntie Whatever it is you most want to.

Siss thinks.

Siss Nothing.
Auntie Is it so locked inside you?

Siss shrugs, looks away. Beat.

Siss Are they going to find her?
Auntie I hope they will every day.
Siss Can I look in her room?
Auntie Of course.

Siss looks.

Do you want to go in?

Siss shakes her head.

Siss Why is Unn the way she is?

Auntie Is Unn not as she should be, then?

Siss Unn's nice.

Auntie And wasn't she happy, too, the other evening!

Siss She wasn't only happy.

Auntie She can't be only happy when her mother died so recently.

Siss There was something else as well.

Auntie What?

Siss I don't know what. She didn't tell me.

Auntie They've been here asking and asking till I'm worn out. I know they've been asking you too. You understand they had to?

Siss I suppose . . .

Auntie You must forgive my asking too – but I am Unn's aunt – and I think there is a difference. Before this she was all mine – an unexpected windfall, if you like, all for me. But now she belongs to everyone, it seems. She didn't tell me anything. (*Beat.*) Did she say something special to you that evening? (*Beat.*)

Siss No. (*Beat.*)

Auntie No, of course not. It's not likely Unn would have told you all her secrets the first time you met.

Siss Can I ask you something?

Auntie Of course.

Siss What will happen if she doesn't come back? (*Beat.*)

Auntie I would not let anyone else ask that, Siss. Though I have thought about it, of course. (*Auntie braces herself.*) If Unn doesn't come back, I shall sell this house and go away. I don't think I can stay here without her. Even though I had her such a short time. (*Auntie hides her tears.*) Well, well, well. We shan't talk about that. Just because Unn hasn't come back yet doesn't mean she won't come back ever.

Siss No.
Auntie And nothing will be changed here, don't worry.
Siss I understand.
Auntie Everything will be just the same.

Auntie and Siss exchange smiles. A moment of shared hope.

Siss Yes. Everything exactly as it was.

But their hope is against the odds and they both feel it.

SEVEN

School.
The class is assembled. There are two empty places: one belonging to Siss, the other to Unn.
The class works in silence, the Teacher is at his/her desk. Siss enters and a ripple of excitement runs around the room.

Teacher All right again, Siss?
Siss Thank you.
Teacher That's good.

Siss sits in her old place.

I'll fetch you a copy of the new book we've started. (*to the class*) And please remember, no gossiping while I am out of the room.

The moment s/he's gone the class erupts with excitement, swarming around Siss.

Students
Here you are!
Welcome back!
Are you better?

Was it awful that night?
You don't look sick . . .
And just think, they can't find a trace of Unn.
It's terrible.
Shh!!
You wouldn't believe it.

Siss answers yes and no . . .

Torill We went out searching too!
Siss I know.
Klaus Now you're back things will be more like before.
Siss I don't think so.
Erik Leave her alone!
Inge What was it? They say Unn told you something you wouldn't –
Siss I can't stand it!

They back away from Siss, surprised by the outburst.

Erik Now see what you've done!

The Teacher returns and the students scurry back to their places, but it's clear that something has happened.

Teacher There's a lot of excitement in the room.
Erik We're just glad to have Siss back.

The Teacher's not convinced, but doesn't want to make a fuss.

Teacher Shall we settle down again now? And please bear in mind what we discussed yesterday . . .

The students return to their work. Siss opens the new book. Looks at it. Turns to look at Unn's empty desk. Turns back. Seems unable to work. She looks for Unn again, then settles to her study. The Teacher remains oblivious to what follows unless otherwise indicated.

A note is passed in secret between the students. It

reaches Siss. She reads it and looks across the desks to a girl. The girl stage-whispers:

Inge Will you play with us at break?
Siss No.

Siss screws up the note, but almost immediately another arrives. She looks at a boy behind her.

Klaus Do you want to go on a ski trip at the weekend?
Siss No.

Siss crumples this note, but now there is a flurry of them winging towards her. Each one she opens brings a new invitation, a babel of whispered friendship. When the frenzy is at its peak, Siss shouts out:

Siss No, that's enough! I can't, don't you understand?

The students go back to their work. Mother appears.

Mother Siss?

Siss scoops up the notes from the desk.

Siss They're not thinking about Unn at all.
Mother Who isn't?
Siss Nobody is. Everyone's forgotten her.
Mother You haven't.
Siss Never!
Mother Listen, Siss. Other people didn't know Unn very well. And they have a lot to think about. Their own lives. You're the one person who can think about Unn all the time.

Siss brightens.

Siss Really?
Mother If that's what will make you happy.
Siss Yes. It will. I'm the one. (*She happily tears up the friendship notes.*) I'm the one.

Mother It's good to see you smile, Siss.

Siss tosses the paper into the air. It falls like snow around her. She laughs.

They say the thaw is coming. The snow has melted off the big ice pile.

Siss When the warm wind brings the thaw it might bring Unn back too.

Mother It might.

Siss I think it will!

Mother Siss . . .

But Siss interrupts, exuberant:

Siss Thank you.

Mother Whatever for?

Siss For the best Christmas present ever.

Mother shakes her head. She taps the Teacher on the arm and s/he comes to life. They shake hands and move away from the students, chatting, obviously concerned about Siss.

Then the classroom door opens and a wind blows in through the room, disturbing Siss's shredded paper. Siss seems to be the only one to notice – she turns around, hardly daring to look. The wind dies down.

A bright light in the doorway: a girl stands waiting to come in.

Seeing Siss, the whole class turns to stare. After a moment:

Siss Who are you?

Selma I'm Selma. I'm new.

There's no response from the startled class, but the spell is broken as Selma closes the door behind her.

I don't know where I'm to sit.

The empty desk is suddenly the focus of all attention. The class defers to Siss.

Selma Is this one free?
Siss No. It's never free.

The girl looks around the class for some kind of explanation but they all look away. She waits until the Teacher returns, ushering in a more normal – if tense – atmosphere.

Teacher This is Selma, she will be joining us for the rest of the year. (*The Teacher bites the bullet.*) You'd better take that desk there. It's free now.

The girl looks at Siss. Siss stands.

Siss It isn't free.
Teacher The desk ought to be used, Siss. I think that would be the best way.
Siss No!

Teacher looks at class. Senses their agreement.

There are desks out in the corridor that aren't being used.
Erik Should I go and fetch one?
Teacher (*to Selma*) The desk belonged to a girl who disappeared last autumn. I expect you read about it in the papers.
Selma Her name was . . . Unn?
Siss If her place isn't there, she'll never come back.
Teacher I think that's going too far. None of us should say things like that.
Siss Why can't the desk stay as it is?
Teacher I respect the way you feel, Siss, but you mustn't go too far. Wouldn't it be better for someone to sit there for the time being? That would be quite natural. Nothing would be spoilt by that, would it?

Siss Yes. (*Stares at new girl. Feeling of ill-will*)
Selma I would rather not sit there. (*Beat.*)
Teacher All right. Fetch another desk.

Erik goes.

Teacher It's not worth spoiling a thing like this.

The class attitude to Selma shifts immediately. They make her welcome.

Inge (*to Siss*) D'you see how we're all in this together?

Siss is suspicious, reluctant.

Friends, Siss.

Siss thinks for a moment, shakes her head.

But you can't stay alone all the time like this.
Siss I'm not alone. And I don't want you to ask me about it again.
Inge You can't go on punishing us like this, Siss. We haven't done anything to hurt you.
Siss It isn't that . . .
Inge There's a ski trip on Saturday – why don't you come with us?
Siss No.
Inge It's the best time for it, now that the drifts have all settled . . .
Siss I can't.
Inge We could go to the ice palace. They say it's incredible now the snow's melted off it.

Siss considers.

Go on, Siss. Just this once.
Siss OK, but only if we go there. To the ice palace.
Inge Agreed.
Siss Agreed.
Inge It's a good start.

Siss It's not any kind of start.

The Teacher taps on his/her desk.

Teacher Thank you . . .

Siss turns away to face front.
Siss's hand shoots up.

Siss I'd like to read.

Everyone is surprised.

Teacher Well . . . if you wish. It's nice to have a volunteer for a change. You know what page we've reached?

Siss nods, stands, reads. As she reads, one by one each class member rises solemnly from their seat and takes up a position on the way towards the ice palace.

By the end of the poem, only Siss and the Teacher remain. The students regard the distant ice palace with reverence, the atmosphere is almost religious.

Siss

We stand here and the snow falls thicker,
Your sleeve turns white and so does mine.
They hang before us like snow-covered bridges.
But snow-covered bridges are dead.
In here is living warmth.
Your arm is warm under the weight of snow, and
a welcome weight on mine.
It snows and snows
On silent bridges.
Bridges that are unknown to all.

EIGHT

The Ice Palace.

The palace appears in all its glory. The others are ahead of Siss. They wait until Siss joins them, observe the ice palace in awestruck silence. This is their tragedy too.

After a while:

Inge Well. Where shall we go next?
Siss I only wanted to come here.
Helle Why here?
Torill Siss must decide. If she doesn't want to come any further it's none of our business.
Siss I'm turning back now.
Inge We'll turn back too then.
Siss Can't you go on as planned?
Erik But why not come with us?
Siss I'd like to be alone here for a bit.

The others look at one another, seem to defer silently to Torill.

Torill You don't want to be with us any more today?
Siss I'd rather not.

Torill shrugs. What can she do? Faces fall.

It's something that I've promised.
Helle We thought everything was going to be the way it was before . . .
Siss How could it?

Her friends give up.

One by one they begin to disappear.

Siss watches for a while, then the roar of the fall draws her back. She shouts over the noise.

Siss There's still no one but you. No one else. You must believe me when I tell you so, Unn.

I shall never forget my promise as long as you are gone.

Siss makes the promise sign.

For a moment, Unn appears inside the ice – clearly, distinctly and dead.

Siss backs away, terrified.

Unn's disembodied voice echoes through the roar:

Unn (*voice-over*) What are you looking for? Here I am. I've been here all the time.

Siss watches appalled until a cloud moves across the sun and Unn disappears again. She shouts out for her friend . . .

Siss Unn! (*She starts to approach the ice, backs off.*) What does this mean? (*She starts to understand . . .*) Oh no . . . (*Siss thinks for a moment longer.*) Unn is dead. (*She shouts at the ice.*) Unn is dead!

Siss runs back down and into the forest, dazed with grief.

She emerges near Auntie's. Stands looking at Auntie's house.

NINE

Auntie's.

Auntie comes out of her house, calls:

Auntie Siss? What a coincidence . . .
Siss Why?

Auntie can see that Siss is upset.

Auntie I was hoping to speak to you, that's all.
Siss There's no news of Unn, is there?
Auntie No.
Siss No.

Auntie Would you like to come in?

Siss shakes her head.

Are you all right, Siss?

Siss I don't know. I can't say it.

Auntie Well I should say something then . . . I believe I promised to tell you if I were to sell and leave.

Siss understands.

Siss Oh.

Auntie I'm certain now that there's nothing more to wait for.

Siss looks back towards the waterfall – she's certain too.

Siss Do you *know* that?

Auntie I don't *know* – and yet I do know just the same. So I've sold the cottage, and I'm going away.

Siss When?

Auntie Tomorrow.

The news sinks in. Siss can feel her last real link with Unn slipping away. Auntie resumes nervously. In many ways, Siss is her last link with Unn.

Auntie It was lucky I saw you. Otherwise I was thinking I'd look in on you this evening. My last evening.

I'd like to go for a walk. I was hoping you might come with me.

Siss Where do you want to go?

Auntie Just around and about.

Siss nods, looks at the house.

Would you like to look in?

Siss creeps to the window. Looks.

Siss Empty.

Auntie Do you want to go inside?
Siss No. Yes.

Auntie nods. Siss enters. The room where everything took place. Now empty. Finished.
Siss comes out.

Let's go now, shall we?
Auntie Just the two of us.
Siss Yes.
Auntie This is nobody's business but ours.

They set out. Through the forest, uphill to a vantage point from which they can look down over the village. The lights on the model village gradually come on.

Auntie Siss, I didn't ask you along just for the company.
Siss I didn't think so.
Auntie I may live alone, but I hear things. You've had a difficult winter. Cut yourself off from your friends at school, even from your parents.
Siss I made a promise.
Auntie Ah. I knew it must be something of the sort. And I suppose I should be grateful to you – for the sake of kinship, so to speak.

Auntie brushes Siss's cheek with her hand, but it's too upsetting a gesture. She pulls away.

I don't want you to tell me any more about it. But you mustn't promise so much that you destroy yourself. Especially when there's no point in it any more.
Siss You don't understand . . .
Auntie You've been ill!
Siss I couldn't stand it. They went on and on about something I couldn't tell them . . . over and over.
Auntie You must remember it was at the very beginning when we had to try everything. None of us realised it was so hard on you.

Siss They've stopped now.

Auntie Yes, they made sure of that.

Siss Made sure of it?

Auntie The doctor who came to see you drummed it into them at school, too. How important it was not to mention it.

Siss (*surprised*) I didn't know.

Auntie You were very depressed. There's no reason not to tell you now that it's over.

Siss Is it over?

Auntie Yes. (*Beat.*) I suppose we must talk about that too, mustn't we?

You mustn't think people have forgotten who they were searching for. They haven't. I know that.

They've given me so much help that now I'm leaving I don't know what to do about it. I ought to have gone round to thank them all. But I can't.

Siss No.

Auntie That's why I'm walking out here in the dark this evening. I daren't show my face.

Siss You must tell me what's over.

Auntie struggles to find the words.

Auntie All right, Siss . . . Unn is gone, and she's not alive.

Siss Have you found something out?

Auntie Not exactly . . . and yet I know it, just the same. What I want to ask you before I leave is that you try to go back to all that you used to have. You said you made a promise. But it can't come to anything now that the other person isn't here any more. You can't bind yourself to a memory, shut yourself away from what is natural to you. Are you listening?

Siss Yes, yes, of course.

Auntie All right: she will not come back and you are freed from your promise.

Siss is taken aback.

Siss Can you do that?
Auntie I believe I can. Shall we say now that it is over? Make an agreement?
Siss How can I know if it's true? Whether you can do it for me?
Auntie Has it gone so deep, Siss? You must have wondered how long you could go on . . .
Siss But it was a promise . . .
Auntie It will be all right, Siss. Trust me. Just so I can be a little happier about going away.

Something moves in the trees. It's something, it's nothing.

It's not right for you to go on as you are. So unlike yourself.
Siss No.

Auntie seems to have made some headway – as much as she can.

Auntie So. That is that. We can cut through here to your house, can't we, Siss?
Siss Couldn't I see you home?
Auntie There's no need.
Siss I'm not afraid of the dark. Not any more.
Auntie All right.

They walk.

Siss It's not cold.
Auntie Not a bit.
Siss What'll you do in the place where you're going to live?
Auntie Oh, I shall find something to busy myself with. You mustn't worry about me.
Siss No.

Auntie I'm a worthless creature.

Siss Don't say that . . .

Auntie The people here have done everything they could for me. Now I'm going to leave without saying goodbye. Don't you think that's poor behaviour, Siss?

Siss I don't know . . .

Auntie You are my consolation . . . Since you went round with me this evening, they'll find out that I walked the village boundary. And perhaps they'll understand that I did it as a way of thanking them. That's something. I'm counting on your telling them. Though I know only a worthless creature would think that way.

Siss No. No, I'll tell them. I promise.

Siss makes the promise sign to Auntie. They are back at Auntie's house now.

Auntie No need to promise, Siss. If you say it, then I know it's true.

Well here I am then. Back where I began.

Auntie seems reluctant to part from Siss.

Let's make an end to it, Siss.

Siss nods.

You *are* free.

Siss and Auntie hug. They stand clasped together for a moment, then Auntie pulls away, trying to hide her tears.

Off you go. Go on!

Auntie 'shoos' Siss affectionately.

Siss raises her hand in a goodbye wave and starts back towards the woods. At the edge, she turns to see Auntie watching. Auntie raises her hand and waves goodbye.

Siss waves back, slips away. Auntie waits a moment, looking into the woods after her.

TEN

Siss's house.

Siss sits over the bowl of water she is about to wash her face in. She stares into it. Her mother comes in.

Mother Siss?
Siss Yes?
Mother Didn't you hear me?
Siss Sorry.
Mother What are you doing?
Siss Nothing.

Mother looks over her shoulder, down into the water. Siss pushes her away.

No, don't.
Mother Is it so wrong for me to want to look at my daughter's pretty face?
Siss I don't want us to look in together.
Mother I hardly recognise you these days.

Siss is confused.

Siss Why?
Mother You're growing up.

Siss looks back in the bowl.

Siss Do I really have a pretty face?
Mother You do. Although it could be cleaner.

Siss laughs. Splashes the water over her face and dries it.

That's better. I was wondering if you could run an errand for me before school?

Siss Where?
Mother Only to the Nedgaards' house. I promised a recipe to Helle's mother.
Siss OK. I better hurry.

Mother helps her on with her jacket.

What's it like outside?
Mother It's fine.

Siss looks out of the window.

Siss It's windy and raining!
Mother Can't it be fine all the same?

Siss laughs. Mother gives her a slip of paper.

Here. You know where they live, don't you?
Siss Of course.
Mother Just checking.

Siss sets out on her journey through the wind and rain. On her way through the forest, she meets Mats coming the other way.

Mats Is that you, Siss?
Siss Yes.
Mats Good to see you again.
Siss And you.
Mats You look different . . .
Siss How?
Mats I don't know . . . more . . .

The two of them are suddenly a little embarrassed . . .

I don't know. (*Beat.*) I'm glad to be back on the main road at last! I've been wading up that slope and the drifts are knee-deep. Heavy too, like dragging your legs through wet sand.
Siss Have you been far?
Mats To the river.

Siss All the way down?
Mats The ice is breaking up.
Siss What were you doing there?
Mats Oh . . . just looking around.

Siss realises he's been searching.

You know how it is.
Siss Yes. Is the ice palace still standing?
Mats Not for much longer – a few days maybe and it'll be gone . . . You can see it from a hill near here if you want to . . .
Siss No. Thanks.
Mats Sure.
Listen – Siss . . . I've thought of saying something to you. Just . . . if I happened to run into you . . .
There's nothing more to be done about it, Siss.
You must think about that now.

Siss stares at her boots.

I'm sorry.
Look . . . I should get home and change out of these wet things.

Siss nods. Doesn't look up.

Don't hide your pretty face, Siss.

Siss looks up.

That's better. Goodbye.
Siss Bye.

Once Mats has disappeared out of sight:

The most important thing . . . when making your way through the forest . . . is to remember that there is nothing bad at the sides of the road. You walk as fast as you can, and wish at the same time that the road would never end.

The space is suddenly filled with her schoolmates playing.

They swarm about, take up positions around her to play 'What's the time, Mr Wolf?'

Torill is the wolf.

The children play the game, creeping closer and closer to Torill. Then she calls:

Torill Dinnertime!

And they run away. Siss stands still.

Torill You're not running.
Siss I'm not afraid.
Torill I could catch you.
Siss I don't think so.

The children creep back, seeing Torill and Siss together.

Erik Are you playing then, Siss?
Siss No. I'm not.

The others turn away, busy themselves with other games. There is a skipping rope turning, a game of 'catch', clapping songs, and the picking of sides for a game. Siss stands on the edge of all this.

A boy, Erik, goes and stands nervously next to her. She moves away. After a while he follows her.

Siss Is anything the matter?

Erik nervously spits out his words.

Erik It can be as it used to be.
Siss Do you really believe that?

He thinks.

Erik No. But it might be possible all the same.
Siss Who sent you?

Erik Sent me?
Siss To say these things to me.

He is obviously hurt.

Erik I can do some things on my own, you know.

Erik walks off in a huff, back into the heaving crowd. Siss calls after him, but to no avail. The others continue playing, laughing, with Siss on the outside. Suddenly she can bear it no longer, summons her courage, calls out:

Siss I have an idea . . .

The playground suddenly stops dead, is silent. Siss is the focus of amazed attention.

I . . .
You . . .
We . . . should go to the ice palace. I heard it's going to fall soon.

A moment of confused silence as the crowd waits for someone to respond. Then, Inge steps forward:

Inge D'you really want to go, Siss?
Helle What'll we do there?
Siss It might be . . . fun. To see it again before it topples down.
Torill Are you making fun of us, Siss?
Siss No . . .
Erik It's a bit out of the blue.
Torill But . . .

Torill looks around the group, sees the eager faces.

We'll go along.

Torill makes the promise sign to Siss, but Siss does not return it. She starts walking again.

Siss The most important thing . . . when making your way through the forest . . .

Mother comes in.

Mother Siss – where are you going?
Siss To see the ice palace with the others.
Mother With all your friends?
Siss They're not my friends . . .

But Mother has linked arms with her, propels her faster through the forest.

Mother Oh – Siss! Your father and I have dreamt of this day . . . we've waited so long for you to be happy . . .
Siss I'm not happy.
Mother No, of course not. Take care, Siss. Enjoy yourself . . .

And Mother waves, drifts away. Siss trudges purposefully onwards. The lights dim, the wind gets higher, there is a loud bang! Siss screams out.
Mother rushes back, with Father now.

Mother What is it?

Siss is terrified, but keeps moving just the same, faster and faster as the panic mounts.

Siss I can't go!
Mother Why ever not?
Siss The window . . . I was sleeping and it flew open, all of a sudden, all by itself . . .
Mother It's just the wind, Siss . . .
Siss It was so sudden . . .
Mother You'll be fine, Siss. You'll be fine . . .
Father See you later! I want to hear all about it!

The lights start to come up again – it's dawn as Siss approaches the fall and stops. Its roaring can be heard in the distance.

Torill appears out of the shadows among the trees.

Siss Are you here already?

Torill I could say the same.

Siss I wanted to be first.

Torill I wanted to meet you before the others arrived.

Siss Well now you've met me. (*Siss turns her back.*)

Torill It was fun to walk home with you yesterday. Everyone thought so.

Siss Did they?

Torill Even you, I think.

Siss Maybe.

Torill But it hasn't been fun this winter.

Siss I think I of all people know that.

Torill The way you treated us.

Siss It wasn't meant to upset you . . .

Torill Did you have to stand apart from us in the playground just as she did?

Siss Don't talk about her!

Torill We missed her too!

Siss You don't know what you're saying!

Torill How do you think that made us feel?

Siss Right! That's it! If you mention her again, I'll . . .

Siss points back to the dirction she came from.

Torill What?

Siss I'll . . .

Siss knows she can't leave. The atmosphere calms down a little.

Torill Siss?

Torill holds out her hand to shake Siss's.

I'm sorry.

Siss looks at Torill's hand. Can't take it.

Siss So much that's impossible is happening.

Torill We're making friends.

Siss But we mustn't.

Torill We must.

Siss No, you mustn't come to me and I must never come to you. And we must never look into a mirror together or it will happen all over again!

Siss starts to run away. Torill rushes after her, grabs her, clumsily hugs her . . .

Torill Siss, you mustn't go off and get upset again.

Siss I know, but . . .

Torill Are you listening to me?

Siss Yes.

Torill Do you understand?

Siss calms down, lets herself be held by Torill for a moment. They hear the others arriving. Siss pushes Torill away, extends her hand. Torill shakes it. Suddenly they are surrounded by the others.

All Hi, Torill!

Hello, Siss!

Inge The sun is so bright today! You can see the palace shining for miles around.

Selma Let's climb it!

Klaus Come on!

They start to move around the fall to find a place on top where they can stand. Siss calls:

Siss No, it's going to fall soon!

Erik You worry too much, Siss.

Torill Let's go!

Torill joins the others. Siss hangs back.

Siss It isn't safe.

Erik Come on, Siss, it's stood this long. Why should it fall today?

Siss Why shouldn't it?
Erik You know no one can see us here. No one in the world. Don't you think that's a good feeling?
Siss I think we should join the others.
Erik Sure.

When they get to the crevice in the ground that the others have leapt over, he takes her hand and they jump together. They loose hands and join the others in the deafening roar. Siss starts to laugh from the exhilaration. Then there is a terrible CRACK! *and the ice vibrates beneath them. They all scramble desperately for safe ground.*

Once they know they are all safe, the laughter of relief breaks out. But Siss does not join in.

Erik It looks as though you were right, Siss.

Siss moves away from the group.

Torill You're not going back, Siss? There's been no harm done . . .
Siss I just want to move a bit further away.
Torill We'll come with you.
Erik Unless you don't want us to . . .

Siss stops for a second. Looks around her.

Siss No, come with me.

They hesitate.

Come on!

Siss heads off again. They follow her down, away from the fall. Torill runs and overtakes her, heads into a patch of sunlight.

Torill Oh!! Feel this. Come on, Siss. Come into the warm!

Erik and Siss join her in the light, soak up the heat, shield their eyes against the sun. Gradually, the light on them fades, comes up on Unn, watching over the model village. Its orange windows gradually light up.

Unn puts her fingers to her lips:

Unn Shhh! (*Unn smiles.*) No one can witness the fall of the ice palace. It takes place after all the children are in bed. Safe in their warm homes, sleeping, dreaming. But in the empty half-cold half-light of a spring night like this one, shattered by the pressure of the water, the palace pitches forward into the white froth from the falls.

Huge blocks of ice are dashed to pieces, then float away, disappear around a bend in the river, before anyone has woken up or seen a thing.

The shattered ice floats on the lower lake, its edges sticking up out of the surface of the water.

It floats and melts, and finally ceases to be.

Unn watches fondly as a bedside lamp fades up to reveal Mother tucking a sleepy Siss into bed. Father waits in the shadows.

Mother Goodnight, Siss.

Siss Night.

Father Sleep tight.

Mother moves to join Father as Siss wriggles down under the covers, eyes tightly closed.

Mother She'll sleep well after the walk.

Father nods, hugs Mother as they both watch over Siss, plainly relieved that she seems to be looking to the future once again.

Mother turns out the lamp, leaving Unn alone.

Unn It is time, now. It is time.

Unn savours her last moments, then blows out the lights in the model village.

The ice palace is illumined for a moment, then blacked out as the sound of its final collapse fills the darkness.

End.

The Mystery at the Heart of Adult Life

Lucinda Coxon interviewed by Jim Mulligan

The Ice Palace was originally part of the first cycle of *Connections* in 1994. Since then the play has been produced in several schools and professionally at the Leicester Haymarket Studio. Looking back on the productions, Lucinda Coxon sees the play as a perfect choice for performers who are relatively inexperienced because the characters exist as functions rather than people. As long as the production is clear it can be done in the space available with the scenes defined by sound, music and light rather than by a built set.

After leaving university, Lucinda Coxon joined Loose Exchange, a writer-led theatre company with whom she worked on short pieces developed from starting points suggested by members of the group. The culmination of this stage of her writing was *Waiting at the Water's Edge*, which had a highly acclaimed production at the Bush Theatre. Film scripts followed, with travel to Italy, Romania and New York.

Since *The Ice Palace* Lucinda Coxon has had several other plays produced in London and, most recently, her play *Nostalgia* premièred in Los Angeles. She has also worked on a number of films, including writing the screenplay for *The Heart of Me*, which closed the Regus London Film Festival in November 2002.

When Lucinda Coxon found *The Ice Palace*, a novel by Tarjei Vesaas, and read a two-line summary of the story – it is about two eleven-year-old girls, one of whom gets trapped in a frozen waterfall – she was captivated, and she determined to release the story dramatically, keeping it as close to the original as she could, without imposing herself on it or interpreting it.

What interests Lucinda Coxon is that, although the story is complex and has layers of meaning, it is open: it is a rite-of-passage story that is free of judgement. It is ambiguous and is about ambiguity. The moral, if there is one, is that mystery is not something you are required to put behind you in order to become an adult. You have to learn that mystery is at the heart of adult life and, once you have accepted that, you are on the road.

> The play is about life and death and love and loss. Siss never knows where Unn has gone. People have suggested that Siss and Unn are the same person, but I like to read it at a much more literal level. Sometimes as a child you may meet someone and just know with absolute certainty that this person will be part of the emotional core of your life. This happens to Siss. It happens very fast and by instinct and then Unn is gone. She is simply removed and Siss has to cope with this.

The story is about a child living in her own head. But there is also a picture of a community which works very hard to look after its children. It sometimes gets it wrong, but it wants Siss to be reintegrated into the community. There is a very strong sense of them wanting her back and in the end, with the help of the community, she has crossed the threshold and become a woman. She owns her experience and is able to let go. Lucinda Coxon is clear that *The Ice Palace* is an open play with no hidden set of meanings.

> People have said it is a play about lesbianism. I simply cannot find that in it. Two eleven-year-old girls take their clothes off together for an instant and, in a sense, that is partly sexual but it is much more about standing in your skin and being vulnerable, being the sum of

> yourself. It is much more about identity than about sexuality.

Lucinda Coxon is conscious that some groups have found that crucial scene difficult to stage but stresses its importance. Most groups have, she says, in the end found acceptable and wonderfully innovative ways to include it.

At the first meeting between Siss and Unn three things happen. They look in the mirror together, they take off their clothes and put them back on very quickly and Unn says she wants to tell Siss a secret. Siss never learns what the secret is, but she is burdened by it. Later on, when Unn is missing and the villagers keep asking Siss if she knows anything, she is trapped because she knows there is something but not what it is.

> As time goes on, the promise of secrecy gets out of all proportion. The promise was about exclusive friendship and devotion, so when Unn goes missing Siss tries looking for her, but she cannot find her. She then does the sensible thing and stands still, trying to turn herself into a beacon to guide Unn home. If she remains exclusively devoted to Unn, if she keeps their promise sacred, this intimate exchange they have had will guide Unn home. The aunt realises this and releases Siss from her promise

Throughout the winter Siss has an emotional breakdown. She starts to imitate Unn and tries almost to become her. Then, at the end, after the community and Siss have accepted that Unn is gone for ever, Torill asks Siss, 'Did you have to stand apart from us in the playground just as she did?' Siss is at first angry and then allows Torill to hold her for a moment. Unn understands her own separateness and at the same time that she is part of the community. Together the children visit the ice palace and stand in the light. A new spring is starting.

Usually it takes Lucinda Coxon at least two years to write a play but *The Ice Palace*, being an adaptation, took only six months

> It was hard to begin with because I was worried about betraying the novel, about maintaining the integrity of the original, and I was over-polite with it. But once I relaxed it was enormously pleasurable to work with another writer. It is a very grown-up play and in the process of writing it I have learned something about growing up.

Production Notes

STAGING AND SETTING

The Ice Palace is set in a remote village at the beginning of winter. Cars and phones are not in evidence because this is a fairy land. It's a community that looks after its members.

The staging needs to be fluid, and to suggest the passage of time from the start of winter through the big freeze to the snow's melting and spring's awakening. The playwright recommends an upper and lower stage level, but there doesn't have to be a massive height difference, just some sort of distinction. There's an area dominated by dredging poles, the Forest, and the Ice Palace itself. The latter might be suggested by lighting and/or moving figures.

A model village is needed to represent as simply as possible Auntie's house, Siss's bedroom and the classroom. It should be dominant at the beginning and at the end it should represent the community huddled together in a cold, remote place. It could be lit from within. It needs to be constant throughout the play.

Please note: it is highly recommended that the company has this model throughout the rehearsal period, so that they can build a relationship with it.

The 'Nude Scene' There is no need to make the girls physically identical. They are the same because they reveal themselves to each other. The important part of this scene is their total exposure to each other. Perhaps only remove one or two items of clothing. Think about how they are removed rather than what's removed, to avoid codifying. For instance, if you are undressing completely then you would take your shoes off differently than if you were slumping in front of a TV.

Lighting is an important consideration when suggesting winter: think of the forest, the moon, shadows, the edge of the lake, the red glow of the sun and the hand-held orange lanterns during the search sequence, against the wintry darkness.

Sound likewise can suggest the cracking of the ice, dripping water, birds singing, a child's lullaby, footsteps, the river, and distant roaring. As well as recorded sound effects, 'live' vocals can be used to suggest, for example, echoes and a babble of whispered friendship.

CASTING

The majority of the cast of twenty-two or more are eleven-year-old classmates. There is the possibility of a certain amount of doubling up, for example, children as Searchers or Shadows. The adults are positive role models, and should ideally be played by older members of the company. Bearing in mind the 'live' vocal effects, it would be good to have a cast with voices of varying pitch. The two main protagonists are Siss and Unn. It's essential that the girls playing these parts have empathy and can work well together.

EXERCISES

Unn and Siss's meeting is a crucible, a test or trial out of which the play proceeds. The two girls are very different, but have a fascination with each other. That first meeting becomes an initiation for Siss into the darker and more difficult areas of adulthood. Siss is very much a young girl at the start of the play, but she matures into a young woman by the end. Unn is further down the road to adulthood. She's experienced a death and shame. She fears being judged, and pushes and tests people and things. Improvise scenes from the girls' back history. Discover how well Siss fitted into the society before she met Unn. Decide if Unn replaced anyone else.

Auntie is obsessed with secrets, and she wants to keep them secret. The exchange of secrets is a crucial aspect of adolescence. Have the cast question what would have happened if Unn had shared her secret with Siss. Decide what you think the secret was. We know that Siss has been to Auntie's home before, so try improvising this scene.

Children's games have changed very little over the years and are similar in different countries. Observe children playing in school playgrounds and in the community. Notice the difference between the games girls play and those of boys. Study the repetitiveness and the rules of the games and recreate some of them.

Similarly, listen to the rhymes and chants of the playground. Remember rhymes you used when skipping. Use a long skipping-rope to help create group games and rhymes. Experiment by speeding up the pace of the skipping, and slowing it down. Manipulate the rope to exclude or welcome specific individuals. Try skipping in pairs, threes, or more, simultaneously.

Take one or more childhood songs and use them as vocal warm-up at each rehearsal. Vary the singing, softly in parts and with vigour at other times. Sing in a circle, while sitting or standing, and then while moving around the space.

As an ensemble, turn yourselves into a search party and see how the direction taken changes, as one person is joined by another, then another, and then the group's leader. Improvise giving instructions and the excitement of a seemingly successful outcome, followed by the disappointment of failure. Repeat the exercise using hand-held torches. See how little or how much more is required to tell the same story while relying on the lights.

Choose a room or other location which gives an echo – for example, a cave, a shower room, a gallery, a disused swimming pool. Experiment with whispers and echoes. Have one member of the group volunteer to be guided around the space by whispers only. Now follow this through to the scene in the play where Unn enters the Ice Palace.

Suzy Graham-Adriani
March 2003
based on a workshop facilitated by Simon Usher

AN ISLAND FAR FROM HERE

Laura Ruohonen

translated from the Finnish
Saari kaukana täältä
by David Hackston

Laura Ruohonen is one of Finland's leading playwrights. She has degrees in dramaturgy, biology and literature, and has written several stage plays, including *Fish or Fowl*, *Olga*, *Love is Paramount*, *Swapman Never Sleeps*, *My Teeth* and *Queen C*. Also a writer for radio and screen, Laura has won several awards and her work has been translated into many languages.

David Hackston lives in Helsinki, where he works as a translator of Finnish and Swedish literature. He is currently working on a Master's thesis at the University of Helsinki on approaches to translating Finnish literature into other languages.

The play takes place in a town by the sea (e.g., Helsinki) in the present day.

There are many different places mentioned in the play; however, it is not necessary to create each one realistically on the stage. The basement and the beach are important, the other places can be identified using one or more points of reference – e.g., a blanket (the girls' room) or a spotlight (the questioning scenes).

A stroke / denotes the point of interruption in overlapping dialogue.

As a guideline, the play requires approximately six female and five male actors.

Other ways of dividing the roles are possible. All stage directions may be altered.

Characters

Lida

Sofia, Lida's younger sister

Old Lady in the basement

Haba, the Old Lady's son

Friend, Sofia's friend

Pal, Friend's pal

Ally, Pal's ally

Headmaster

Bloke A

Bloke B

Friend's Parents

Lida is about fourteen to seventeen years old,
Sofia and the other girls about nine to thirteen.
Haba and the Blokes are late teens, early twenties.
The Old Lady is 'old'.

ONE: A HAND IN THE DARKNESS

The basement. A patch of light against a stone wall.
A hand appears in the light.
Blackout.

TWO: MONKEY ISLAND

The girls' room.
Night. Sofia, half-asleep, shakes her sister awake.

Sofia Do you remember Monkey Island?
Lida This is different.
Sofia You said I wasn't really Mum and Dad's child, but the Princess of Monkey Island.
We were going to move there, to the island where anything you wish for can happen.
Lida This island's different. This one's real.

THREE: A VOICE IN THE DARKNESS

A telephone rings. There is a single patch of light in the darkness. A hand picks up the receiver. We cannot see clearly who is speaking.

Old Lady Who is this? Who? I haven't seen him round here. No. Not for donkey's years. Why would he come here now? I don't care if he owes you money, he's got nothing to do with me. What? On holiday? Surely they can't just let them out. What do you mean, on his way? What did you say? Going to visit his old mum? (*She slams the phone down.*) At that point I put the phone down and started packing. But I'm not afraid.

Blackout.

FOUR: A LETTER TO MUM

The girls' room. Lida shakes Sofia awake. In her hand she is holding a piece of paper with a heart drawn on it.

Lida (*angrily*) What's this?
Sofia What?
Lida This letter. Who wrote it?
Sofia Someone else.
Lida Who else would write a letter to our mum saying 'I Like You, Mum'?
Sofia Maybe it was some passer-by.
Lida What?
Sofia Someone was just passing by and made a mistake.
Lida Look, she doesn't deserve your . . . our . . . (*Decides not to say it.*) It's all her own fault. Promise you won't speak to her or listen to her. You can nod or shake your head, but do not listen to a thing she says.
Promise me!

Pause.
Sofia nods her head.
Lida tears up the letter. Sofia watches her.

FIVE: THE GIRLS IN THE BASEMENT

Lida I went down to the basement to get my fishing rod when I got this odd feeling. It was too quiet. Then,

I saw a piece of bread on the floor. Who would come down to the basement to eat bread? Down here there's only concrete walls and a dusty little window by the ceiling and heaps of junk piled up, sofas and tables and old newspapers and rugs and /

Sofia Have a sniff.

They sniff the air.

Lida What?

Sofia Nothing. (*She sniffs the air.*) It's like a . . . a new smell.

Lida And when I stopped to listen, it was almost as if someone was listening to me, as if someone had held their breath and was listening.

Sofia What, here in our basement?

Lida Yes.

Sofia (*hesitates*) You don't think . . .?

Lida No. I called and checked. Dad's at that woman's place and Mum's still away.

Sofia Maybe it's an animal.

Lida Maybe.

They step forward cautiously and peer into the darkness.

It's made itself a nest. Look, on the sofa, it's gathered up cushions, blankets and supplies for the winter.

Sofia Maybe it's a dog. Maybe it's a St Bernard puppy and we could take it in.

Lida It's got a handbag. (*She points at the handbag.*)

Sofia Maybe it stole it.

Lida A St Bernard? It's not a dog. It's taking medicine.

Sofia Dogs can be ill too, you know. When Elisa's dog was on heat the bottle had her mum's name on it: 'Mrs Tina Falk, to prevent arousal.'

Lida It's not a dog.

Sofia (*enthusiastic*) But it might be a criminal. Why else would he be hiding? (*Pause.*) Maybe he's killed someone.

Lida Or he's about to kill someone; he's setting traps. One by one people in the house start going missing.

Sofia Where is he now then? Don't you think we should call Mum?

Lida No! (*She suddenly stops, then slowly backs off.*) Let's go. He's not here any more.

They exit.

*

Lida (*alone*) I said no, there was nobody there, even though there was. A little bundle of black, sitting quietly by the cupboard – not very big, I don't know what it was, who it was. Didn't look very nice.

SIX: THE BASEMENT

A voice and a figure in the darkness.

Old Lady I can hear footsteps coming from upstairs, they're his footsteps. I know exactly how he walks, how he flops down on the sofa, how he turns on the tap. Ordinary sounds, ordinary movements, I've seen them all, the way his hands and feet move, right from the time he used to kick around in his cot. The way he takes a step backwards, so he has enough space to swing his arm properly, so that his fist hits its target so hard and so sharply that he even surprises himself. Was it really his mother standing there in the way of his fist?

The sound of a rock hitting metal.

SEVEN: THE UNTRUTH ABOUT LOVE

Sofia is writing something with her head dangling downwards.

Lida Why are you here all by yourself? Hello? Answer me.
Sofia They won't take me with them.
Lida Why not?
Sofia Because I'm not in love.
Lida What?
Sofia You can only join in if you're in love with this one boy. Everybody else is. I'm not.
Lida Say that you are, then.
Sofia But I'm not! I hate love.
Lida Well, that's exactly how you can trick everyone.
Sofia What?
Lida People that are really in love can do just about anything to each other, they torment each other and cheat on each other and lie and stab each other in the back and that's supposed to be love, so compared to that you'd be doing someone a really big favour if you just say that you love him and then leave him alone.
You don't even have to say anything, just nod your head.
Sofia When we were by the sea yesterday, I saw how all the male ducks attacked this one female, one after the other, they kept her head under the water and every time she tried to come up for air they hit her on the head with their beaks, and by the end of it she was all battered and covered in blood. And then our teacher just said: 'Such are the follies of love!'
Lida (*laughs*) You could be a real cow to that boy and if anyone wondered why you could just say, 'Well, that's love for you,' and no one would suspect a thing.
Sofia Yes . . . just think about that woman and Dad and Mum /

Lida (*interrupts*) What is that? What are you doing with your head?

Sofia If your head's upside down, there'll be more blood going to your brain and you'll remember things better.

Lida What do you want to remember?

Sofia Everything! My life. Here's all the evidence, all that woman's letters, all the dates and the times when Mum pretended she was dead, so when Dad comes back and asks /

Lida (*interrupts*) He's not coming back.

Sofia But /

Lida (*interrupts*) He's not coming and he won't be asking. Sorry.

EIGHT: THE BASEMENT

The sound of a rock hitting metal.

Old Lady Too much junk, too much stuff, too many trivial memories. I'll take care of all of this, once everything else has been taken care of.

Heavy, dirty chests.

When he was a little boy he used to collect stones.

When he grew up he threw them. Now he's become just like them. Hard, and when he hits you it hurts.

The sound of a rock hitting metal.

NINE: THE PLAN

Sofia's friends are examining a large hand-drawn map. They quickly hide it when Sofia enters.

Pal Get lost!

Sofia But I am.

Pal What?
Sofia You know. Like you.
Ally Huh? What?

Sofia pulls a strange face.

Friend In love?

Sofia nods her head.

Pal Is she in love with X?

Sofia nods her head.

Ally You weren't this morning.
Pal Right!
Friend A person can fall in love in a flash, it's actually really classical, love at first sight. Things just go click.
Pal Yeah well, she can just go and click somewhere else.

Pal and Ally laugh.

Friend (*happily*) Now we have to let her in. Everyone else is.
Ally Well you'd better not muck this up!
Friend Look. This is the plan. Here's the map.

They open out a large hand-drawn map.

Pal It's a map of the swimming pool.

Sofia nods.

This is the girls' changing room.
This is the door into the boys' changing room.
When our class goes swimming tomorrow and when X comes out of that door /
Sofia (*interrupts*) X?
Ally Like, does she even know who we're talking about?
Friend Of course she does, don't you?

Sofia nods her head uncertainly.

Pal Right, so when our class goes swimming tomorrow, we'll spread soap – (*She produces a bar of soap.*) – all along the floor at point A – (*She indicates a place on the map.*) – and so when X comes out of the door, he'll slip on the soap, fall over and break his leg!

Sofia doesn't understand a thing.

Ally Don't you get it?
Friend Then we'll run in and be the first ones to help, we'll take him to hospital, visit him every day and – he'll fall in love with us!

Sofia doesn't know what to say.

Pal Well?
Ally Are you in or not?
Sofia I don't . . .
Ally Well? Do you love him or not?

Pause. Sofia nods.

Pal You see, love isn't just words, it's deeds as well.

TEN: BY THE SEA

Haba Some old logger told me about how one day in
late autumn he was wandering about by himself in the
middle of the woods when this huge boulder, the size
of a house, left there since the ice age,
suddenly cracked,
like thunder, it split in two.
That sound in the wilderness . . .
A single, enormous stone,
which for hundreds of thousands of years has weighed
down on that same spot,
cracks,
and

the only person in the whole world
to see it
is me.
That would be,
that would be something.

The distant sound of a rock hitting another rock.

ELEVEN: THE QUESTIONING

Sofia, Friend, Pal, Ally and the Headmaster.
The girls are staring at the floor.

Head Why did you do it?

Silence.

There's no need to be scared – out with it. It's important to find out what really happened. You nearly split that boy's skull open with all that soap. You must have had some reason. What? Come on, girls, surely you wouldn't do something like that for no reason whatsoever.

Silence.

Has he done something to upset you?

Sofia shakes her head.

Nothing?

Sofia shakes her head.

So there was no reason at all?

Silence.

Was he bullying you?

Sofia shakes her head.

Don't you understand that this is a serious issue? That boy might even have broken his leg and had to go to hospital.

Friend (*excited*) Exactly!

The others stare at her in horror.

Head Did you want to hurt him? Why?

Friend Well . . . /

Others Shhhhh!

Head So? What was it all about?

Friend Well, just love.

Head (*getting up*) Right, you can just sit here until you come up with a better explanation. I'm very disappointed in you. Love's no laughing matter, you know. (*He leaves the room.*)

Sofia No, it's deadly.

Friend This boy in school hit me on the head with a stone and it hurt like mad, but then everyone just said, you should be pleased, he really likes you. Pleased, that some fatso schizo throws stones at you and doesn't even get punished?

Sofia I hate love.

Ally I hate X. Without him, none of this would have happened.

Pal Right! This is all his fault.

Ally We'll make him pay.

Friend Right . . . (*Pause.*) Once he's recovered and come back to school.

Sofia I'm never going to fall in love.

Friend How can you stop it happening?

Sofia It's like smoking. If you don't start when you're young, you won't get hooked.

Ally I haven't exactly started. He was the first.

Sofia Yeah, and look how it turned out! I'm never going to love anyone! Never!

Friend Me neither!

Pal Me neither!
Ally Me neither!
Sofia No, let's stick together and never love anyone!

They all embrace each other.

Friend (*excited*) You're all great. I love you!

The others stare at her in shock.

Well, just . . . you know.

The Headmaster returns.

Head Well then, girls? Have you thought things through? Why were you bullying that boy?
Friend We hate him.
Head Why's that?
Pal We've had to suffer quite a lot because of him.
Head Aha. What did I say? Come on, girls, let's go and have a chat over in the dining hall.
Now we can sort all this out, I think we understand each other.

TWELVE: THE LOCK

Haba enters carrying a bag; he rummages amongst his things for a while, then produces a key.

Haba When I went up to the door, I wondered whether she was waiting for me. The old key still worked. The locks hadn't been changed. (*Laughs.*) Last time they were. I still don't know whether she's waiting for me.
But I'll be waiting for her.

He opens the door and goes into the Old Lady's flat.

THIRTEEN: THE KEY

Sofia and the Friend in the basement.

Sofia I saw her! She's old, really old, at least fifty or sixty or seventy.
Friend What was she doing?
Sofia Sleeping.
Friend You mean, lying down?
Sofia Yes.
Friend Are you sure she's not dead?
Sofia Hard to say, really, all old people look a bit mummified. If we could weigh her, then we'd find out.
Friend What?
Sofia When someone dies, they lose 120 grammes. It's been tested.
Friend Why?
Sofia (*shrugs her shoulders*) The soul leaves the body . . . I suppose.
Friend (*worried*) Is the soul really that light?

Sofia nods.

Maybe we should call / someone.
Sofia No.

A voice from the darkness as Sofia speaks.

Old Lady No! Please, don't say anything to anyone!
Girls (*together, scared*) No, no, no!
Old Lady Especially if there should be
a man
young
a young man who comes asking for me.
He might . . .
Best if he thinks I've gone away.
For a few days.

I'll be here for a few days and then I'll leave and I won't bother you again. I won't hang around, just four days – I'll be quiet as a mouse – four days and four hours.
Then you'll never hear of me again.
I could even pay you.
Sofia No, there's no need.
Old Lady I have got money, you know.

A rustling sound. The Old Lady is frantically rummaging through her things.

Aah! I've hidden the money. I hid it in a panic, because I just couldn't think straight. It's still sitting there at home, and if he finds it it'll all be gone. He'll sniff out where I've hidden it, and if he can't find it then he'll force me to tell him, of course. Please help me, girls, and then I'll pay you, go and fetch my money and bring it down here to me. Quick before it's all gone.
There's the key. It's door number 2B, it's in a big red photo album on the shelf with 'Beloved Memories' written on the cover.

A hand appears out of the darkness. It is holding a key on the end of a piece of string. The hand drops the key onto the floor, then disappears from sight. Silence.

*

Friend Do you think we should call someone?
Sofia Who then?
Friend Well . . . (*Thinks hard; gives up.*) What are we going to do?
Sofia Help her.

Sofia picks up the key from the floor.

FOURTEEN: BY THE SEA

Lida is sitting on the edge of a rock; she is fishing.

Haba enters, opens a can of beer and looks at Lida. He drinks from the can.

Silence.

As Haba opens another can, Lida gets up and is about to leave.

Haba What are you staring at?
Lida Nothing.
Haba Stop it.
Lida What?
Haba For Christ's sake, I know what it means when a girl like you starts looking at me like that.

Lida tries to say something.

Don't butt in. Quiet!
Carry on like that and soon you'll be telling me you love me.
Lida What? Never. What's it got to do with you anyway?
Haba Oh, it's got nothing to do with me, has it? That's rich!
Isn't it just bloody incredible, how there are no limits in this country, no laws, nothing stopping people jumping out of the bushes and falling in love with you? If someone hates you and goes around calling you an arsehole, you can take them to court, it's a matter for the police, but if some tosser starts rambling on like, darling, sweetheart, I love you, for no reason whatsoever, then you're just completely at their mercy and no one can stop them. Then you've just got to smack them one yourself, and that doesn't do any good either. No sooner turn your back than they're running up behind you, whinging away, 'It's

not your fault you hit me, love, I'm sorry, I was asking for it,' and there's never been a fucking truer word said!

Lida I was just looking at the sea. And those islands.

Haba OK. Let's leave it at that, OK?

Lida OK. (*She is about to leave.*)

Haba You shouldn't hang around here, this is a dangerous place.

Lida (*looking at Haba*) What, in case some nutter turns up?

Haba Yep.

You come here by yourself, the sun's setting and those islands start kind of floating on the horizon. You're just sitting there watching them, then you notice there's some big bloke standing behind you. He lifts his hand and you think you're about to get knifed, but no, he puts his arm round you and sits down to enjoy the view. That's when all hell breaks loose.

You're sitting there together and you start thinking that the waves lapping on the beach and the mighty thunderstorm, the scent of the rain and the first snowflake are all thanks to that person, you run up the aisle together, have a couple of kids, and then it starts to dawn on you like, hang on a minute, that wasn't love, it was just a nice view.

Don't you see? This is the sort of place you should only come to by yourself.

Lida That was the point.

Haba OK then.

Silence. They look at each other.

Fine. I'll be off, then.

Haba gets up. He walks over to Lida and kisses her. Lida is speechless.

Don't worry, I don't go for under-age girls.

Lida And I don't go for over-age boys.

Haba (*self-consciously runs his fingers through his hair*) Erm . . .? How old do you think I am, then?

Lida About . . . twenty, or twenty-six or . . . thirty . . . five?

Haba (*shocked*) Thirty-five?

Lida Well, it's not my fault older men all look the same.

Haba This face is older than me, OK?

Lida So's this one, OK?

Haba Right, listen: Grandpa's golden rules numbers two and three:

Number One: To catch a fish round here you need the right tackle.

Number Two: Round here, fishing is prohibited. (*He makes to leave, then turns around.*)

Got any dry bread on you?

Lida You hungry? (*She gives him a sandwich.*)

Haba For the swans.

Lida I hate them.

Everyone's always harping on about how once swans have mated, they're faithful to each other for the rest of their lives, and if one of them dies, the other one never mates again. But no one ever tells you what jealous lunatics they are. If another couple of swans comes swimming down the same bay, then the males attack each other and beat each other half to death – even though there'd be enough food and space for all of them. But oh no, they don't just offer it to each other like, 'Tuck in, help yourselves to a few of these rotten rushes, we've got twelve tonnes of them.' No, it's just me me me all the time.

Why do they have to be so stupid, when they could all swim about together in peace, there'd be plenty of food and space for everyone, no problem? But no, this lot go out of their way to start a fight and they're always worrying about making sure they get to keep everything for themselves and leave nothing for anyone else.

Haba Just like humans. Except you get a decent pillow out of a swan. Humans are no use to anyone.

Lida Yes they are.

Haba What then?

Lida They keep mosquitoes going.

Haba Thanks for that, that's given me the will to live for a while.

Come on, I can show you how to catch a bird like that. You need a bit of bread and a plastic bag. (*He rummages in his pockets and produces lots of plastic carrier bags.*) Swans are a bit big and moody, but even a beginner can catch a pigeon or a duck. You put a bit of dry bread inside the bag, the bird goes in to get it, then you quickly close the bag – it's all right, as long as the head's inside – and twist the bugger's neck. Come on, they don't teach you this at school.

Lida (*starting to laugh*) No, they won't.

Haba OK?

Lida OK!

They exit.

FIFTEEN: THE PHOTO ALBUM

Inside the Old Lady's flat.

Sofia and her friends enter. Sofia is carrying the key.

Ally Whose place is this?

Sofia Shhhh!

Pal It's that old granny's, the one in the basement. You stay by the door and keep a look out for anyone.

Ally Why don't you?

Friend Maybe we should call someone's mum.

Sofia Just look for the photo album, it's red. Quick!

Ally She's got some weird stuff.
Pal What's this? A whip?
Ally There's an empty beer bottle over here. She's an alky!
Sofia What was that?
Pal What?

They listen.

Sofia (*shakes her head*) Nothing.
Pal Why does she want an old photo album?
Ally Bring back memories, I suppose.
Friend (*finds the photo album*) Look! They must be bad memories. Look at this!
Pal Why have all the heads been cut out?
Sofia What? That boy used to live here. When he was fifteen, he threw the TV and the stereo out the window and when his mum said she wouldn't buy him new ones, he stuffed her into a suitcase and kept her there for three days.
Friend Oh. Then did she buy him new ones?
Pal He looks really normal.
Friend He looks like a typical idiot.
Ally So, a normal boy, then.

Two young men enter, Blokes A and B. They glance at the girls as they walk past, but do not say anything. They have a carrier bag full of lottery scratch cards with them. They sit down and begin to scratch the cards.

The girls are silent and are all standing stock-still. The silence continues for so long that it cannot carry on any longer. Sofia slowly begins to make her way towards the door. She still has the photo album in her hands.

Bloke A (*calmly*) Give it to me.
Sofia What?

Bloke A The thing in your hand.

Sofia shakes her head.

Friend It's not yours.
Bloke A Whose is it, then?

The girls remain silent.

Bring it here.
Friend (*to Sofia*) Give it to him.

Sofia gives the album to Bloke A, who begins to leaf through it. Suddenly he begins to laugh.
He takes a wad of cash from inside the album.

Bloke A Well well. Girls like that, eh?
Friend No we're . . . not.
Pal This is the first time – here. I mean, it's the first time we've ever been anywhere / . . .
Bloke A (*interrupts*) Give me the key.

Sofia hesitates.

I'll get in anyway.

Sofia gives him the key.

Drop by sometime! But don't come round unless the landlord's in, otherwise I might have to have a word with your parents. I'm sure we can keep this one between us, all right? Hey, you. You!

He means Sofia. She stares back at him.

Go on, shake your head again. I like seeing your curls swing about. Just like an angry little ram. (*He hands the Friend some money.*) Go and get us a beer.
Friend But I'm a child!
Bloke A Well spotted. (*to Bloke B*) Looks like you're off, then, old boy.

He gives the money to Bloke B, who has been feverishly rubbing scratch cards the whole time. Bloke B exits.

Silence. Bloke A resumes rubbing the scratch cards; the girls do not dare leave.

Bloke A Give us a hand, will you, girls?

The girls pick up scratch cards and begin to rub them excitedly. Bloke A tries to add up his total winnings.

Pal Scratch cards!
Ally There are tons of them here!

They continue to scratch the cards.

Bloke A (*throws a bundle of cards to the Friend*) You count them.
Pal They're almost all empty!
Ally It's a fix!
Pal This is daylight robbery. Imagine, people buy these cards and then they don't even win anything!
Friend (*has added up the winnings*) Three hundred and ten.
Bloke A Is that it? Every damn card in the shop and a lousy three hundred quid? We should report it to the police!

The girls look at each other.

Friend Can we go now?
Bloke A Don't go yet. Let's talk, have a discussion, a chin-wag. It's not every day you get to meet nice little rogues like you. Come on, let's have a chat. (*to Pal*) You. What are you going to be when you grow up?
Pal A soldier.
Bloke A (*surprised*) Why?
Pal It's the safest profession there is.
Bloke A Huh?
Pal Didn't you know? In war nowadays it's always the women and children and old people that die first.

Soldiers just sit around in their base all day and every now and then they bomb hospitals and play-groups in poor countries.

Ally That's why sometimes women aren't allowed to be soldiers, otherwise there wouldn't be enough people to kill. It's not a good idea to become a child soldier, though, they usually die pretty quickly.

Bloke A How do you want to die, then?

Ally Well . . . if there was a nuclear war, then me and my friend would run to the nearest sweet shop and eat as many sweets as we could before we died.

Bloke A (*to Sofia*) How about you?

Sofia does not answer.

Friend (*answering for Sofia*) In the woods or at sea.

Bloke A You're not afraid a bear might come along and eat you?

Ally Ugh!

Pal Imagine being eaten, ugh!

Friend That would be a great death! It would be wonderful if people remembered her as 'that girl Sofia, she got eaten by a bear' than if some idiot on their mobile ran you over on a zebra crossing. That would be really humiliating.

Pal I don't know . . . imagine, a bear's tongue, ugh!

Bloke A What about you?

Friend The old-fashioned way. Just like Sofia.

Bloke A Maybe I should start flogging exotic, extreme-death holidays to Finland: freeze to death in a snow-drift; drown shit-faced in a frozen lake; choose your own bear, mad cow's disease or a high-speed car crash with a moose . . .

Bloke B enters with a couple of six packs and begins to hand them out to the girls.

Bloke A Us girls are having a whale of a time talking about death. Some of them think it would be better to go through the digestive system of a large animal before finally ending up as compost, others prefer more technical solutions.

Bloke B I'm with the animals.

Forests are full of snakes and bears and none of them has ever bothered me, but there's not one day goes past without some dickhead ruining it for you. You could get a team of huskies to take you off to the most remote glacier they can find, and still some Norwegian's bound to turn up with a grin on his face just to take the piss.

Bloke A Norwegian?

Bloke B It's because they haven't had a proper war for hundreds of years, so the whole country completely loses it if one measly wolf walks across the border for the first time since 1753. The army is alerted and mental-health organisations open up a crisis centre so the country's positive mood won't suffer. But I don't have anything against Norwegians; Swedes are far worse: arse-licking clowns, who sell Finnish inventions to people round the world as if they were their own, rake in all the money and the fame and it serves the Finns right. A bunch of bitter, anti-sociable lunatics, who are too busy deciding whether to hang themselves or stab their neighbour.

Ally Yes, it would be far more civilised to shoot him.

She starts to hiccup. The Blokes laugh.

Bloke B Humans are the only species who get hiccups – they can't even breathe properly! Lions, elks, even the smallest little shrew, they're all far superior to us.

Bloke A What are you on about now?

Bloke B I used to share a cell with this guy and he was so thick, I couldn't stand listening to his yacking.

I had to go and sit in the library and read nature magazines all day.

They take a swig of beer.

Bloke A Drink up.

Some of the girls take a cautious sip out of their cans. Sofia carries on staring at the floor and shakes her head.

Bloke B Did you know that all the water we have on Earth is here right now? We won't be getting any more. Every single drop of water in rivers and oceans, every drop of beer in this bottle, even urine in your bladder, just keeps on going round this same system for ever. This is all we've been given. Therefore, I suggest we treat this particular form of water with the respect it deserves.

Pal (*to Ally*) What's wrong with you?

Ally Just feel a bit funny . . .

Bloke A (*to Sofia*) What about the mute girl?

Sofia does not say anything.

Friend She's just thinking.

Bloke A (*slightly drunk*) What's she thinking? Say something.

Friend Well, that /

Sofia puts her hand over the Friend's mouth to stop her saying anything.

*

Sofia (*as if she were alone*) I was thinking that . . .

Pause.

Animals are just the way they are, they follow their nature, neither good nor bad, but / (*She vomits.*) Can a human ever be good?

SIXTEEN: THE ISLAND OF DREAMS

The girls' room.
Sofia is in a bad way.
Lida enters with her fishing gear and a fish.

Sofia (*crying*) Where were you?
Lida Calm down.
Sofia I didn't know where you were!
Lida Sorry.
Sofia Mum came up to me, but I didn't speak to her. Why didn't you come home? I had to drink beer.
Lida There, there.
Sofia Don't. When I was little, someone told me that Hell was a place where everyone's starving, even though everywhere you look there are huge great cauldrons full of food. All the spoons in Hell have two-metre long handles, and no matter how hard all the sinners try, they can't get the food into their mouths. And guess what Heaven is like?
Lida Well?
Sofia It's just the same. Except that the people there use the two-metre long spoons to feed each other.

Lida tries to hug her, but Sofia won't let her.

Even my best friends are scared of wolves and bears and snakes, but they just think it's normal that hundreds and thousands of people get run over every day.
Lida Don't shout at me. I agree with you.
Sofia What can we do, then?
Lida We'll leave. We'll move to Lapland or to a desert island, we'll find a place that's so barren and poor and miserable that no one will want to follow us. These morons can carry on sitting in their cars on their mobile all day, frightened of every step and smell and raindrop, let them stay here and lie to each other and

get drunk and shag whoever happens to come along, it suits them. Be my guest.

But we've got to learn to be hard and to be by ourselves. To live so that we'll become different, the complete opposite of everybody here. We've got to learn how to hunt and fish and recognise all the mushrooms we find.

Sofia I'll gut that perch for you if you like, since you don't know how, even though you're older.

Lida And it's completely wrong that people like us, who try to do things right, end up having to leave. It should be the other way round, all the arseholes should be kicked out. People are always whinging about how hard it is to change the world. Rubbish. It would be simple, if we really wanted to.

Sofia How?

Lida All you'd have to do would be to exterminate all the evil people in every country – it's probably only about ten per cent of the population. Once you'd got rid of them, we'd all have a much better time.

Sofia Who would kill them?

Lida That's the only problem with this plan. Putting it into practice.

Sofia (*thinking hard*) Yes . . .

Lida But you'd better not do anything stupid. Got it? Did you hear me?

Sofia What?

Lida You heard.

Sofia Yeah, yeah.

Pause.

But when? When can we leave?

Lida As soon as we've got the money together.

Sofia Hm, money stinks.

Lida There won't be any money on our island.

Sofia Good. Or love.

Lida (*pause*) What if someone falls in love, though?

Sofia Two warnings, then you either get expelled or executed. It's up to you.
Lida That's quite harsh.
Sofia It has to be. Otherwise it'll just end up like everywhere else.
Lida True.
Sofia We don't need anyone else there. You and me and maybe, maybe if Mum /
Lida No.
Sofia But /
Lida No.
Lida Everything there will be pure and severe.
Sofia And beautiful.
Lida And beautiful.
Sofia There'll be a path to lead you there, and you can't tell whether it was made by humans or animals.

SEVENTEEN: INTERLUDE

The Blokes are carrying things across the stage. Furniture and other items from the Old Lady's flat.

EIGHTEEN: THE BASEMENT

Lida and Sofia enter the basement. Lida is carrying the photo album.

Lida Hello? You, Mrs? We've brought you your photo album.
Sofia (*to Lida, whispering*) She won't come out.
Lida I'll leave it here on the floor.

Lida places the photo album on the floor at the edge of the darkness.
Silence.

Sofia (*to Lida*) Tell her!

Lida (*to the Old Lady*) There's just one thing, though. Er . . . the money.

Clatter.

There were a couple of men there.

Clatter.

It wasn't your son, though, they were different. Well . . . they took . . .

Old Lady They're all the same. (*angrily*) Get out! Go on, out! Now!

Lida But /

Old Lady (*interrupts*) Don't bother coming down here again. Just go away. I'll be gone by tomorrow. Don't speak to me any more.

Lida But he's sitting out there waiting.

Old Lady Who?

Lida Your son.

Pause.

Old Lady (*hushed*) Does he know where I am?

Pause.

Lida No, but /

Old Lady I don't know anything about him, I don't know what makes him tick. He's a stranger to me, someone I'd rather watch from a distance, through a glass wall – from as far away as possible –

If he comes too close, things will all turn black again.

Sofia (*tugging at Lida's arm*) Come on!

Lida (*to the Old Lady*) Do you know what I think? / I think

Old Lady Be quiet.

Lida Tell me why the heads have been cut off these photos?

Sofia Let's go!

Lida Children don't just hate their parents for no reason at all.

Old Lady Since when did God hand out trophies for being a good mother?

Lida No. We do that.

Old Lady You ask him if he can remember just how much I loved him when he was born, I thought my heart would burst I loved him so much. I thought there's no other child in the world I could ever love as much as I loved him. Ask him if he remembers sitting in his mother's lap. He must remember! Can't he remember a single time? You just ask him!

The girls leave.

The Old Lady shouts after them.

He can't remember because he's got a short memory and a f—ing temper on him!

Sofia (*to Lida*) Maybe he just didn't like all that swearing.

Lida What do you think happened?

Sofia What, with the son?

Lida No! With her. What's she done to make her so afraid of her son?

The Old Lady gets up, takes a stone out of her son's collection, clenches her hand around it and squeezes it tightly in her fist. We see this in the beam of light.

She stands there waiting.

NINETEEN: THE ENDURANCE CAMP

Sofia and her friends with woolly hats on, underneath a mountain of blankets.

Sofia This extreme camp is to test our endurance of the cold: windows wide open and all the radiators off!

Pal How cold is it?

Ally Minus fifteen.

All Yeah! Yippee!

Ally How long have we got?

Sofia One minute left, then we'll stick the sauna on, shut all the windows, whack the radiators up to full and turn on the oven and all the hotplates! We've got to learn to endure hot and cold and solitude. (*to the Friend*) Have you got a barbecue?

Friend (*slightly concerned*) I don't really think we . . . /

Pal Bring in the barbecue!

One of the girls comes in pushing a smoking, steaming barbecue on wheels.

Ally Look, we can't harden up if it's just a bit warm or a bit chilly, this has to be full on! Full power! Get everything on full blast!

Pal Yeah, quick, before your parents get back.

Friend They won't be back until late. They said they'd be back about ten o'clock and they're always at least a couple of hours late.

The barbecue continues to glow.

Ally I'm really starting to sweat in here.

Pal We've got to be careful not to fall asleep. It could be fatal. One night my uncle had a heart attack in the sauna and in the morning all they found was his dried up skin. He'd been baked and shrivelled away to nothing.

Sofia The word's emulsified, actually.

Ally What?

Sofia Or coagulated. Forty-two degrees is the temperature at which humans and eggs congeal into a tough kind of jelly. (*to the Friend*) What are you doing?

Friend Getting a thermometer. I don't want my head to boil like an egg.

There is a noise at the door.

Sofia That'll be my sister.
Pal She's not coming. She popped round and said so just before you arrived.
Sofia My sister?
Pal Yeah. She's gone to the beach with some boy.
Sofia My sister?
Pal Yes.
Sofia What boy?

Pause.

Friend That same one.

Sofia runs out.

Ally What's wrong with her?

More noise at the door.

Pal Who's that, then?
Ally Oh no, it's your parents! Quick, they're coming!

The Parents enter.

Parents Bloody hell!

The girls run away carrying blankets, pushing barbecue, etc., offstage.

TWENTY: BY THE SEA

Haba is by himself; he is throwing stones into the water.

Haba There she is, cowering like a rat in a hole; blind and fat like a mole, just sitting there snivelling, she'll run away and hide if she can and if she can't, she'll bite. (*He laughs.*) Mummy. (*He throws a stone.*)

Lida enters.

Lida She's there. Why didn't you come?
Haba I was afraid.

Pause.

Not of what I'd do,
not even of what she'd do.
I was afraid of what would happen if we both walked into the same room.

Pause.

Does she know I'm here?
Lida Yes.
Haba Has she known all along?
Lida (*nods*) Yes.

Silence. Haba stands up.

Can I ask /
Haba No.
Lida Why did you come here if . . .?
Haba I just thought I'd see
whether . . .
what might happen.
Lida If you met up?
Haba Yes.
Lida And?
Haba We didn't meet up.
That's it. Don't give a shit. (*He is about to leave, but then turns to Lida.*) Where do you think I should have gone? Who could I have gone to?

Lida doesn't know what to say. Haba leaves.

Lida The first time I realised that I was old was when I was standing watching a toddler, about two years old, running around all happy and clumsy and laughing, then running back to Mummy's arms and everyone else started laughing and I would have given anything just to be able to be like that again.

But . . .
When they looked at me, they didn't see something soft and downy and sweet-smelling, something that's easy to love. No, they saw a pair of eyes which looked deep inside them and saw things that they didn't want anyone to see. They stared back at me with stony eyes and then they looked away.
I was five years old.

TWENTY-ONE: THE BASEMENT

The Old Lady is sitting in the dark. She hears something, but stays put.

Haba enters. He stops and stands behind his mother. She does not turn.

Silence.

They are both waiting for something, but it does not happen.

Haba turns and walks away.

Very slowly, the Old Lady turns her head, but Haba has already gone.

TWENTY-TWO: THE BETRAYAL

Night. The girls' room.

Lida is hurriedly packing things into a backpack: a pocket lamp, a black woolly hat, etc. Sofia enters in her pyjamas.

Sofia Where have you been?

Pause.

Where are you going?
Lida Did you know there's an island really nearby and no one lives there. It's about half an hour away by

boat. There's an old mine, a well, empty houses – don't you see? – empty blocks of flats on an island . . .

Sofia Who are you going with?

Lida This one guy and a couple of his mates. They've got a dinghy. There's still loads of pots and pans in the kitchens, kettles on the stove, as if the owners had just popped out, children's toys lying on the floor /

Sofia It belongs to the army.

Lida Maybe. Listen, I'll go and check it out, see what kind of place it is. If it's all right . . . Imagine, it could be a place for us, really, it could be just the right place.

Sofia walks out.

Where are you going?

Sofia (*voice, off*) I'm getting dressed.

Lida (*looks at her watch*) I'm going now. It's best to go when it's dark.

Sofia enters. She has put her coat on over her pyjamas.

See you, I'm off.

Sofia I'm coming with you.

Lida Not now.

Sofia Why not?

Lida Don't argue.

Sofia I'm not arguing. I asked you why not.

Lida Listen, next time, OK?

Sofia I want to come with you.

Lida Look, of course you can come . . . later. But this time it's best if I just go by myself.

Sofia (*cold, blankly*) Why?

Lida Don't argue.

Sofia I'm not arguing. I just asked you why.

Lida That's enough!

Sofia turns and walks off.

Hey, come on . . .

Sofia You're already different.

Pause. She makes the 'liar' sign at Lida. This can be any sign the sisters have devised and it is clear that they both understand the significance and strength of it.

No, you're the same, you're just the same as everyone else. (*Exit.*)

Lida looks at her watch, hesitates for a moment, then leaves.

TWENTY-THREE: MUSHROOM PICKING

In a forest. Sofia is picking mushrooms, she has a basket and a mushroom field guide with her. Her friends are somewhere nearby.

Sofia We all went into the woods, me and my friends, it was getting dark and we couldn't really see whether the mushrooms we were picking were actually the same ones we thought we were picking.

Sofia picks a mushroom, begins to examine it and reads from the field guide.

'The Bitter Bolete, *Tylopilus felleus*. This mushroom is most probably not poisonous, but it is so bitter that even the smallest piece when mixed up with other mushrooms will ruin an entire meal.'

Sofia chuckles and puts the mushroom in her basket. She picks another mushroom and reads from the field guide.

'The Witch's Cap, *Coprinus atramentarius*. The cap is initially bell-shaped, but widens as the gills begin to secrete ink. The stipe is white and hollow. Edible when young, but contains coprine which, when combined with alcohol, has effects similar to antabus. Even drinking beer the following day can cause severe symptoms: vomiting, diarrhoea, etc.'

Sofia puts the mushroom in her basket.
The other girls enter.

Friend What are you doing?

Sofia does not answer.
Pal takes a mushroom out of Sofia's basket, examines it, then reads from the guide book.

Pal 'The Web Cap Mushroom, *Cortinarius rubellus*. The poison in this mushroom causes serious damage to the kidneys . . . The Roman Emperor Claudius is said to have died after someone deliberately served him a meal containing poisonous mushrooms. The poison has been confirmed in animal tests.'
Ally That's awful! Poisoning animals.
Pal (*to Sofia*) Are you planning to kill your stepmother?
Friend No. Her sister won't let her. If her stepmother dies, Sofia will be the prime suspect. Now she just dips the old cow's toothbrush in the toilet every time she goes for a wee.
Ally Her sister doesn't let her do anything. Even though it would be really easy to plug in the hairdryer and throw it in the water when the bitch is sitting in the bath and – zzzzzhhhhhh – nobody would be able to prove a thing!
Pal Why are you picking these?
Sofia To solve over-population.
Friend Sofia, look. I don't want you to go to jail.
Sofia I won't go to jail.
Friend Throw them away.
Sofia They can't prove anything. (*Smiling.*) I'm just a little girl.

Friend You'll end up somewhere. Then I'll be all alone.

Sofia thinks for a moment. Then all of a sudden she takes a mushroom out of the basket and stuffs it into her mouth. They all frantically try to get it out. Eventually she manages to get it out of Sofia's mouth.

Sofia It was only a chanterelle!
Friend A chanterelle?
Sofia You ought to know your mushrooms a bit better.

They are all relieved and play-fight with Sofia.

TWENTY-FOUR: THE BASEMENT

Old Lady This is the final day. Every time I heard footsteps upstairs I hoped and feared that soon this would all end.
It was quiet. I couldn't hear a thing any more, not a sound all night long. I just lay here and listened to his deep sleep.
I couldn't bear the silence.
Then I went back – home – but he'd gone. All that was left was a dent in the pillow and a crumpled duvet.
He had slept in my bed.
Now he was gone.
What had he come back for? Money? What was he looking for?
His mother? (*She gently strokes the pillow.*)

TWENTY-FIVE: THE QUESTIONING

Lida, Haba and Blokes A and B, each sitting on a chair, each in turn under the spotlight.
The blokes are in high spirits throughout the scene.

Lida We got caught – of course we did, it was an island.
I could see how, the whole time we were there, the police were thinking, that girl, she's a different breed from those blokes, she's a good girl, even though I was standing right there with them.
And just . . . for a moment I almost wished that I wasn't, because it was all so unfair.
And yet . . .
I wonder if, somewhere along the line, perhaps I got the tiniest crumb more;
a hug at the right moment;
a gene or some beautiful landscape or a joke we could all laugh about.
Was that enough
to make
a difference?
We lay on the ground on our stomachs, so the dogs wouldn't get nasty.

Bloke A (*laughs*) My old man taught me how to kill a wolfhound. Just twist its neck round like that. Piece of cake. That's what my dad taught me. We could have . . . if we'd wanted to.

Lida They wanted to let the dogs loose on us but they couldn't, because I was there, a good girl. Is it my face? This face that looks like all it's missing is a convertible and a pair of sunglasses.

Bloke B Well, we rowed to the beach and covered the dinghy with leaves and twigs . . .
Stupid . . .

Bloke A Completely bloody stupid, but what kind of life would that be if you just plan things out all the time and think about what would be best and what would be right and sensible? Sometimes you've just got to let go and see what happens.

Bloke B And you can be pretty sure something'll happen!

Bloke A On the other side of the island there were a couple of ships moored in the harbour, ships belonging to the coastguard and the navy, but apart from that the whole dark, empty island was ours; it was full of deserted houses, lorries parked by the roadside, petrol in the tank, cargo in the boot . . .

Bloke B And it was just like they said, pots on the stove, not your average pots though, but ones big enough for fifty soldiers. What we didn't know was that in the middle of the island there was a set of barracks and when we looked through the window we saw long rows of artillery, neatly stacked up like ploughs at a farming convention. We opened the door /

Haba 'What did you use to break in?' they asked . . . so I showed them my Swiss army knife.

Lida (*angrily*) I mean, it's a disgrace that such dangerous weapons are guarded so badly that any amateur can just come along and break in and all they need is an army knife. One stupid padlock on the door!

Some criminals might break in there!

Bloke A Cardboard boxes full of hand grenades, pistols, all individually wrapped in tissue paper like in a cosmetics shop.

Haba (*to Lida*) Did you take anything?

Lida Yes.

But I put it back.

I just somehow felt like /

Haba Good.

Pause.

Lida (*to Haba*) Did you take anything?

Haba doesn't answer.

Bloke A Don't get personal.

Bloke B We were walking down these paths in the pitch dark.

New boots got completely ruined. (*to Bloke A*) And he was scared of the snakes!

Bloke A I was not. I just don't like them, that's all. They bite.

Bloke B The only person I know who's ever been bitten by a snake is my old Auntie Elsi. She had to go out to the bushes during the night and managed to crouch right on top of a grass snake and bam! We had to take her to hospital.

Bloke A Grass snakes aren't even poisonous.

Bloke B I know, but this one had dirty fangs and my Auntie Elsi got this really nasty inflammation, her whole backside swelled up.

They laugh.

Bloke A Things were going really well until they didn't. We had to push a truck to get it started and then we drove around until she fell off.

*

Lida (*alone, in the spotlight*) I'm not in love. It was enough for me that there was someone, someone with warm skin and a ticket to a world I could never enter by myself.

Because there's nothing much
good left in the world,
then I hoped that
at least my body could be happy.
I could make love by the sea, surrounded by everything that's beautiful in the world, and for a moment I could feel as if I'm a part of it.

TWENTY-SIX: RECONCILIATIONS

The girls' room. Night. Sofia is writing something, sitting upside down. Lida enters. She goes over to see Sofia. Sofia turns the paper over so that Lida cannot see what she is writing.

Sofia The police came round to talk to Mum about you.
Lida What did she say?
Sofia Not much. She's asleep.
Lida Aha.
Sofia Yes.
Lida Good.
Sofia She's still got her wellies on.
Lida Has she?
Sofia Yes.
Lida Well.
Sofia Yes.

Pause.

Lida Let's go and take them off.
Sofia What?
Lida The wellies. Let's take them off. They're probably really hot.
Sofia (*nods*) Yes. (*Nods again.*) Yes, let's.

Sofia takes Lida by the hand and they walk off together.

*

Haba (*as if writing a letter*) This is a bad ending. A happy ending would have been if I'd lost, if I'd disappeared in a ball of flames, in a burning car flying towards the black water, which would take me with it deep down, me and everything I've done, which you don't know a thing about. But deep inside you, there would already be a new beginning, a new person, a child, and you'd quietly walk up to my mother . . .

Lida (*has entered with a letter in her hand; as if she carries on reading*) I'd walk up to your mother and she'd say . . .

The Old Lady comes out of the darkness for the very first time.

Old Lady She'd say:
I'm waiting.
And then I'd ask . . . I'd ask her what he was like . . . that boy.
My son.

The End.

Fireworks Exploding in Your Head

Laura Ruohonen interviewed by Jim Mulligan

Laura Ruohonen is one of Finland's leading playwrights. She was born in Helsinki, where she now lives and works.

An Island Far from Here explores two sets of relationships: two sisters who, disappointed by their parents, dream of escaping to an ideal far-away place; and an old woman hiding in their cellar from her abusive son who is returning from jail.

> There are two parallel stories in the play. In both stories you see the relationships between parents and children even though the parents' generation – the middle-aged – is completely missing from the play. One of my aims was to show how uncompromising children can be in the way they see the world. In many ways I find their moral ideals much stronger and more severe than adults'. The fact that there is also a lot of humour and laughter in the play is thanks to the fact that children have an immense power of imagination and a capacity to live in the here and now.

Structurally the play also works on two parallel horizontal levels: there is the basement, the darkness beneath the surface; and the other is the dream of a more honest life in the open air, deserted woods and islands no human has yet destroyed.

Lida, the older sister, and Haba, the Old Lady's son, can be seen as mirror images of each other. They both have pasts that are unknown to us. Laura Ruohonen does not reveal their personal history in detail.

> I am not very interested in painting look-alike portraits of different characters. I am more concerned

> with ideas and language. I want to see how people's ideals and dreams collide rather than just find psychologically relevant explanations for why people say nice or rude things to each other. That kind of drama is already being very well taken care of by television.

And yet the experience of loving and being loved is central to the play. The young people certainly come from dysfunctional families. Children learn early on that parents are not be trusted – or loved – if one doesn't want to get hurt. Lida recalls a time when she was five years old, and her parents were staring at her with stony eyes before flinching away because they believed she was looking deep inside them and seeing things they didn't want anyone to see. And the Old Lady admits her son is a stranger to her, the son she loved so much she thought her heart would burst. Lida therefore asks herself, 'What's she done to make her so afraid of her son?' Not the more obvious question, 'What has *he* done to her?'

> People do the most terrible things to each other in the name of love, so you may decide you don't want to be any part of that kind of deception and dishonesty. In their own way these young people are afraid that every time you love you take such a huge risk that it's better to decide not to let love into your world. Even the youngest girls in the play learn their lesson: 'I'm never going to fall in love.' 'How can you stop it happening?' and 'It's like smoking. If you don't start it when you're young you won't get hooked.' At first glance the attitudes to love in my play look bleak, but there is also the tremendous power of love, even in its absence. I don't want to give up hope although I recognise that loving someone forces you to make compromises that you shouldn't have to make. We can have successful relationships.

In one sense the play, set in the Finnish landscape with its barren islands, rocks and stones, is a quest to leave behind the materialism of city life and to live a life close to nature.

> I understand that young people in the UK will not have experienced this kind of deserted landscape, but all children are able to imagine wild, fantastic places and people of all ages react against the materialism of our societies. Children in Finland, just like anywhere else, get computers and mobile phones and focus on the screen instead of getting out and experiencing the reality around them. So I am sure young people in the UK will be able to relate to the play. Some details in the play will be strange to them but the relationships will be recognisable. In fact, that little bit of distance might even help. It is easier to look at the more painful parts of our lives when they are not immediately recognisable as our own.

An Island Far From Here is going to make demands on actors and audiences. It asks serious questions and looks without sentimentality at how families make and break children. It looks at our disconnection from nature, history and each other and it asks young people to reflect on how they can live and – perhaps – love.

> I believe drama can be intellectually cathartic. I remember seeing Camus' *Caligula* when I was seventeen. It was a freezing night in Helsinki, minus 35 degrees Centigrade, and I lived six kilometres from that theatre, but I was so excited I ran all the way home from the performance, my head exploding. Good theatre can be like fireworks in your head. It can light up things that you have only vaguely known are there. It can make your thinking take a leap.

An Island Far from Here does not even give the consolation of a clear-cut ending. According to the young scoundrel, Haba, a happy ending would have been if he had disappeared in a ball of flames, purged of everything he had done, and left Lida with a child, a new chance. Instead Laura Ruohonen brings the Old Lady out of the darkness for the first time to ask Lida the question forgotten long ago: 'What was he like . . . that boy . . . my son.'

There is so much longing in this play, so much need for love, that perhaps young people will be able to feel the pain and see a little more clearly some wonderful, strange and dangerous things they already know.

Production Notes

The play is best approached as a 'phenomenon' or object that has to be discovered. Sometimes it's best not to explain everything. A sense of mystery should be kept. A play often grows out of intuition, and works on an audience both consciously and subconsciously.

Laura Ruohonen

STAGING AND SETTING

The play takes place in the present day, in a town by the sea, somewhere in Finland. A number of locations are mentioned. The basement and the beach are important but it's unnecessary to create either realistically onstage. The play works best if the staging is quite fluid. Many of the locations can be suggested or representational. For example, two blankets could be the girls' bedroom.

The play is full of literal and metaphorical references to light and dark. It begins with a hand turning out a light (most plays begin with lights going up). This could be achieved by using a tight spotlight, or creating a shaft of light using a gobo. The sequence of scenes is often light/dark/light/dark. Not all the scenes in the dark take place in the basement. Scene Three, 'A Voice in the Darkness', occurs in the Old Lady's home.

Darkness, for the Old Lady, is representative of her damaged relationship with her son. She is also hiding in the dark of the basement. They represent fear. Traditionally children are afraid of the dark, but here the Old Lady is afraid of the light. It is only at the end of the play that she steps forward into the light when she sees the truth about her relationship – that she does not know her own son and is still waiting for him to come home.

When staging scenes, be aware of the time of day the action takes place.

The play requires approximately 6 f and 5 m actors including an old lady. She is often in half-darkness. The incidental roles of headteacher and parents could be detached voices.

THEMES

Children This is a play about children and growing up, hard experiences and exciting discoveries. It is interesting that the middle, parental, generation is missing. There are children (Sofia and the other girls are 9–13) and there is the Old Lady. The children have to grapple with big, difficult concepts in order to make sense of their lives. The play explores boundaries where fantasy and reality collide.

Love The play examines many different types of love: familial, sexual, love as dark as well as light. It can be a painful, complicated force. Love is often closely bound up with fear in the play. It can be cold, unyielding and numb, like a rock, or it can be open, free and romantic, like a floating island. Swans mate for life, but they also fight and attack each other. In Finnish, love is a very strong word. It is used less often than in English and therefore implies a more extreme emotion.

The character Haba is on leave from prison, and in the past he has been quite violent. In Finland there is much depression and violence in rural communities due to isolation. Haba is violent, yet the girls find him attractive and charming. His character can be seen through many different lenses. He is something of a paradox, and symbolises the difficulty and confusion of 'love' in the play.

Finland In Finland, as in the play, many things collide. (Rock hitting rock or metal). Cultures collide, often within one family. The play is partly an exploration of barriers and the transgression of borders.

It is not surprising that Sofia knows the Latin names of mushrooms in Scene Twenty-Three. This sort of field-craft is more common in Finland.

Language and Translation Laura has crafted the rhythms of the language very carefully. There is a musical phrasing in the language that David has tried to capture in translation. In Finnish, words tend to be longer, which gives the language a poetry and lyricism that cannot be directly translated. Be aware of the 'music' of the text: its rhythms, sounds and pauses. Look out for short, snappy scenes that are followed by longer lingering ones and allow these contrasts to happen.

The 'liar' sign on page 328 could be a sign representing plucking something out of the air. An English equivalent could be the 'chine chin' sign (stroking your chin).

Landscape There are lots of islands in Finland. So an island has an important metaphorical meaning in Finnish. Finnish islands tend to be rocky or stony, which has metaphorical resonance with the motif of rocks and stones (symbols of aggression and hostility) throughout the play. The island of the play also has the sense of something that is forbidden (the army base) and dangerous.

An Island Far from Here is an open-air piece. In Finland there is much more of a sense of permeability between the outside world and the interior of buildings. There is a great sense of isolation in the Finnish outdoors.

Animals There are references to animals in the play. Animals are used frequently in Finnish discourse and are common cultural referents. Humans are often compared to animals, as on page 320: ' There'll be a path to lead you there, and you can't tell whether it was made by humans or animals.'

Story-telling There are strong story-telling elements in the play. At the end of some scenes, characters turn to the audience to comment on an action (for example, at the end of Scene Three). There are different levels of reality within the play, it does not exist entirely on one plane. It should always be clear whom an actor is talking to.

EXERCISES

Have the actors run a scene from the play while passing a football backwards and forwards. In order to speak they must pass the ball on the last word of the line of the speech. The force of the ball needs to take on different energies. Try having the actors get the ball from the others if it suits the impetus of the line. Encourage the actors to experiment by keeping the ball moving during a long speech by bouncing or juggling it. The ball can begin to represent the 'meaning' or focus of the scene, the thing that is at stake.

Units Separating the script into units, or beats, is a useful way for the director and actors to harness the action and be clear about what story they are trying to tell. It's a subjective process; there are no rules or right or wrong answers but a collaborative activity of negotiation and discovery.

Broadly speaking, a unit of action is one in which one action is initiated and completed. Take Scene Fourteen, for instance, where Haba is trying to chat up Lida and make her stay. Lida is uncertain about Haba, but is attracted to the character and wants, against her better judgement, to remain with him. As a rough guide, a new unit often starts when a new character enters or exits or attempts to. In Scene Fourteen, units are built around Lida attempting to depart, or agreeing to remain. In the end she stays.

Within a unit there is normally a point of change or transition. Pay heed to punctuation and the spatial arrangement of text, as these can often give clues to where pauses and breaks suggest a change in direction or emphasis.

A unit often ends when two characters reach some sort of agreement about a proposition. For example, on page 309:

> **Haba** OK. Let's leave it at that, OK?
> **Lida** OK. (*She is about to leave.*) [*End of unit.*]
> **Haba** You shouldn't hang around here, this is a dangerous place.

Haba's last line here is the initiation of a new action: trying, and succeeding, to keep her with him.

Once the units have been put in, you could then try to give them titles. These should be active and contain an active verb, so that they give actors a target. The titles could be put up on a wall and the actors encouraged to improvise around them. The units can also be a useful basis for blocking the scene; for example, consider that each new unit displays a difference in the physical relationships between the characters.

Suzy Graham-Adriani
March 2003
based on a workshop facilitated by Edward Kemp

MOONTEL SIX

Constance Congdon

Constance Congdon's best known play, *Tales of the Lost Formicans*, has been produced in Helsinki, Brixton, Manchester, Tokyo and over one hundred locations in the USA. *Casanova* and *Dog Opera* were both staged at the Joseph Papp Public Theatre in New York. Her play about the first woman President, *Lips*, commissioned by Speilberg's Dreamworks, was produced in New York in 1998. *The Automata Pietà*, written for ACT in San Francisco, was seen again at the Magic Theatre in 2000. The Profile Theatre in Portland, Oregon, devoted an entire season to her works, and their production of *No Mercy* included a new companion piece, *One Day Earlier*. Her new verse version of *The Misanthrope* premièred at ACT in 2001. *Mother*, based on Gorky's *Vassa Zheleznova*, will open at ACT in Spring 2004. *Earthrise*, a new opera for which she wrote the libretto, will première at the San Francisco Opera next year. Congdon is an alumna of New Dramatists and currently teaches playwriting at Amherst College and the Yale School of Drama.

Characters

Uberbeth
Older female teen. Part luminescent jellyfish. Just began her genitive. A reluctant mother-figure for Toyn. Sceptical of most people

Zipper
Older male teen. Part lizard and part moth. Serious, concerned with his future and the well-being of others

Emo
Male teen. Mixed genes from Earth mammals. Naive. Given to outbursts of uncontrolled emotion. Sexually ambivalent

Toyn
Boy. Completely human but speaks like a technical manual. Refers to himself in the third person. Suffers from severe allergies and, maybe, asthma. Mature beyond his years but still a boy

Geenoma
Older female teen. A genetically-warped valley girl. Knows she is beautiful. Wants to be the leader but frequently fails. Devoid of maternal instinct

Meema
Female teen. In constant quest for answers. Fearless. Knows her power. Capable of holding her own in arguments. A doer rather than a follower

Seven
Male teen. Highly intelligent. A maths-brain. Logical. Finds comfort in probability. A misfit in a group of misfits

Yuseef
Older male teen. Human. A protection officer for the human population on the Moon. Recently from Earth. A lost soul desperately looking for a future

Sark
Female Moon-being of indeterminate age. Eebee's mate

Eebee
Female Moon-being of indeterminate age. Sark's mate

SCENE ONE

Several kids in a sort of line-up, facing the audience.

Uberbeth We just want to explain what happened.

Zipper They made us leave.

Emo They didn't want us.

Zipper At Moonstead Estates, either.

Emo Particularly there.

Zipper They didn't want us around their kids.

Uberbeth Because we have these weird genes –

Emo – which we didn't ask for.

Uberbeth But we wouldn't be who we are without them.

Emo Yeah. There's nothing wrong with us. We're made the way we're made and we're fine with that.

Zipper Uberbeth here is part luminescent jellyfish. (*to Uberbeth*) Anything glow yet?

Uberbeth Not so far. But I just began my genitive.

Emo Yeah, we all have in some way. Zipper's started to pupate.

Zipper I'm waiting for wings and then I get to mate.

Uberbeth That's really why they didn't want us.

Emo The whole 'mating' thing. As if we'd really even want to date their 100 per cent human Moonstead snobs.

Zipper We have our variations, but we're proud of them. Right?

Uberbeth Like, I have trouble digesting anything with lecithin in it. I'm not sure what lecithin is except it's in anything that has a shelf-life estimate on it.

Zipper So – you don't mind me telling them, do you, Uberbeth?

Uberbeth Lecithin makes me flatulent.

Zipper And we eat a lot of shelf-life products here.

Emo We like to think of it as her 'special power'. And me – I have some genes from some Earth mammal that was supposed to make me strong, but small and dainty. That didn't work out at all.

Zipper And I'm part lizard as well as moth. Since lizards eat moths, I have some concerns about my future.

Emo And we're not 100 per cent pure human but, from what I've seen, that's totally fine.

Uberbeth Only Toyn is totally human. But he has allergies and stuff.

Zipper (*chastising Uberbeth*) Uberbeth, you said his name. Now he'll come out.

Toyn enters and looks at them. He's holding an inhaler and a 'lovey toy' – some shapeless stuffed animal, now unrecognisable. He looks at the audience with suspicion, takes a hit from his inhaler, still looking at them.

Toyn Downloading. Please wait.

Processes, then suddenly points to individual audience members and identifies them for the kids.

Analog. Analog. Analog. Analog. All analog. (*Looks closely at one audience member.*) Digital. (*Another audience member, but one that pleases him.*) Vacuum tube unit! Classic.

Emo Toyn! You're bothering them.

Toyn Do not disassemble this unit. Disassembling this unit can cause electrical shock. To you. Danger. Danger.

Zipper They're not humans. They're bots, Toyn.

Toyn All digital? Like Toyn?

But this doesn't make Toyn happy, and he begins to breathe with difficulty – he goes into an attack. Uberbeth calms him.

Zipper So, the deal is, we thought we were Good, but we were perceived as Evil, Bad and Wrong.
Uberbeth So we're hoping you'll understand.
Emo If you understand the whole story.
Zipper It started with the socks.
Emo No, it didn't. It started with Geenoma.
Uberbeth It started with the probability of seeing the ship!

They exit to reveal Meema lying on the ground, looking up at the 'sky'. Seven enters, sees her, looks up too.

Seven The probability of you seeing it again is very, very small. And, indeed, we might alter its path by observing it.
Meema Seven, stop thinking so much and just freaking look up?
Geenoma (*entering with a large bag*) I, like, I, like, I, like, like, like, I can't, like, STAND the, like CHAOS AND FILTH WE LIVE IN ANY MORE!!

She dumps the contents of the bag on Meema. It's a zillion pairs of dirty socks. Geenoma exits.

Meema (*spitting and wiping her mouth free of sock debris*) Sock scum! How could she do that to me?
Seven (*smells them*) Yeah, they're not even your socks. (*Smells them.*) They're mine. (*Smells them again.*) Well, that one's yours.

They look at the mess for a beat.

Meema Well, are you going to help me clean this up?
Seven No, but I'm going to help you understand how it happened. You see . . . when you lose one sock, it leaves behind its mate. Or partner. Let's call it 'partner'. So you wear the next pair and you lose one of those. Because it's actually more likely that you'll

lose one of a matched pair than one of an unmatched pair because you rarely wear an unmatched pair because most people are less likely to wear and then wash the unmatched sock, unless they are us who have stopped washing them altogether, so the odds are even greater that the next sock to get lost will be part of a pair. Are you with me?

Meema I hope not. Because this is some flaming convoluted boom-boom you've got going here.

Seven It's important, Meema. It's important to understand how the world works.

Meema But we're not on the world. The world is a planet. We're on the Moon – a satellite of the Earth. And not a planet.

Seven I know it is futile of me to try to explain this to you, yet again, but: the Moon is a planet. It travels in an orbit, therefore, it is a planet. Just because it doesn't orbit the *Sun* doesn't mean it is not a planet. It is as much a planet as the Earth is.

Meema You just can't accept the fact that we are satellite-dwellers.

Seven If you can't get your total left brain Nazi to give up your solarcentrism and consider –

Meema Left-brain? Left-brain? I am *right*-brain, totally. *You're* the left-brain, Math Boy! Dweak!!

Seven Try to grok it this way –

Meema Don't you Heinlein me, Seven! That's not fair!

Seven It's a matter of perception. We can be anywhere we want to by using our access to simstem reality.

Meema Seven, you are in denial.
Which is a river on Earth.
Where we are not.
Because we're on the freakin' Moon!
Even Toyn can accept this –
Oops, I said his name.

Toyn enters. Long beat. He waits for something from them.

Seven We're sorry, Toyn. Meema just said your name because she likes your name. You go rest now.

Toyn Don't activate unit until you are ready to use it. (*He exits.*)

Seven Back to the task at hand. Let's say you have ten complete but distinct pairs of socks, meaning each pair differs from another, then it will be over a hundred times more likely that the result will be the worst possible outcome.

Meema Cleopatra!! Hellllllo!! Worst Possible Outcome?? Seven – *this* is the Worst Possible Outcome! We're living it! The fact that only an abandoned moontel could be our home! The fact that no one cares what happens to us, except the ones who want us sterilised. Like the wonderful folks in Moonstead Estates who raided our group home and chased us through the hydroponic gardens, through the air tunnels, through the entrails of this community until we ended up in this place. And the Very Worst Possible Outcome is after they find us, which is inevitable – do you deal with inevitabilities in your happy probable world?

Seven The Best Possible Outcome would be seven complete pairs left. Drawing two socks at random even from a drawer full of complete pairs is most likely to produce nothing but two odd socks. And, here's the interesting part –

Meema THERE IS NO INTERESTING PART!!

Seven My point is, if you draw two socks at random from a drawer full of complete pairs of socks you are going to, probably, get two *odd* socks . . .

Meema Seven, you're starting to scare me now. Are you there?

Seven More than ever, Meema. Facts make up the world, so probability is a religious experience. For me.

Meema So you were praying? With the socks?

Seven With the numbers.

Meema You are so very odd.

Seven And you're *not*?

Meema (*sees something in the sky*) There it is. And you just don't want to face it because you don't understand it. Seven – just look up.

Seven (*looks up, sees something*) All right. There's something there.

Meema Lie down.

Seven lies down.

See? There it is.

Seven It's most probable that it's a fault in the dome.

Meema Then why haven't we seen it the million other times we looked up?

Seven Because we haven't paid attention.

Meema No. We didn't pay attention at Moonstead Estates. Since we've been running, we've paid attention.

Seven But not to the sky. (*Sees it.*) Wait.

Meema See it? It moves.

Seven Total Galileo Moment, my Meema. (*Seven jumps up.*) Something is on me!

Meema Oh, Seven, you're such a – (*Sees something on his back.*) Uh-oh.

Seven (*whimpering*) 'Uh-oh?' 'Uh-oh?'

Meema brushes 'it' off and then steps on it.

Meema (*noticing similar bugs on the floor*) Ooo. There're lots of them.

Meema steps on and pursues lots of 'them' – a big killing spree. Seven has freaked out and has escaped somewhere offstage.

Meema Seven, come on. I killed them all. Come on.
Seven (*re-entering*) This place – is getting – uninhabitable, Meema. I still feel like I've got something on me. Indulge me and check.
Meema Turn around.

Seven turns around and there is a huge bug on his back.

Just a little dirt, Seven. Just look up and tell me what that phenomenon might be. In the sky. We don't want to miss it. (*Meema removes the bug carefully.*)

Seven It looks like someone or something is pinching the sky and then making a crease
And now the crease disappears over the horizon.

Meema throws the bug offstage.

However, the probability of that being an actual crease is very low.
I purport star surf. A wave. A wrinkle in the sky.
Meema (*finishing with the giant bug*) Uh-huh.
Seven (*suddenly*) It's a ship, Meema. It's a ship!! See? It's a ship crossing the starfield. Right? And blocking out the stars as it passes, *therefore*, creating the semblance of a ripple in the sky.
Meema A ship?
Seven Right.
Meema Where is it, then?
Seven It went to the other side.
Meema You mean, the dark side?
Seven Dark in that it never sees the Sun. Or the Earth, in fact.
Meema Stop quibbling with me about everything!! The question is, why would a ship go to the other side?
Seven I don't know.
Meema But, could it be, might it be, a ship that would carry us off this barren satellite –

Seven – planet –
Meema – to somewhere we might, you know, you know, like, be OK.
Seven I don't know that either.
And, even if, say if, we found that ship, how could we get to it without air to breathe along the way? And getting everyone to move again –

Geenoma enters.

Geenoma I, like, like, like, can't stand it, like, one, like, like, like, moment more!! We are, like, down to shelf, life two-thousand-oh-two Ramen Noodles! And, like, that shit is nasty!! AND WHAT ON BUZZ ALDRIN'S GREY EARTH IS THIS??

Geenoma produces the bug that Meema just disposed of and throws it somewhere else and exits.

Meema I think Geenoma would go.
Seven In a minute. But what about the others? Emo, Zipper – even Uberbeth – are assuming that we've found a safe place here, as long as we don't bother anybody.
Electronically Amplified Adult Voice
Kids?
We're so glad we found you.
Walk toward the light.
No one will hurt you.
We promise.
Just walk toward the light.

Start of music – some Barry Manilow or other bland tune made more bland by muzak, or something by Nirvana or Pearl Jam done on the cheapest synthesiser possible.

Kids Oh no. They've found us!

General pandemonium. The kids run around, on- and offstage, gathering stuff and bringing it on and taking some off again.

Geenoma Like, like, like, like STOP!

They all stop where they are.

OK, like – OK. OK. Like, we – all – have to, like – get into a, like, *line*, and *exit*. Like now. The air tunnels are that way!

They all exit, led by Geenoma, but Seven gets mesmerised by the light.

Electronically Amplified Adult Voice
Geenoma, Meema, Seven, Emo, Zipper, Uberbeth.
You are, like, totally, like, busted.
We are, like, so glad we, like, found you.
No one will hurt you.
We promise.
Just, like, walk toward the big, friendly light.

Meema (*grabbing Seven*) Seven, look at me, not the light. Now, let's go!

Long beat.

Toyn enters, holding his lovey object and his inhaler. He looks around, isn't bothered, particularly. He waits, takes a hit from his inhaler, waits, looks around, then addresses something that might have an answer for him.

Toyn Does the cable you are using have the correct connector?

Long beat.

Le câble n'est peut-être pas connecté correctement?

Beat.

Do you have the correct cable attached?

Beat.

In Spanish, and a new tactic to get an answer.

Sino estan en la pueblo con las regulaciones –

Pause.

– ese unida puede casar descarga electrida de shoke.

No answer from anything or anybody.

I don't feel so good. (*He lies down as the lights go down on him.*)

SCENE TWO

Immediately following. In the entrails of the domed Moon city. The kids are still moving quickly, being pursued, but they're hunkering down, getting into smaller and smaller spaces.

Emo Where are we going?
Geenoma These air tunnels are the only way we can escape!
Like, like, like, keep moving!
Uberbeth I'm cramped.
Meema Who isn't?
Zipper Are we being followed?
Geenoma How did it, like, know our names?
Emo I don't know.
Uberbeth Excuse me. (*Smells flatulence.*)
Seven Uberbeth!
Uberbeth I'm sorry – I'm tense.
Meema You get in the back of the line.
Uberbeth There's no room.
Emo We'll make room!

They squeeze her past them. She gets to the back of the line.

Uberbeth Hey, where's Toyn?

Seven Oh. Well, don't worry. You said his name – he'll come.

Silence. They wait and then realise Toyn is gone, then emotional pandemonium.

All (*not together*) Where's Toyn? Oh no! What are we going to do? Toyn! We left him!!

Meema We have to go back.

All (*not together*) Right! We have to! Absolutely! Let's go!

But they have a failure of courage and don't move.

Seven I'll go.

Meema (*grabbing Seven's sleeve, surprising herself and Seven*) No!

Emo I'll go.

Geenoma No. Like, no one will go.

Uberbeth Geenoma!

Geenoma Like, we can't go. All of us are, like, totally genetic freaks and, like, something they, like, want to do away with. Toyn, is, like, 100 per cent human. They might be good to him.

Zipper Good? *Good?*

Uberbeth She means they won't, you know, fix him.

Seven (*what a stupid word for it*) Fix? *Fix?*

Geenoma Like, like, like –

Meema Just spit it out, Geenoma! They want to fix us, they want to sterilise us!!

Emo Oh, is that all? Couldn't we all just take really good showers? I mean, how sterile do they want us all to be?

They decide not to inform Emo of what sterilisation means.

Uberbeth (*speaks in coded language to protect Emo's innocence*) Look, I don't mind being really, really 'clean'. If they wanted to 'clean' me, that would be fine.

Zipper Uberbeth, what are you saying? You can't mean that!

Uberbeth Zipper, I think the flatulence genes should end with me. (*She starts to crawl out of the tunnel, going back in the direction they came from.*)

Emo Uberbeth! Don't go!

Zipper They'll get you!

Geenoma I, like, order you to come back here!

Uberbeth (*produces flatulence as she exits*) Oops!

She's gone, but the odour remains.

Emo Woa! Bad one!!

Uberbeth (*offstage, about the flatulence*) Sorry!

Geenoma Like, bye, Uberbeth! (*to everyone else*) This is, like, sad.

Meema I know.

Emo Maybe they'll let her take a bath instead of a shower. And then she could soak for a while. Would that be clean enough for them?

Seven I hope so.

Emo I know baths aren't considered to be all that sterile –

Zipper Can someone tell him? Can I tell him? Emo, sterilisation means they want to – (*Stops – it's more difficult to tell than he thought.*)

Meema Go ahead.

Geenoma Explain what they want to do to us.

Zipper They want to –

Emo Uh-huh . . .?

Zipper I can't.

Seven They want to take away our ability to pass on our genes.

Emo How can they do that? All that stuff's inside our bodies. They'd have to – (*Realisation. Overwhelmed. Passes out cold.*)

Zipper I think he finally gets it.

Meema Wake him up. We have to get going.

Geenoma Like, Meema's right.

Zipper Aren't we going to wait for Uberbeth to bring Toyn back?

The others just look at each other.

Seven The probability of her being successful is very low.

Zipper What is wrong with you guys? We let her go!

Meema Zip, we have to think of ourselves.

Geenoma They won't, like, exactly, like, kill her – they'll just, like, fix her.

Emo comes to.

Zipper Yeah, they'll spay her, like an Earth cat.

Emo passes out again.

Emo!! Wake up! Come on!

Emo wakes up.

We have to go.

Lights down as they all start crawling in line again, continuing their escape.

SCENE THREE

Back at the moontel. Uberbeth enters – she's just emerged from the entrails of the domed Moon community. She looks around, doesn't see Toyn. Suddenly, the electronically amplified voice is right on top of her.

Electronically Amplified Adult Voice
Geenoma, Meema, Seven, Emo, Zipper, Uberbeth.
You are, like, totally, like, busted.
Walk toward the light.
No one will hurt you.
We promise.
Just walk toward the light.

Uberbeth hides.

Geenoma, Meema, Seven, Emo, Zipper, Uberbeth.
You are –

The announcement stops. Enter a young man, wearing colourful jockey briefs, large fireman-type boots – and nothing else. This is Officer Yuseef Cho-Chee-Buchanan-Stein He carries a small, hand-held programming device which he is fiddling with. Uberbeth can't believe her eyes and stands up, then, realising she's endangering herself, crouches down again, as he reprogrammes the announcement.

Electronically Amplified Adult Voice
(*reprogrammed announcement*)
Geenoma, Meema, Seven, Emo, Zipper, Uberbeth.
You have gone too far.
You will not survive.
Please turn yourself in.
We only want to take care of you –

Can't stand the bullshit of the message, reprogrammes.

We only want to do a small laser surgery that will leave you unable to ever have children of any kind because we are evil.

That is satisfying, but he can't do that.

We only want you to turn yourself in to Officer Yuseef Cho-Chee-Buchanan-Stein because he is desperately lonely on this stupid rock that looks so much prettier from the Earth.

Back to the proper announcement.

We only want what is best for you and for all of us.
We won't hurt you. We promise.

Yuseef OK. Music select.
Anything current on here?
Oh – 'I Eat Your Heart and Spit it Out.' Too sentimental. (*Finds something.*) OK, here's something from the last five years.

He programmes to play. Out comes a song that is the equivalent of one note against a complicated repeating rhythm, with a lyric that consists of an occasional shrieked and/or whispered repetition of 'Now!' 'Sex.' *He finally rejects that, too.*

OK. Back to old standards.

Muzak version of some classic rock. Yuseef starts singing to it, but with his own lyrics. He starts to dance to it.

I hate my job. I hay-ate my job.
I hate my job. I hay-ate my job.
I hate my job. I hay-ate my job.

Uberbeth makes herself visible.

Uberbeth Then why do you do it?

Yuseef What! Wait! You wait right there! You're under arrest!

He exits, dropping the programming tool. She picks it up. He re-enters, getting into a jumpsuit and grabbing his protective gear and gas mask. She quietly sits and turns off the muzak

All right! You can sit! But don't move!

She quietly watches as he jumps around, putting everything on, and then grabs his goo gun.

OK – which one are you?

Uberbeth What is that thing?

Yuseef It's a goo gun. One shot and the perps are encrusted with an invisible goo that makes them stick to *anyone*, including themselves, thereby preventing escape.

He puts on his gas mask and then throws a can towards her. She picks it up.

Uberbeth What is this?

Yuseef Stun gas.

Uberbeth Why would you want to use this in a sealed, domed community with only one source of air that is circulated all over?

Yuseef I – I don't know. I was issued a carton of these.

Uberbeth Aren't you supposed to pull this tab *before* you throw it – to activate the gas?

Yuseef Don't mess with me, Missy Mutant! You throw that can and you'll be the one not breathing. I have a gas mask on. You don't. So you just forget about exuding your tentacles and zapping me with poisonous spit from your proboscis, because I am protected by the Families Against Species Confusion in Space Town Settlements. They have given me my authority to arrest you.

Uberbeth (*a statement about his sexiness*) You're really hot.

Yuseef An officer does not think about his physical well-being. He only serves to protect the lives and property of the Family Always Serves Community In Setting Things Straight.

Uberbeth I'm a little peckish. How about you?

She opens the can. He ducks and covers. She takes out some little snack pretzels and munches on them.

Mislabelled cartons – happens a lot up here. Now, have you seen a smallish kid with breathing problems? Carries a stuffed creature we're not sure what it is? (*about the opened can*) Want some? The shelf life on these is usually fairly recent. (*Realises her mistake. Stops eating them.*) Uh-oh. (*Flatulence.*)

Oops. Oh man. Darn it.

Yuseef Now don't think you're not still under arrest, but I'm going to take off my gas mask.

Uberbeth Oh, don't! Please! You need it!

Yuseef The stun gas is a can of pretzels!

He takes off the mask, anyway. She waits for him to react to the smell of the flatulence and really suffers as he comes closer and looks her over. But he doesn't react.

You don't look like a mutant.

Uberbeth I'm not! I'm just genetically altered, but only slightly.

Yuseef They told me you were part luminescent jellyfish.

Uberbeth I am, but I've never been able to figure out which parts are affected.

Yuseef I don't know if it's the extreme heat of this suit they make me wear or just stress in general from being in this very strange environment, but I'm beginning to have just a few little bitty questions about my mission.

I'm really hot. (*He starts to unbutton the top of his jumpsuit.*)

Uberbeth That's what I thought when I saw you.

Yuseef But I was in my underwear.

Uberbeth Yeah.

Yuseef Wait a minute – here I am, letting my guard down, about to step out of my protective uniform. I know what you're doing. I'm on to you. You are *toying* with me.

Toyn enters.

Uberbeth Toyn! Toyn! (*She goes to him and hugs him.*)
Toyn This unit needs to go to technical support. Now.
Uberbeth No, Toyn. Once we get out of this moontel and into – ah – somewhere else where the air circulation is better – you'll be able to breathe easier.
Toyn (*about his inhaler*) Peripheral needs recharging.
Yuseef Both of you! Stop! Where are the others? I demand that you take me to the others!
Uberbeth (*about the inhaler*) You need a new one. What are we going to do? (*to Yuseef*) Can you break into the Moon Mall? We've been pilfering his inhalers from there.
Yuseef I am an officer of The Family Always Serves Community In Setting Things Straight! And you are *not* going anywhere!
Uberbeth (*to Toyn*) Come on. And we can tell the others that there's no need to worry because it's just a rent-a-cop chasing us.

She starts to exit with Toyn.

Yuseef *Rent-a-cop!?*

She has exited with Toyn. Yuseef fires his goo gun in the direction of their exit.

Uberbeth (*offstage*) What? What have you done?
Toyn (*offstage*) Breathing with difficulty.
Uberbeth (*offstage*) Toyn, it'll be all right.

Toyn and Uberbeth hop back onto stage, stuck together.

Look what you've done!
Yuseef I'm so sorry. (*He goes to them, trying to help.*)
Toyn Being sticky is very bad for electronic circuitry!

Yuseef tries to unstick them.

Uberbeth You are a horrible person!!

Yuseef I was just doing my job!!

Uberbeth I thought you were hot, but you're *not*! Get away from us!!

Yuseef I'm trying to apologise.

Uberbeth Too late! Now leave!

Yuseef I – I can't.

Toyn This unit's functioning is further impaired.

Uberbeth I said, I'm not interested in your apologies! We're your captives – Big Policeman of the Moon, working for the F.A.S.C.I.S.T.S. (*He doesn't put it together.*) *Fascists?*

I mean, can you even spell? Or read?

Yuseef I never realised . . .

Uberbeth Be careful who you work for!! You gotta serve somebody – make sure it's the Forces of Good. The Earth Prophet Dylan said that. Don't you even know your own history?

Yuseef For your information, that is a Hemisphere Number Two Prophet, *and* it's George Lucas.

Uberbeth Dylan!

Yuseef Lucas!!

Toyn Gummy is bad for components.

Uberbeth Get out of here! Because of you, we're stuck!

Yuseef So am I.

Uberbeth What?!

They all try to get unstuck, can't.

Toyn I have experienced condensation. It is time to drain my waste liquids.

Yuseef What?

Uberbeth just looks at Yuseef, totally disgusted with how dense he is. Yuseef finally gets that Toyn needs to pee. Resigned, Yuseef and the other stuck-together two hop offstage.

Toyn (*offstage*) This unit needs to perform this function in private.

Uberbeth *and* **Yuseef** (*offstage*) Well, you can't!

SCENE FOUR

Further down the tunnel. Everyone is progressing. Suddenly, Geenoma, who was towards the head of the line, stops.

Meema What?
Emo Why have we stopped?
Zipper What's going on?
Geenoma I'm, like, getting claustro –
Emo Don't even say it!
Geenoma I mean, like, this looks not too good.
Meema (*to Seven*) Seven, we may have reached the end. All I see is darkness ahead.
Seven Spare me the metaphors, Meema.
Meema No, really. Look.
Seven Oh no.
Emo Oh no?
Zipper What?
Emo He said, 'Oh no.'
Zipper I'm backing out. I'm heading back.
Seven Wait. We can't go back.
Emo (*covering his crotch with his hands*) No way am I going back.
Geenoma OK. OK. OK. So, like, I'm the, like, oldest. So, like, I'm going to go into that dark and find whatever it is. A precipice. A, like, wall. Whatever.
Seven I should go.
Meema No, you're not. (*She grabs Seven and holds on, surprising them both.*)

Zipper I'm going. (*He heads for the dark.*) It's time for my chrysalis period, anyway. Something in me seeks a dark place to metamorph. (*He exits into the dark.*)
Emo Zipperrrrrr!

But Zipper's gone.

Geenoma (*crying, upset*) Oh, like, like, like, that's terrible. (*Trying to comfort Emo, but can't because he's way down the line*) Like, like, there, there, Emo. (*to others*) Pass it on?

They do.

Like, Zipper will be, like, all right. (*to others*) Pass it on?

They do.

I, like, hate to see you, like, so upset. Pass it on?
Meema He totally can hear you, G!
Geenoma *and* **Emo** (*really upset*) Zipper? Zip?
Seven The probability of us having a good day just keeps decreasing.
Meema For just once, can you keep your facts to yourself?
Geenoma I, like, totally apologise. I have, like, totally pulled myself together. Nobody may have ever wanted us. But I'm not going to, like, die crying. I'm going in after Zipper. (*She exits into the dark.*)
Emo Noooo! Zipper! Geenoma! (*He squeezes past and goes in after Geenoma.*)
Meema (*grabbing Seven, who is acting like he's going in too*) Stop right there. Haven't you ever seen a horror movie? 'Oooo, I'm scared out of my mind. Let's go down to the basement.'
Seven Pheasant! You're nothing but a pheasant!
Meema You have the wrong Earth bird.
Seven Chicken?

Meema I'm not that either. Get out of my way. (*She passes him and goes into the dark.*)

Seven (*following her*) Meema! Why does it always have to be about you? Even our probable death!? (*He follows her into the dark.*)

SCENE FIVE

Uberbeth, Yuseef, Toyn hop onstage.

Toyn Ahhh. This unit always operates better after a draining of waste liquids.

Yuseef *That* was totally disgusting and embarrassing.

Uberbeth You have problems with the human body. I can't believe I thought you were hot.

Yuseef First of all, you're *not* human. And secondly, I am so hot, I'm sweating!

Uberbeth I may be a variation on being human, in that I am part jellyfish, but I am still pretty much human. And Toyn is totally, 100 per cent human.

Toyn This unit is an electrical component. This unit is digital. This unit is not human.

Yuseef OK. So Toyn is human. I remember reading that in the records, but *you're* a freak!

Toyn Not human, digital.

Uberbeth Don't upset him.

Yuseef I can't stand either of you!! You're a freak and he's insane!!

Uberbeth Well, YOU ARE A HORRIBLE PREJUDICED DIRT BOY!

Yuseef 'Dirt boy?' *That* is so *racist*!

Uberbeth I can smell the dirt on you. You are from the *Earth* and you are a *dirt boy*. Dirt boy! Dirt boy!

Yuseef Genetic freak! Genetic freak!

Toyn Analog! Analog!

All Three I'm getting out of here!!

They try to escape from each other and end up just hopping off.

SCENE SIX

The dark side of the Moon. Two figures call to each other across the stage.

Sark Eebee?
Eebee Sark?

They run to each other and make happy noises.

Sark Ship come.
Eebee More trash.
Sark Good trash.
Eebee We make what now?
Sark More bots. More and more bots.

They exit.

SCENE SEVEN

On the dark side of the Moon. The light from a torch – it's Zipper. He enters and looks around.

Zipper Wow. Cool.

Geenoma enters.

Geenoma Whoa. Zipper!
Zipper We're alive!

Emo enters.

Emo G, you're OK. And Zip! Zipper, Zipper, Zipper! Where are we? (*Looks at the sky.*) Oh no! Where's the Earth? Where did it go?

Zipper You can't see it from this side of the Moon.
Geenoma It's, like, hard to see anything through this dome.
Emo What company had this dome made?
Zipper Some company that went broke, it looks like.

Emo starts to hyperventilate.

Hey, Emo. You're fine. The dome is fine. It works. Look at me – I'm breathing fine.

Emo calms down.

Geenoma Like, it's, like, if you didn't know, like, the Sun existed, like, you wouldn't, like –

Emo grabs her.

Emo Stop saying 'like'! Stop it! Never say it again!! Just say what you mean!!
Geenoma No Sun in sky. I here. No see Sun. No ever see Sun. Not know Sun exists.
Zipper I don't think she can talk another way.

Sound of scurrying in the dark.

Geenoma Hey, guys? Are there, like, animals on the Moon?
Zipper Nothing but insects that we brought by accident.

More scurrying.

Geenoma Well, I think there might be some, like, really big ones here. Check your bags for glow trash.

They pull out some glowing, lighty things.

Zipper See any bugs?
Emo Thank heaven Seven isn't here. The idea of big bugs would freak him out totally.

Seven enters.

Seven I heard my name! I couldn't believe it. I was stumbling in the dark and I heard my name! And then I saw your lights.
Where's Meema?
Geenoma We haven't seen her.
Seven But she was ahead of me! I have to find her!

Sound of scurrying.

Oh, she's hiding in the dark here. Trying to fool me.
Zipper We don't think so.
Emo No way.
Seven I can see you're lying. You're just covering for her.

More scurrying – closer.

I'm going to find her.

He heads into the dark corners, following the sound of the scurrying.

Geenoma Like, like, totally a bad moment coming.
Seven (*from a dark corner*) Yikes!!
Geenoma I, like, told you.
Seven (*from the dark*) Oh, you're kind of cute. And there are two of you.

Coming back on, leading a very reluctant Eebee, who is squeaking.

Look what I found.
Eebee (*about the light*) What this? Ow!

Very quickly, Sark enters, grabs Eebee and exits with her.

Emo What was that?
Geenoma Some, like, creatures!
Zipper They looked like us – sort of.
Seven But where's Meema? This is terrible.

Emo (*about the weirdness of the creatures*) Zipper, could there be other mistakes –

Zipper Like us? We're not mistakes. Our genes are fine.

Emo And we don't need any operations.

Seven Where is Meema? I've lost Meema.

Meema (*from far off, in the dark*) Seven? Seven, are you talking to me from the Next World?

Emo No, it's more like the next room.

Meema (*from far off*) Seven, I've never believed in anything like that.

Seven It's all right, Meema. Just come to my voice.

Meema (*from far off*) I'm not ready to leave my mortal shell.

Geenoma Meema, like, just, like, stand up and, like, walk out here.

Meema (*from far off*) I hear Geenoma. Is she – there, too?

Geenoma We're all here, Meema.

Meema (*from far off*) Ohmygod, this is so profound. And to think I never believed in an afterlife. I was such a fool.

Seven Meema, sweetheart. Just listen to the sound of my voice and walk towards it.

Meema (*from closer*) It's so scary. To finally be leaving the dark tunnel of life and walking into the light.

Seven Will you just crawl out of the freaking tunnel and come out here?

Meema (*from closer*) Don't be angry at me, Seven. Now that we're dead, I can tell you that I love you.

Seven You do? Oh, Meema. And I love you –

Zipper Oh for crying out loud!

Zipper walks to the tunnel opening, reaches in, grabs Meema or some part of her and drags her out.

Zipper Here!

Meema (*hugs Seven*) Life and death. They are just a few steps from each other.

Seven Meema, we're not dead.
Meema Keep up your spirits, Seven, that's the spirit. Because we're all spirit now.
Emo Can someone just shut her up!
Geenoma Meema, like, we're *alive*. Like, this is just the, like, dark side of the Moon. OK?

Beat. She gets it.

Meema I didn't mean it when I said I loved you.
Seven Me, either.

Light beams down on them from overhead.

Electronically Amplified Adult Voice
Kids?
Thank you for coming.
We told you we wouldn't hurt you.
And we kept our promise, didn't we?
Please get in line.

The kids line up and start to walk as a subway arrival ping sounds.

Now
Walk Toward The Light.
Walk Toward The Light.
Mind the gap.
Walk Toward The Light.

Meema Seven? Seven? Don't look at the light. Just look at me.
Seven And Meema? Look at me.

They look at each other and find that they can break away. Finally, they break away totally.

What about the others?

They exit.

SCENE EIGHT

On the light side of the Moon. Uberbeth, Yuseef and Toyn, still stuck together, are lying down.

Yuseef Well. This is great.
Uberbeth We've fallen and we can't get up.
Toyn Uhn. Uhn.
Yuseef Stop moving that way! It doesn't work and it always hurts me.
Uberbeth Well. We can't stay here for ever!
Toyn Uhn. Uhn.
Uberbeth Look, the only way we're going to be able to stand up is if we work together.
Yuseef Oh, please. Spare me the do-gooder globalisation parables.
Uberbeth I'm serious.
Yuseef So am I.

Uberbeth – flatulence.

Uberbeth Excuse me.
Yuseef For what?
Toyn (*reacting to the odour of the flatulence*) Eeeuuuw. Uberbeth.
Yuseef Stop flailing, Toyn!
Toyn Have to disconnect! Bad smells are hard on components.
Yuseef I showered this morning! OK! It's been a hot day and I can't help it. I sweat!
Uberbeth You smell OK. You smell kinda good, in fact.
Yuseef Well, I wouldn't know. I have no sense of smell.
Uberbeth Really?
Yuseef Yeah. It's some genetic fluke in my family's genes, *but* it happened naturally, after generations of normal, human mating. We're not mutants. Or freaks.

Uberbeth I'm ignoring the mutant-bashing you engage in constantly and have decided to move beyond it because I am a better person, however genetically 'Other' I may appear to be. And why this change of heart on my part? *Because* you are a freak, too, although you have been assimilated and brainwashed and deprived of the proper conduits to your true culture of the genetically altered. You have the low self-image typical of the assimilated because you don't know Who You Are. You are, in fact, identity-challenged, and have, in typical fashion, over-identified with the dominant non-genetically-altered culture, hence your employment as an officer in the dominant-culture police force.

Yuseef Are you finished?

Uberbeth Yeah, OK. I'll put my foot here. And Toyn will move that way. Toyn?

Toyn Instructions received.

Yuseef Good. Now, if I put my hand over here, then –

With a lot of grunting, they co-operate and stand up.

All We did it!!

Sound of muzak approaching and the light.

Toyn Digital unit?

Yuseef Uh-oh. It's them.

Uberbeth Who?

Electronically Amplified Adult Voice
Good job, Officer Cho-Chee-Whatever your name is! You have apprehended the mutants.

Toyn begins to have a breathing incident.

Uberbeth Toyn? Stay calm. (*to the 'Voice'*) You're scaring him! Stop it! (*to Yuseef*) I thought *you* controlled the voice.

Yuseef Unless it's overridden by my . . . employers.

Uberbeth Rent-a-cop! Rent-a-cop!

Electronically Amplified Adult Voice
You have been apprehended by the Family Always
Serves Community In Setting Things Straight.
Prepare for paralysation to precede sterilisation.
Have a nice day.

Sound of an electronic something revving up.

Yuseef Wait a minute. She's the only mutant. He and I are human!!

Uberbeth (*to Yuseef*) You – horrible *human*!

Yuseef (*to Uberbeth*) Get behind Toyn and me. (*to Toyn*) Come on, Toyn – hop around so we're in front.

Uberbeth You monster!

Yuseef (*still to Toyn*) They won't want to shoot humans. Get in front of Uberbeth – we'll be a shield for her.
I'm trying to protect you!
Will everyone just do as I say?

Electronic sound revs up again and increases. Yuseef gets ready to take the hit. Electronic sound revs down.

Yuseef See? See?

Uberbeth I saw.

Toyn Goo deactivated.

Uberbeth (*grabs Toyn, then Yuseef, by the hand*) Now let's get out of here.

They exit.

Electronically Amplified Adult Voice
Officer Yuseef Cho – whatever your name is.
You are no longer in the employ
Of the Family Always Serves Community In Setting
Things Straight.
Have a terrible day.

SCENE NINE

Geenoma, Zipper, Emo.

Zipper Where . . . are . . . we?
Emo Have they done it yet?
Geenoma Like, open your eyes, Emo.

Uberbeth gets pushed in.

Zipper Uberbeth! You're here!
Geenoma Uberbeth, are you, like, OK?
Emo Where's Toyn? Oh, poor little boy – they've fixed him.
Uberbeth First of all, he's not a little boy. And, secondly, I got recaptured because of him. Have – have any of you seen a policeman? Tall? Not too ugly?
Geenoma Uberbeth, are you, like, OK?
Emo But where IS Toyn? Poor little boy.
Toyn (*offstage*) This unit does not recognize your operating system! This unit has confirmed that you have experienced information deterioration!
Emo That's Toyn!
Geenoma I, like, never heard him, like, talk so much!
Zipper Who is he talking to?
Uberbeth He has issues with the Digital Unit that keeps pursuing us. He wouldn't shut up and that's how we got caught again!
Zipper Hey, where are Meema and Seven?
Emo They've got them first! They're lasered and fixed like earth pets!
Electronically Amplified Adult Voice
Please be quiet.

Beat. Everyone gets quiet.

Thank you.

You are scheduled for sterilisation in twenty minutes.
You are scheduled for sterilisation in twenty minutes.
Have a nice day.

Toyn enters as if pushed.

Toyn Bad code! Bad, bad code!

Electronically Amplified Adult Voice
Shut up, little boy.
Have a nice day.

Uberbeth Oh, Toyn, why couldn't you have been quiet? They would never have found us.

Emo That voice! I can't stand it!

Zipper They're not going to kill us, Emo. And it won't hurt. I promise.

Uberbeth The flatulence gene ends here.

Emo I'm too easily upset to be a good father, anyway.

Geenoma And I, like, have this, like, bad speech problem.

Zipper We'll just have to be each others' kids, I guess.

Uberbeth I was kind of hoping to grow up. Not be a kid, any more. (*to Toyn*) Do you know what they're going to do to us?

Emo Don't tell him. Ignorance feels better.

Toyn This unit . . . will never be replaced . . . by a newer model.

All (*not together*) Yeah. That's true. Sad. That's deep. Beautiful, man.

Offstage.

Seven Meema, the probability of them being in there is about a hundred to one!

Meema While you figure it out, Seven, I'm just going to bang on every door!!

Sark No need.

Eebee We fix. Turn this toggle switch.

Seven But, what if –

Meema enters.

Meema We're breaking you out of here!

Seven enters.

Seven Dammit! Why do you have to be right all the time?

All Seven! Meema!

Emo Why did you guys leave us?

Seven To get help.

Zipper What are those?

Meema These are some Moon dwellers.

Seven On the dark side of *planet* Moon.

Sark *and* **Eebee** This is fun. Now what happens?

Yuseef enters.

Sark *and* **Eebee** More company!! Happy!! Happy!!

Yuseef Ex-Officer Yuseef here! And I've come to do the right thing! Because I know evil when I see it. Don't make me use this goo gun.

Sark Who he?

Eebee Hero.

Uberbeth You're all right! You found us!

Yuseef Again.

Meema These little Moon residents have an entire communication system that they have made from all the garbage *you*, the Family Always Serves Community In Setting Things Straight, have been dumping for years!

Seven And you've been getting paid a lot of Earth rubles for that illegal, immoral and horrible practice!!

Yuseef And I have reported you via satellite!!

Emo So you'd better let us go!

Zipper Yeah! Right! (*to the others*) Go where?

Electronically Amplified Adult Voice
Hang on – the mutants have guns
And satellite connections.

Moving to Enron procedure
And immediate evacuation.
This robot will now self-destruct.
Have a nice day.

Offstage sound of electrical burnout.

Zipper They've gone.
Emo *It's* gone.
Yuseef For now.
Emo Where can we go?
Sark Garbage ship.
Eebee Androids drive it.
Sark We give you bots to help.
Eebee You take. We have extras.
Sark Go to your planet.
Eebee Wherever it is.

They laugh to each other.

Seven It's just on the other side of here.
Sark There is nothing on the other side of our planet.
Seven 'Our' – what? 'Our PLANET.'
Eebee Our planet is dark.
Meema Well, our *true* planet is green.
Emo But it looks blue. From the Moon.
Eebee *and* **Sark** If you say so.
Geenoma Like, like, who made you?
Emo Did you come from a lab, like us?
Zipper Weren't you genetically altered for space travel or something?
Eebee We come from Map and Pap.
Sark Dog made us. Dog made all.
Meema If you need us –
Seven – to free you –
Sark You go. Bye-bye.
Eebee Ciao-ciao.

Everyone exits, leaving Sark and Eebee.

Sark Eebee, I told you there were aliens.
Eebee Good. Now we colonise more planets with our bots.

SCENE TEN

On the bridge of the garbage ship.

Emo So that's what happened.
Zipper And we appreciate you letting us on your ship.
Emo It doesn't smell all that good, though.
Zipper It's a garbage ship, Emo. But we're very thankful for it.
Meema I wonder if it's got a name.
Seven How about the *Uberbeth*?
Uberbeth Guys.
Yuseef I can't smell a thing. I think 'Starship *Uberbeth*' is a great name.
Uberbeth (*feels like she emitted some flatulence*) Oh. Excuse me.
Zipper Hey, I don't smell anything.,
Emo Maybe someone's morphing.
Zipper Hey, I can feel something on my back . . .
Emo Nubs of wings, bro. I can see them.
Uberbeth What about you, Emo? Feel any different?
Emo (*in a lower voice*) No, I feel the same.
Zipper But your voice is lower. Or are you faking that?
Emo Yes.
Yuseef Who is captain of this ship? Shouldn't we have a human captain?
Geenoma Like, like, you have so much to learn!
Emo And you're still on trial, 'officer'.
Toyn You shot Toyn with goo.
Seven I think Meema should be captain.

Meema Only if you do the navigation, Seven. I mean, numbers, and everything.

Toyn Computer pilot. All digital.

Seven You know what's really strange? The odds of two lost socks finding each other is astronomical, but to make pairs from a random collection of odd lost socks, well, that's unheard of. That's all I was trying to say.

Uberbeth I feel funny.

Zipper Check it out!

Emo No way!

Uberbeth I feel strange.

Geenoma Like, like, like, I'm speechless.

Meema Uberbeth . . .

Seven You're lit up. You're –

Toyn Luminescent! Like a beautiful . . . person!

Uberbeth I know. I know!

Yuseef Beautiful.

The light on Uberbeth gets brighter and brighter.

I hear the engines firing. Everyone get ready for take-off!

Meema, Seven *and* **Zipper** You're not the boss!

Toyn We go! We go!

They all look expectantly out to the android, bot and human audience as the ship slowly rises off the Moon.

End of Play.

A Faustian Bargain

Constance Congdon interviewed by Jim Mulligan

Constance Congdon comes from a family of great story-tellers. Her father worked in the oilfields of Oklahoma and she spent her early years moving from one small town to another, living in apartments, motels or single-room accommodation. Eventually the family settled in Des Moines, which had one of the best public-school systems in the USA. She began writing poetry at the age of nine after the death of her mother and a move to live with relatives in Colorado. Constance Congdon wrote the 'High School Column' in the local paper and the editor actually paid her, so that at sixteen she was a paid journalist. Critics see Constance Congdon as a trail-blazer. Her play *Tales of the Lost Formicans*, they say, prefigures the time-tripping chronology of *Pulp Fiction* and the conspiracy-rich paranoia of *The X-Files*. Not bad for the story-telling girl from Des Moines.

Moontel Six creates a culture set in the future on the Moon, which has been colonised, and a group of rejected young people, strange genetic mixtures, appeal for understanding from the audience.

> I imagined they were a group from Moonstead Estates – my comment on upper-middle-class gated communities. I concluded that, once the Moon becomes developed, a lot of money will come from private corporations as well as the government and that scientific research will soon give way to mining and such like. I envisaged a prosperous society, with people living under huge domes and where children are born a generation after the original settlers –

> mostly labourers and scientists – have put down roots. Moonstead Estates is just like Carter 9 in Oklahoma where my grandfather and father lived in a community of families. All the men worked on the oil derricks owned by Carter oil company.

At the core of the play there is a debate about genetic modification, how far it should go and what we should do if things go wrong.

> There is a lot of bizarre research going on at the moment. I have read for example that geneticists have put spider genes into goat DNA to see if the goats could produce thinner, stronger hair. It's terrifying, and at the same time genetic research is one of the most exciting things happening today. It really is a Faustian bargain. Any technology can be bought and then people can do what they damn well please if they have the money.

In *Moontel Six* things have gone horribly wrong. Or have they? One of these strange people, Zipper, part lizard and part moth says, 'We're not mistakes. Our genes are fine. And we're certainly not freaks. We thought we were Good but we were perceived as Evil, Bad and Wrong.' The rest of the play is an appeal to the audience to understand. Should they be allowed to procreate or should they be sterilised by the Fascist authorities?

> Once the story started in my head, I saw that the first problem they were going to have is: do these kids have the right to procreate? It is probably the single most important issue we are going to face as human beings. The idea of what it is to be human is changing. I don't believe in the soul, one part of you that goes off and has an independent consciousness. We are our brains and our bodies and if we are genetically altered does that make us any less human?

Only Toyn is totally human, but what a strange boy he is. He has allergies and he speaks almost as if he believes himself to be a robot – 'Don't activate unit until you are ready to use it.' His parents are not around and he has taken refuge with this group of social outcasts.

> Somehow Toyn is a throw-away kid. Somebody in the human society has totally rejected him. There are a lot of these kids all over the world and even in the USA we have an alarming number of them. They're on the streets and in institutions or even in homes, where they are physical and emotional throw-aways with no family connections.

Despite the pessimism inherent in a world where scientists mess about with genes and financial corporations control what happens to experiments, there is an upbeat ending. Sark and Eebee – brilliant re-cyclers – supply the kids with a junk spaceship, the robot that is hunting the children self-destructs and as the young people take off back to earth Sark and Eebee gleefully set about colonising more planets with their bots. But the questions still have to be faced. What will happen to them? Will they be allowed to live, never mind procreate?

> As long as there are human or humanoid types like these kids then there is hope, but I have to say things look pretty bleak a lot of the time. However, if you are emotionally sound, if you are capable of love, you have a good chance that you will be all right.

Constance Congdon does not think young people in the UK will have any difficulty with *Moontel Six*. She feels that culture is only part of who people are.

> Why else would literature work across cultures as it clearly does all the time? I think young people involved in the play are going to have a lot of fun.

> I hope the audience will bond with some of these strange kids and will be moved by these characters. I hope it will help them consider further the questions they are already asking themselves about genetic research and what it means to be human.

According to Constance Congdon, *Moontel Six* is not a difficult play to stage. She wrote it for a bare stage with all the spaces being created by the actors' imaginations and physical movement.

> My play makes no more demands on the audience than on the people who paid a penny to stand and watch Shakespeare's plays. *Antony and Cleopatra* has twenty-three locations, after all. Audiences can go anywhere the actors take them.

Production Notes

STAGING AND SETTING

On the Earth's Moon in a not-so-distant future, a group of genetically altered teenagers have gone into hiding after being pursued by the Moonstead Estates, a security-obsessed community that hates having adolescents with questionable genes near their perfect children. Meema, Zipper, Emo, Seven,Toyn and Geenoma find they have to leave the abandoned motel that has been their refuge and head into the bowels of the Moon base where they have to find a way to save themselves and get back home to Earth.

The play begins and ends on the bridge of a garbage ship, which could be suggested with stage blocks. The light and dark sides of the moon might be achieved through lighting changes. Connie Congdon suggests that the kids hold torches when on the dark side. The extraordinary lunar locations can be created very simply. You might consider performing the play in more than one location. It may be a promenade performance where the audience move with the characters as they travel through the story. The different locations could be suggested by a team of supporting performers creating the tunnel and lunar landscape.

Moontel Six doesn't require the actors to do big-step slow-motion moonwalking. We need to assume that the moon community has been established long enough to have sorted out gravity issues. But you should think about the texture of the Moon surface to help set the tone and environment. The characters are always moving from one part of the Moon trying to reach one another. The sense of never resting in one place, of unrest, of progression is always there. Consider too what natural locations you have at your disposal; the cast might use the entrances and exits through the audience via the gangways. You might choose to stage the play in a non-theatre venue, or a venue playing to the audience on more than one side.

Sound includes muzak, Barry Manilow or other bland tunes, or something like Nirvana or Pearl Jam produced on the cheapest synthesiser possible. Consider a muzak version of some classic rock songs such as 'The Sunshine of Your Love', by Cream. There is an electronically amplified adult voice. Think of this as another character. The effect might be achieved live or through pre-recording. You can decide if it belongs to a human or robot.

The end of the play focuses on Uberbeth and her transformation. She is growing out of her old self and into her new self. The staging of the pivotal moment needs to be considered carefully. Her transformation affects not only herself but the rest of the group. It's a spiritual moment, an acknowledgement and celebration of their differences, of changing from a child to an adult. It also continues the journeying theme by highlighting an individual's journey and change within the group. There is trepidation and excitement within the group as they witness the transformation. The moment of vacillation between these two strong emotions is fundamental to understanding the play.

Costumes Connie's notes in the play on the central characters describe what influences them genetically. This will have some bearing on what they look like physically, but avoid clichéd futuristic clothing and work on adapting current fashions for the cast to wear. This is a very physical piece of theatre, so make sure the costumes don't inhibit movement.

Casting This is a play written for a cast of five males and five females. Extra actors can be used as creatures on the dark side of the Moon.

EXERCISES

There is a chain of roadside motels in the USA called Motel 6. They are bland, anonymous and everywhere. The title, *Moontel Six*, is a play on the name of this chain but it is also a reminder to us not to take for granted the world we live in. Have the cast imagine a time when something that we consider ordinary in this world becomes ordinary on another planet. Have them imagine what the world might be like in a hundred years' time. Travel to the Moon and life there would not only be the concern of governments and scientists but something possible for the public. If the Moon was to be colonised and inhabited, then it is likely that certain fundamental earthly structures, such as towns, road systems, residential areas and motels, could be established there too. Have the cast create an aerial view of the Moon of the play.

The characters we meet in *Moontel Six* who have been genetically modified have been altered by scientists on Earth. The Earth doesn't want to keep them. Instead they have been exiled to the Moon, though it isn't clear if they have fled or been forcibly removed from the Earth. Improvise this part of the characters' joint back history.

The moon's inhabitants are unhappy with the possibility of living with children who are genetically different. The inhabitants of Moontel Six are now concerned that these children (except Toyn, who is pre-adolescent) are on the cusp of puberty and therefore able to pass on their particular and peculiar genetic coding. The children understand that the local community considers them a threat. They need to escape being caught because the consequence is sterilisation. Give the other Moon's inhabitants, who aren't seen in the play, an identity. Improvise an encounter between Uberbeth and her friends and some of the adults who have not been genetically modified. Have the improvised scene demonstrate why the children have real cause for concern.

At the beginning of the play there is a convention established where the characters address the audience directly. This is used only once as Connie wanted to establish two distinct worlds, the one we live in and the possible world of the future. When the doors of the spaceship close, the characters no longer speak directly to the audience. Have the cast experiment with delivering the lines in the following ways:

- Just above the audience's head.
- Then directly to the audience as a group.
- To the audience looking them in the eye.
- Picking out individual audience members and aiming larger sections of the dialogue to them.

Have the actors discover how far they can go to include the audience directly in this first scene.

Three characters – Uberbeth, Toyn and Yuseef – get stuck together. Get the cast to play the party game 'twister' (someone's bound to have it, or it can be obtained from most toy shops). See how the group finds ways of working round each other. In groups of three, set the cast tasks such as making a cup of tea, using the bathroom, loading a shopping trolley. See how these tasks can be accomplished when they're joined together and discover the comic possibilities.

Suzy Graham-Adriani
March 2003
based on a workshop facilitated by Frank Nealon

MULTIPLEX

Christopher William Hill

Christopher studied drama and theatre studies at the University of Kent, where he specialised in theatre direction. His many works for the stage include *Tenth from the End*, *Stealing the Smile*, *Lam*, *Song of the Western Men* and *Blood Red, Saffron Yellow.* He has also written for radio, and is currently under commission by Plymouth Theatre Royal, where he is Writer in Residence, and by the Northcott Theatre, Exeter.

Characters

MALE

Mouse

King

Spike

Geach

Dillon

Elton

Fish

Jay

FEMALE

Whizz

Cass

Jo-Jo

Twiglet

Princess

Mags

Tash

Empty stage. No set. Location is indicated by lighting only. The Ushers assemble, dressed in the uniform of the multiplex cinema. Spotlight on Dillon.

Dillon There's three types of ushers, right. There's Plankton . . . that's like the lowest of the low. Don't know shit. Then there's Dudes, they're, you know, cool. But they don't know movies. And top of the food chain, there's the Buffs. Know everything about every movie ever made, and to them, right, cinema . . . it's not just entertainment, it's life.

Ushers Interior. Multiplex cinema. Day.

Dillon So that's it. Plankton, Dudes and Buffs.

The Ushers sing the Pearl and Dean theme beautifully, in close harmony.

It's like a ghetto, you know? A fifteen-screen, all-singing, all-dancing multiplex ghetto.

Ushers (*in unison*) As staff of the ICL multiplex corporation we have a duty to our guests: to provide quality entertainment and service with a smile – no matter how fucking rude the guests are. No earrings will be worn, no smoking, no chewing gum on duty. No swearing. So fucking watch it. Happiness will be kept to a minimum at all times. Too sodding right. We will not moan if our wage slips come through late. We will not grumble when we mop up sick, will not cringe when we wipe shit from the floor. It is our duty. Part of the challenge – the ICL experience. Amen.

The following is played directly 'to camera'.

Elton Favourite film? *Sudden Impact*, Clint Eastwood. 'Go ahead, make my day . . .'

Whizz Dunno. Comedies, I s'pose. I like comedies. Can I think it over?

Tash (*to Jo-Jo*) He wants to know what your favourite film is.

Jo-Jo signs The Silence of the Lambs.

Tash (*translating*) She said *Silence of the Lambs*.

Jo-Jo does the Anthony Hopkins fava-bean lip-smack.

She's deaf, see? So you got to give her a job, and me, 'cause I'm her translator. Else it's discrimination, right? You can get done for that, yeah?

Fish *Sound of Music*. Mum says I've got a developed maternal side. And she'd know, wouldn't she? That bit with the lonely goatherd. Really gets to me. Chokes me up every time. Shit-hot, man. Had a big crush on Julie Andrews. I mean, sex kitten or what? I could never look at nuns in the same way. Not that I had to much.

Whizz OK, so I've thought it over. *American Pie*. Comedy, see?

Jay Dunno, it's not a feature film or nothing. Didn't say it had to be a *feature* film . . . it's a sex-education film. My dad's got hundreds of them. He's not a perv. It's professional. He's a biology lecturer. You ever seen sperm swim? Goes really bloody fast.

Tash My favourite film? Of all time?

Spike *Bullitt*. Steve McQueen . . .

Tash *Forrest Gump*. Yeah? OK?

Geach *Toy Story*.

Spike . . . Kind of model myself on Steve McQueen.

Geach 'Buzz Lightyear to the rescue. To infinity and beyond!'

Mags (*sinisterly*) *Halloween*. Episodes one onwards . . .

Cass The old ones are definitely the best. Romantic. Girl meets boy, girl falls in love with boy . . .
Mags (*smiling oddly*) . . . boy dies in fatal accident.
Princess It's a chick-flick kinda thing.
Twiglet Difficult. James Bond, I'm really into James Bond. Sean Connery in particular –
Princess . . . *Something About Mary*. You know, the spunk bit. Cool.
Cass (*passionately*) That film with Burt Lancaster and Deborah Kerr . . . where they roll over and over in the waves . . . but they don't drown, they're just in love.
Twiglet – although I had like a *major* crush on Timothy Dalton. Not that keen on Pierce Brosnan, he's got funny eyes and too much hair in the wrong places . . .
Cass *From Here to Eternity*.
Twiglet All right. Sean Connery. *Goldfinger*. 'Do you expect me to talk?'
King (*intense*) *The Third Man*. Directed by Carol Reed. Starring Joseph Cotton, Orson Welles, Alida Valli and Trevor Howard. Classic.

Spotlight on Dillon.

Dillon That's King. He's like the *über-usher*. Undisputed master of the multiplex, *capisce*? And me? Favourite film? *Metropolis*. Fritz Lang. Black and white and silent and shit-hot. 'Cause I'm a Buff. Top of the food chain.

King steps forward from the group of Ushers.

King Making a new film
Spike Shit-hot, man.
Dillon And then, once in a while, a couple of times a year, something fucking wonderful happens. King makes a film. He's out there and he's doing it. He's making it happen . . .
Geach Where you gonna film it, King?

King Down the industrial estate.

Spike Urban. Cool.

Princess Cast it yet, King?

King No. Not yet.

Princess Looking for someone sexy?

Spike Why? Know someone, do you?

Princess Piss off.

King Haven't thought of cast yet. Still storyboarding.

Spike What's it about then, King?

King Kind of set in the future . . .

Elton Cool.

King The Earth's dying . . .

Spike Harsh.

Elton Meteor . . . or flesh-eating virus or something?

Spike Princess could play the flesh-eating virus.

Princess I'm gonna knee you in the nuts if you don't shut your hole.

Spike Class, isn't she? Pure class.

King You listening, or what?

Spike Hanging on your every . . .

Elton . . . word.

Spike Yeah.

King Post-apocalyptic, I reckon, there's been a war . . .

Elton War. Cool.

King It's wiped out most of the planet.

Elton But there's survivors, right?

Spike 'Course there's survivors. Right?

Princess Wouldn't be much of a film if there weren't survivors.

Elton Like I was thinking.

King And they're fighting for survival, to stay alive.

Elton And they eat each other, right? Cannibals, yeah? Mutant, flesh-eating . . .

King Tell you what, I'll just shut up and you make your own fucking movie.

Elton Sorry, mate.

King Gonna be shot in black and white, give it a harsh edge. Do it like a documentary . . . fly-on-the-wall kind of thing. Like you're there with these people . . . see them falling apart.

Elton But not eating each other?

King Where did this whole eating thing come from? I never said nothing about people eating each other. Did I?

Spike No.

Princess No.

King This isn't some zombie flick.

Princess So what, romance then?

King (*frustrated*) It's not romance. 'Course it's not romance. They're all *dying*.

Princess But in love, yeah?

King shoots her a withering glance.

Dillon That's it. That's who we are. United through film. And for a while you feel like you're somebody. 'Cause for a year or so, you're part of the movies. Living it, man. It's real. Everybody wants to be your friend, and with free tickets to the multiplex you can pull dead easy. Just like . . .

He clicks his fingers. Lights up on Geach and Spike.

Jay Interior. Screen One. Day.

Spike I've got Fat Jackie from the Spar on the corner, pulled the short straw. Fat Jackie's got greasy hair, lank like she washed in butter. She smiles but I don't smile back, because her eyesight's shit, so there's no point. She's getting frisky and her glasses start steaming up, so I give her a tissue to wipe them off and she chins me, right hook like Lennox Lewis.

Jay Bloody good punch she's got. Hits like a heavyweight.

Spike Who'd you take?

Geach Nicky Banks got chickenpox, so she sent Mellie Wilson instead, and Mellie's like, bugger, she's like beautiful, and she's got a funny laugh, and her funny laugh makes me laugh. And she says, 'You've got a funny laugh,' and we both sit there laughing. Laughing funny. Till King says . . .

King Stop bloody laughing.

Spike Kiss her then, did you?

Geach Just sat their laughing quiet, but we're still laughing funny. And she puts her hand on my leg and I'm sitting there thinking, 'Thank the dear Lord and sweet Jesus too,' because she's got her hand on my leg . . .

Jay Go on.

Geach Nothing else.

Spike That's it? She just kept her hand on your leg?

Geach All through the film.

Spike (*sarcastically*) Cool.

Geach Yeah, cool.

Cross fade to Whizz, Cass and Twiglet.

Whizz . . . And Gary, he's fit and Michelle Burns fancies him, so I'm like, yeah, up for it, mate. So I gave him a free ticket. Didn't see much of the film, though . . . if you get my meaning, ladies.

Twiglet Dirty slapper.

Whizz Got a reputation to uphold.

Twiglet But Gary, he's a complete twat.

Cass How come?

Twiglet He's into Harley Davidsons and all that shit. He got really pissed and went into this tattoo place . . .

Cass They're not supposed to do you if you're pissed.

Twiglet Well they did, OK. Don't believe me, ask him yourself. He was pissed all right, he got the bloke to tattoo 'Hell's Angles' on his forehead.

Cass *Angles*?

Twiglet Yeah, told you he's a twat.
Cass Dyslexic?
Whizz No, but the bloke in the tattoo shop was.
Cass Shit.
Whizz He's got a nice smile, though.

Cass and Twiglet laugh. Snap spot on Whizz.

Whizz It's not that I like boys, more that boys like me. Got magnetic charm. Sex appeal, innit? I'm the honey pot, they're the bee. They're like, 'Want a snog?' so I'm like, 'Yeah, up for it.' Even if I'm not. Reputation, right? Not that I'm a slapper or nothing. 'Cause Dad reckons I'm a slapper. So I'm like, 'Piss off, you twat, who gives a toss what you think?' Now Mum, *she's* a slapper. Seven kids, and each one got a different daddy. Take a family photo, it's like a Benetton ad. Multicultural, see?

Spotlight on Dillon.

Dillon Now me. Romantically, how do I fit into all this? Good question . . .

Lights are raised on Princess.

Princess Can't you just piss off?
Dillon Ever wondered what the plural of multiplex is?
Princess You what?
Dillon Plural . . . you know, like . . .
Princess I know what plural means, shit-wit.
Dillon Multiple multiplexes. Multiple multipli. It's like Elvis, yeah? What's the plural of Elvis? Is it Elvises or Elvi?
Princess Fuck off, you're creeping me.
Dillon But . . .
Princess No, honest, you're really weirding me out.
Dillon Is this the brush-off?
Princess No, it's the 'piss-off'.

Dillon Yeah, right. Cool.
Princess I can still see you.
Dillon Sorry, man.

Pause.

Yeah, right.

Spotlight on Dillon.

Babe magnet, see? Princess, she's like the fittest usher of the lot. Way out of my league, but it doesn't stop me trying. Got to keep it real, man.
Mags Interior. Multiplex foyer. First day of filming . . .

Princess stands downstage.

Princess How do you want me, King?

King enters with his digital camera. He is followed by Spike, Elton and Cass.

King Less make-up.
Princess It's only lipstick and eyeshadow.
King This is post-apocalyptic, end-of-the-world.
Princess And they can't get hold of make-up? I find that hard to believe.
King Look, wipe it off or I'll get somebody else to play the part.
Cass I'll do it!
Princess (*angrily*) OK, OK. I'll wipe it off.
Spike What's the look you're going for, King?
King Docudrama. Ken Loach style, that kind of thing. Keeping it real.
Elton Real. Right.
Princess And?
King And what?
Princess What am I supposed to be doing?
King Just standing.
Princess Just . . .

King . . . standing. Looking.

Princess At what?

King Taking things in. The world around you.

Princess Singing maybe?

King Not singing. Just looking. For fuck's sake, the world's been wiped out. Why the hell would you be singing?

Princess Cheer myself up.

King No.

Princess Just standing. That's all you want me to do?

Spike Maybe the part's too challenging?

Princess Oh piss off.

King OK. Rolling.

Elton (*snapping a clapperboard*) Take one.

Fade. Spotlight on Cass.

Cass King's dead gorgeous. Like Tom Hanks, Brad Pitt and Ewan McGregor all rolled into one. And really fit too. 'Cause he works out, I've seen him. Going down the gym. Not spying on him or nothing. Just see him there. And one day I'll kiss him. When he's just stood there, thinking. I'll come up and snog him on the lips. Stick me tongue down his throat so he can't say nothing. Kiss him and kiss him, till he can't think of nobody in his head but me. Then he'll go out with me, we'll get married, have a flat together and make babies. Then he'll divorce me, and pay child support. And I'll move into a bedsit . . . and start smoking. And wear pedal pushers, and jumpers from the Salvation Army, and eat doughnuts and maxi packs of crisps and go on *Trisha*. Then I'll die. The end.

Beat.

Yeah, got my life sorted.

Spotlight on Dillon.

Dillon That's it, in a nutshell. We like films, so we work in a multiplex. King likes films, so he makes his own movies. Simple. And then something happens, kind of out of the blue. But that's the way things happen. Just when you're not expecting them.

Mouse enters, stands centre, a sheet of paper in his hand.

Fish Interior. Manager's office. Day.
Mags Close-up on face of Mouse. Sixteen, but only just. Enters the multiplex and stands at the desk. Application form filled . . .
Dillon This kid comes into the cinema. Sixteen. Small kid, right. Wouldn't reckon nothing to look at him.
Spike Favourite film? Think carefully now.
Mouse *Citizen Kane*. Orson Welles.

The Ushers stand, stunned. Snap cross-fade.

King He said what?
Elton *Citizen Kane*. Orson Welles. I heard him.
Jay But that's, like . . .
Spike Out of the ark.
Jay Yeah.
King Knows about film then, he reckons?
Mags Knows all there is to know, they say.
Princess Anyone ask you?
Mags No.
Princess Then shut it.
King Movie buff, yeah?
Spike Say he's got an encyclopaedic knowledge of film. Photographic memory, see? Click. Flash. All stored away.
Geach Photographic? Like a camera?
Spike Yeah, that's right, dip-shit. He's got a camera planted in his brain.
Geach No shit?

Spike Yeah, no shit.

Spotlight on Dillon.

Dillon And this is Mouse.

Cross-fade to light on Mouse, Spike and Elton.

Spike So you're the new usher?
Mouse Yes. I've just come from –
Elton We didn't ask where you came from. Don't give a flying fuck, mate.
Spike You're here. That's all that matters.
Elton What do they call you, then?
Mouse Mouse.
Elton 'Cause you're small, or 'cause you like cheese?
Spike Shut the fuck up.
Elton Gotcha.
Spike Welcome, little Mouse. I'm Spike, this is Elton.
Elton Pleased to meet you.
Dillon Now the thing about Spike and Elton, they're like henchmen, see? King's heavies. Not that King wanted heavies, they just kind of chose him. Spike's the brains . . .

Spotlight on Spike.

Spike The thing about school, the teachers always seem to think if you're bright you *want* to learn. Like how wrong can you get? Can't wait to get out the fucking place. I can count to ten in three languages, so I reckon I'm educated enough. GCSE revision would be a fuck of a lot easier without the teachers there to distract me. Maths, English . . . piece of piss. So I spend half my time trying to find ways to get thrown out. So many foolproof ways. Art, for instance, a gleaming example. You could shit on a piece of paper and call it postmodernist sculpture. So I did. This does not impress old Mr Vincent. 'Call this art?' he says, 'Yes, sir,' I said, 'Very Tracey Emin, don't you think, sir?' 'Tracey Emin my arse,' he says. 'It's a load of crap, that's what it is,' and we all piss ourselves laughing, 'cause that's exactly what it is. 'It just won't wash,' he says. 'This is state education not the fucking Tate Modern.' He said buggering, not fucking, but I think fucking's what he meant. We call him The Dick, old Mr Vincent, cause he's a bit of a dick. The clue's in the nickname. And the tosser says, 'Spike, you always have to have the last word.' So I say, 'Yes.' So then I get suspended, which means I can have a lie-in. Don't need to get up. Dad's pissed off to bugger-knows-where with Gran's care assistant, and Mum's on the alcopops, so basically my life's my own. And our deputy head, he's a prick, he keeps phoning up and saying, 'You can come back to school as soon as you've learnt your lesson. Have you learnt your lesson yet?' So of course I say, 'Not yet, sir. Might take another week or two.' And the twat can't think of nothing to say, so he says goodbye and hangs up, and I go back to watching porn on cable.

Beat.

Cushy number really, school.

Spotlight on Dillon.

Dillon And Elton's the brawn. You look at him and think, what the hell's going on inside your head?

Spotlight on Elton.

Elton Life depresses me, man. Always had this kind of fear . . . more like terror, I suppose. This terror that when I die I'll come back reincarnated . . . you know, born again . . . reincarnated as, like a fish or something. 'Cause I can't swim. Got an allergy to chlorine, so Dad never took me. What if I'm reincarnated as a fish and I can't fucking swim? Like, typical or what? Come back as a fish and I fucking drown.

Lights revert to normal.

Spike Heard you quite fancy yourself.
Mouse What?
Elton Quite up yourself, that's what we heard, wasn't it, Spike?
Spike Those words exactly. Bit of a film buff?
Mouse I like films.
Spike That's why you're here, yeah?
Elton In a multiplex fucking cinema.
Spike Language, Elton, you're intimidating the man. Don't be intimidated, Mouse.
Mouse I wasn't.
Elton Do what?
Spike Think you're clever?
Elton Shall I show him the power gloves, Spike?

Jay enters. A moment is held.

Spike Careful, little Mouse. We'll be keeping an eye on you.
Elton An eye. Yeah.

Spike and Elton exit.

Jay Want to watch it with Spike and Elton.
Mouse How come?
Jay Just keep your head down, you'll be all right.
Mouse I'm Mouse.
Jay Yeah, I know. Jay.
Mouse What did he mean about . . .
Jay Power gloves?
Mouse Yeah.
Jay A pair of gloves Elton carries round in his pocket.
Mouse What kind of gloves?
Jay Just ordinary. Knitted.

Mouse What does he do with them?

Jay Hits people.

Mouse Why?

Jay Elton's trademark, really. Hitting people. Sort of hobby, I suppose. And he's good at it. Remember the first time I got hit with the power gloves. Second day here. I was walking up to Screen One, and he was stood there, just leaning against the wall. So I go –

Tash Cut to.

Whizz Flashback. Interior. Multiplex foyer. Day.

Jay – 'All right, Elton?' and he goes . . .

Elton What?

Jay So I go, 'All right, Elton?' but louder, and he goes –

Elton Taking the piss?

Jay – And I go, 'No,' and he goes –

Elton You are, you're taking the piss.

Jay – And he reaches into his pocket, real slow, and he pulls out the pair of gloves.

Elton Know what these are?

Jay – he says. 'No,' I says, 'cause I don't.

Elton Power gloves.

Jay 'Cool,' I say, 'cause I'm like, really confused now.

Elton Gonna hit you with them.

Jay And being a man of his word, he did. Beat the crap out of me.

Whizz Flash-forward. Interior. Multiplex foyer. Day.

Jay But you learn, right. You get wise to it. He's like fine till he's got the gloves on, then he's this lean mean fighting machine. He's an animal. And you know when you're in trouble, when he's going to reach into his pocket and get those power gloves out. But you try and stop him. Try and will him to do something else . . .

Mouse 'Will him'?

Jay With your mind. So he thinks of something else, takes his hands out of his pockets . . . you know, does something else. Make him laugh or something. 'Cause if he's laughing, he's not thinking about making you bleed, right? Happy thing, laughing. Not punching and blood. Smiles and shit.

Tash Interior. Canteen. Night.

Lights up on the canteen. King enters, followed by Princess, Spike and Elton. King lies on his back, holding the digital camera, focusing on Princess. Mags watches silently.

Dillon OK, so back to the film. The thing about King . . . he's cool, cause he hasn't got any competition. He's top of the heap. Pig in shit. Happy, yeah? But ever notice how fucking flimsy life is? Just when you think you've started to understand things, got some system sorted out, some little prick comes along and fucks things up. In this particular case, Mouse . . .

Elton (*with clapperboard*) Take four.

Princess So what am I doing now?

King Walking. I keep telling you. This is the fourth time.

Spike One foot in front of the other, simple really.

Elton Maybe she's got attention deficit . . . you know, that thing.

Princess Walking? First I'm just standing, now I'm just walking.

King OK, look. This is a long shot, right. We see you, lost in this canteen . . .

Princess Maybe I get a cup of coffee?

King No, you don't get a cup of coffee. And why not?

Spike 'Cause the world's come to an end. No cappuccino, no latte . . . no Nescaff.

Princess Oh yeah, right. Shit.

King Go back. Do it again.

Elton Take five.

King The soundtrack's heavy . . . *moody*. You come into the canteen . . . there's no one there . . .

Princess acts to King's directions.

You're scared. Shit-scared. You hear a sound . . . you turn. You're not alone . . .

Mouse enters. Pause. King puts the camera down.

You're in shot.
Mouse Sorry.
Spike Get *out* of the shot.

Mouse steps to one side.

King Yeah. What?
Mouse Nothing.

Mouse continues to watch. King is visibly unnerved.

King Well?
Mouse Just watching.
Mags (*quietly, nervously*) Maybe Mouse is a survivor too . . . like Princess.
Elton And maybe Mags is one of the flesh-eating zombies.

Mags smiles awkwardly. Spike laughs.

King Fucking hell, Elton, how many times have I got to tell you? There's no flesh-eating zombies.

Spotlight closes in on Mags.

Mags Got horror in me head. Hammer Horror and stuff, all the way through. *Nightmare on Elm Street*, *Halloween . . . Blair Witch*. *Exorcist*. How cool is that, to have your head revolving? Mum, she doesn't understand, takes me to see all sorts of crap. Not really into blood and gore, says I take after my dad. Everything in the house is pink. She collects thimbles, and plates with painted dogs from Sunday magazines. I mean, sick or what? And she thinks there's something wrong in *my* head. No she doesn't, no she doesn't. I never said that. You didn't hear that . . .

Beat. She collects herself.

Makes me sit there on the settee with her, and watch these crappy movies. *Breakfast at Tiffany's*, *Barefoot in the Park* . . . all that shit. Jane Fonda, you know. If I could spend an hour alone in a room with Jane Fonda and a pickaxe. (*She smiles.*) Cool.

Fade back to the canteen.

King OK, so try it again.
Elton Take six.
Spike Better make it good this time, Elton can't count past seven.
Elton Funny.

Princess walks forward.

King Walk, walk, walk. Horror. Turn.

Princess freezes.

What?
Princess It's him. I can't concentrate.
Spike Piss off, Mouse.
Mouse Maybe if you started again . . .
Princess Do what?
Mouse You know. You've kind of lost the moment. It's not real any more . . .

An awkward pause.

King So what, you know about film-making now, do you?
Mouse Yes.
Spike You what?
Mouse I've done a bit. Before I moved here . . .

Spotlight on Dillon.

Dillon And that was it. Wanky, I suppose, but kind of the moment everything changed. One thing that hadn't changed, that was Elton. Like the missing link in man's evolution.

Mags Cut to.

Tash Interior. Boiler room. Night.

Dillon The boiler room, nobody goes there. Just King, Elton and Spike. It's where King goes to think . . . and Elton goes to hit people . . .

Grim light illuminates the boiler room.

Tash Extreme close-up on the face of Elton. He's got a mean look in his eyes, flecks of foam round his mouth. Rabid, man.

Jay You just don't want to make him mad.

Elton Shut it.

Jay 'Cause once he's got his power gloves on . . .

Elton What did I just say?

Jay 'Shut it.'

Elton So how come I'm still hearing you?

Jay Tinnitus? Echo maybe.

Elton Funny bugger.

Pause.

Think you're something, yeah?

Mouse No.

Elton 'Cause that's what King reckons. That you think you're something. And if you think you're something, then it makes King get jumpy, yeah. 'Cause if you're something, what does that make him? Something or nothing?

Mouse I don't know.

Elton It wasn't a question. And if King gets jumpy, then we start getting jumpy too. And if we start getting jumpy, something has to be done about it, yeah? Settle the balance, yeah?

Elton removes the 'power gloves' from his pocket.

Jay There, see? Power gloves. What'd I tell you?

With great ceremony Elton puts the gloves on.

Elton As far back as I can remember, I always wanted to be a gangster . . .
Mouse What you going to do?
Elton Hit you.
Jay See, told you. Dead hard, Elton is.
Elton Are you going to shut it, or am I gonna have to hit you too?
Jay No, mate. Mouth shut. Won't hear another –

Elton gives him a sharp punch on the arm.

Mouse You don't have to do this.
Elton You're wrong. I do.
Mouse Do you expect me to talk?
Elton No, Mouse, I expect you to . . .

Tash enters.

Tash Elton.
Elton What?
Tash Parky wants to see you in the office.
Elton Can't it wait? I'm busy.
Tash Says he wants to see you now. Says you've put too much syrup in the cola machine.
Elton Shit. (*He stares hard at Mouse.*) You'll keep. (*He exits.*)
Jay Don't take it personally, Mouse. If he wasn't hitting you, he'd most probably be hitting me. Survival of the fittest. See?

Spotlight on Tash.

Tash They say life is like a box of chocolates. I always get caramel. I hate caramel. This is life, right? It sucks. You aim for strawberry cream but you always get the fucking caramel.
Mags Cross-fade to . . .

Slow cross-fade to multiplex foyer, day. Fish and Whizz stand side by side. Whizz drinks a slushy.

Jo-Jo Interior. Multiplex foyer. Day.

Fish Heard Weasel's been sacked?

Whizz Yeah, I heard that.

Fish And Elton's got it in for Mouse.

Whizz Heard that too.

Fish Oh. Right. Heard anything new?

Whizz There's nothing new.

Fish What are we going to talk about then?

Whizz Do we have to talk about anything?

Fish I've sold one tub of popcorn in half an hour. If I don't talk to somebody, I think I'll end up . . . you know . . . slashing my wrists or something.

Whizz Won't get any complaints from me.

Fish I really love the bond we're building.

Whizz (*sarcastic*) Yeah, lovely, isn't it?

Fish Got any hobbies?

Whizz You what?

Fish Hobbies. Things you like doing?

Whizz No. You?

Fish Not really, no.

Whizz So pleased we had this chat.

Fish All right, things you look forward to in life?

Whizz You shutting the fuck up.

Fish Apart from that.

Whizz Don't know. You?

Fish Being recognised.

Whizz What?

Fish Recognised. People remembering me. Knowing stuff about me.

Whizz OK.

Fish Kebab shop on the corner. I feel special, you know? 'Cause I walk in, and they always know the way I want it. 'Cause I'm a regular. They *know* me.

Ushers All right, mate?

Fish Yeah, cool.

Ushers How's it hanging ?

Fish To the left, up and over.

Ushers Usual, mate?

Fish Yeah, cool.

Whizz The usual?

Fish Doner kebab, salad, easy on the onion. Chilli sauce one side, mayonnaise the other.

Ushers Chips with that, mate?

Fish Large chips, no salt. Ketchup one side, mayonnaise the other.

Whizz You eat that?

Fish Yeah.

Whizz Sick.

Fish And all these blokes are stood there, leaning against the counter. And they're looking at me, you know, like in awe, like I'm the king of kebabs. The master of pre-formed meat. And the little guy's shaving slivers off the doner, and there's like . . . there's like joy in his eyes. And for once I actually feel like something. Somebody. Not some prat in the crowd, but a real somebody. You know what I mean?

Whizz No.

Fish 'Cause they know me. I'm not a nobody.

Whizz And what? That's all you look forward to in life?

Fish Aim low, that way you can never be disappointed.

Whizz Triffic.

Fish Go on. Ask me anything on the menu.

Whizz What?

Fish I memorised it.

Whizz You did what?

Fish Memorised it. The whole menu. I memorise things.

Whizz Why?

Fish I don't know. Listen. Starters: hoummos, tarama salad, dolma, mixed meze, prawn cocktail, salad in pitta. Kebabs, all served with salad in pitta bread, lamb doner, chicken doner, shish kebab, kofte kebab, saslik, chicken shish . . .

Whizz All right. I believe you.

Fish . . . the Kebab Maximus, that's like a super deluxe no-expense-spared kebab. You know, the mother of all kebabs. You've got to be well hard to eat a Kebab Maximus . . . or crazy.

Whizz That it?

Fish That's it.

Whizz Great, that's thirty seconds of my life you've wasted. Could have had a fag.

Fish Could have been run over by a bus.

Whizz Least I wouldn't have had to listen to you talking crap.

Fish takes out a bar of chocolate.

Fish Want some?

Whizz Aren't you supposed to be on a diet?

Fish No need. I've got big bones and a fast metabolism.

Whizz Shouldn't that make you, like technically, you know, *thin*?

Fish Freak of nature, eh?

Whizz Thought you had those stick-on patches for chocolate addiction?

Fish I ate them.

Whizz Do you suffer from low self-esteem?

Fish Depends if you're gonna snog me or not.

Bored, Whizz looks at her watch.

Whizz Eyes open or closed?

Fish If you've got your eyes closed, can I grope you?

Whizz Open then.

They kiss.

What you trying to do, kiss me or revive me?

Fish Bit of both, really.

She smacks him. Pause.

Whizz So what did Weasel get the sack for, then?
Fish Pissing in the slushy machine.

Beat. Whizz pulls away from the slushy. Snap fade.

Dillon That's what it's like, man. Like the kid said, 'Aim low and you'll never be disappointed.'

Spotlight on Fish.

Fish Used to dream I was Catholic. Used to lie in bed and imagine I was in a convent. You know, somewhere with nuns. Used to dream that Julie Andrews would come in. But she never did. I'd call out, 'Sister', and then this nun would come in, and I'd look at her, but it wouldn't be Julie Andrews. She'd be like ugly, or really small or something. So I'd call again, and under my breath I'd be going, 'Please be Julie Andrews, please be Julie Andrews, please be Julie Andrews'. Then the next nun, she'd come in. And it wouldn't be Julie Andrews. So I'd try again and again. But it was never bloody Julie Andrews. And like the really strange thing, the nuns right, they wouldn't go away. They'd just stay in the room. Staring at me. Nuns. Everywhere. Bloody nuns.

Beat.

Funny thing, imagination.
Princess Cut to . . .

Lights up on Jay, Tash and Jo-Jo in the canteen.

Geach Interior. Canteen. Day.
Jay Can't I just talk to her on my own?
Tash No, you're stuck with me.
Jay Thought she could lip-read.

Tash She can. But she said you've got a strange mouth.

Jo-Jo signs again.

Not strange. *Weird.*

Jo-Jo nods.

Jay What's weird about it?
Tash Just difficult to read, that's all.
Jay So how come you can sign then?
Tash Mum's deaf.
Jay Harsh.
Tash Not really. I can piss off out and go clubbing when she's asleep and she doesn't know I'm gone.
Jay Cool. Wish my mum was deaf . . . or blind or something.

Angrily, Jo-Jo signs 'Hurry up.'

Tash Yeah, right, keep your hair on. So?
Jay What?
Tash What do you want me to say?
Jay Shit, I don't know.
Tash Terrific. Good start.
Jay Tell her I think she's gorgeous.

Tash signs this to Jo-Jo. Jo-Jo laughs.

Why's she laughing?
Tash She thinks you're cute.
Jay Cool.
Tash Yeah cool. Keep going.
Jay Tell her I think she's got eyes like . . .
Tash Oh *please.*
Jay . . . eyes as blue as the sky.
Tash I'm gonna hurl.
Jay Thought you said you'd help me.
Tash OK. OK.

Tash signs to Jo-Jo.

Anything else you want to say?

Jay Tell her my granddad's deaf . . . got a hearing aid and everything.

Tash So?

Jay So, I like . . . *understand.*

Tash (*ironically*) Yeah, good. She'll like that.

Tash signs to Jo-Jo. Jo-Jo signs 'Piss off.'

Jay What she say?

Tash Piss off.

Jay No, really. What did she say?

Tash signs to Jo-Jo. Unmistakably, Jo-Jo gestures 'wanker'.

Jay Oh, right.

Lights fade on Tash and Jay. Spotlight on Jo-Jo.

Jo-Jo In my head, all I'm thinking is 'Knob off, knob off, knob off, knob off . . .'

Pause.

They look at me strange, kind of wondering, if she's deaf how come she works in a cinema? What's the point in that? 'Cause if she can't hear stuff, she can't get much fun out of watching films. Poor deaf cow. But I'd argue, 'Cock off. Don't be so pissing ignorant.'

Jo-Jo signs 'Cock off, don't be so pissing ignorant.'

But of course they wouldn't understand. They can't really.

Pause.

Sitting there in the dark, and watching those faces on the screen. Just stretching there in front of you. I hear their voices so clear in my head. Like magic things in my brain. Like colours and things. I hear colours.

Tash Cut to . . .

Geach Interior. Boiler room. Night.

King enters with the digital camera. Elton, Princess and Spike enter.

Elton Take three.

Princess I'm shagged.

King Work with it.

Princess I don't *want* to work with it. I want to go back home.

King You haven't got a home. It's been destroyed.

Elton Cut.

King Did somebody tell you to cut? Did I tell you to cut?

Elton Sorry, King.

King Come on, Princess.

Princess I don't want to. I'm pissed off.

King Of course you're pissed off. The fucking world's come to an end.

Spike (*quietly*) Intense. Stanley Kubrick moment.

Elton Red rum, red rum . . .

They laugh.

King Shut it.

Beat.

OK, everything's dead. What do you do?

Princess Can't I just go . . .

King (*angrily*) Everything's fucking dead. Where *can* you go? What do you *do*?

Princess I don't know.

King You can't go home, there's no home to go to. Your family's dead, your friends are dead. Everything you've ever known, destroyed . . . gone. What do you do?

Princess (*upset*) I don't want to do this.

King You don't know what to do. You're scared. Almost out of your brain with fear. You think it's irrational, maybe you shouldn't be feeling like this. Maybe there's nothing to be scared of. Not really. But deep down, you know that everything you think, it really is as bad as that. Worse, maybe. Even worse than you think.

King closes in on Princess's face with the digital camera.

And all the time there's this scratching noise. You don't know what it is. You think it's something rubbing against the door . . . something normal. But it hasn't stopped. It's always there . . . *unnatural.*

Elton (*quietly*) Flesh-eating . . .

Spike Shut the fuck up.

King Always scratching. You don't know what it is. You thought you knew what it was, but you don't. It's changed. It's something else. Something different. And you know that if it gets in, that's it. It's over. You can't let it in . . .

Princess (*screaming, terrified*) Shut up. Shut up!

King (*calmly*) OK, that's it.

Spike What?

King takes the digital camera from his eye.

King It's done.

Spotlight on Princess.

Princess I look up at the screen, and it's me. My face filling the picture. Highlights and new teeth. Me. No bugger else. Me. And it's wonder. That's what it is. Wonder. It's what King's done. What King's made of me. I'm not *me* any more. I'm someone special. I'm it. I'm fucking it.

Tash Interior. Multiplex cinema. Night.

Dillon Nobody knows shit about anybody. Just trapped here. Like I said, the ghetto, right?

Spotlight on Jay.

Jay My success rate with girls is not good. Actually, it's a fucking disaster. Mum thinks I've got 'odour issues'. She had laser surgery for snoring and hasn't been able to smell anything for four and a half years. 'Maybe it's your pores,' she says, 'maybe your pores are clogged.' Like she'd know. But it gets me thinking. Maybe I give off odours that I can't smell. Microscopic things crawling over me, farting. You know, too small to smell on their own. But *together*. Timed or something, so they do it *together*, at the same *time*. A little wave of microscopic, farting *things*.

Snap cross-fade. Lights up on Twiglet and Mags. Mags mops the floor. Jay smells himself.

Twiglet What you doing?
Jay Nothing. Why?

Twiglet shrugs. Pause.

Jay Still at school, then?
Twiglet College.
Jay Right.
Twiglet A-Levels.
Jay Cool.
Twiglet You think?
Jay Nah. You?
Twiglet (*smiling*) Nah.
Jay What you taking?
Twiglet Modern History, Biology, French and German.
Jay Four A-Levels. Brainy, yeah?
Twiglet Nah.
Jay Nah? Come on.
Twiglet What?

Jay Say a bit of German.
Twiglet No.
Jay Go on.

Pause.

Twiglet *Haben sie einen Meerschweinchen?*
Jay That it?
Twiglet *Nein, ich habe keine Meerschweinchen.*
Jay Meaning what exactly?
Twiglet Have you got a guinea pig?
Jay And?
Twiglet No, I haven't got a guinea pig.
Jay And have you got a guinea pig?
Twiglet No.
Jay So, like, limited use then?
Twiglet S'pose.

She smiles. Jay smiles back.

Mags I had a guinea pig once.
Jay Yeah?
Mags It died.
Dillon Dysfunctional, see?

Spotlight on Twiglet.

Twiglet I'm gonna be a stand-up comedian, like Jo Brand, but thinner. That's the plan . . . long term. I write a bit. Gags, one-liners. Make people laugh, that's got to be a good job. Go on the club circuit, do my own set. Ten minutes, and off. Get noticed by a comedy agent and the BBC. Have my own show on the TV, probably get a BAFTA. Then another BAFTA. Buy a great mansion in the country with a jacuzzi and swimming pool. Get another BAFTA . . .

King enters, followed by Spike and Elton.

Spike Finished it, then?

King Yeah.
Spike How's it look?
King Dunno yet. OK, I s'pose.
Elton When you gonna screen it?
King Tomorrow night.
Spike Gonna let Mouse come?
King Why not?
Spike Just thought . . .
King Just thought what?
Spike Dunno. Just thought.
King Well don't, right?
Spike Right.
Elton Thinking just screws your mind up.
Spike You should know.
Dillon Then there comes that point when King finishes making one of his films. He knows this projectionist, so when the multiplex closes down at night he screens his films. And we all come to see them, kind of on pain of death. But it's great, yeah. 'Cause we're pulled together.
Twiglet Interior. Platinum Class. Screen One. Night.

Spike strides forward. The Ushers enter, awed.

Spike You are now viewing 'Platinum Class'.
Dillon This time it's a bit different, 'cause we're christening Platinum Class. A new concept in multiplex entertainment. Least, that's what it says on the posters . . .
Fish Like, how cool is this?
Spike Leather upholstery.
Whizz The sweet stench of dead-cow hide.
Princess Effing cool.
Spike Extra large seats, for the wide of girth.
Fish Even better.
Jay Blindingly cool.

Spike Something a little different, a little special, for the discerning moviegoer. Observe.

Spike clicks his fingers. Lights up stage left, then right.

Fish Shit!
Spike Ladies and gentlemen, I give you the future. The shape of things to come.
Fish Even got a built-in drinks holder.
Jay Shit-hot.
Spike This, my friends, is cinema heaven.
Dillon 'Cause this is the future and everything's changing. Gone supersonic.

King enters.

King All right?

A burst of applause from the Ushers.

Spike Ready, King?
King Yeah.
Cass What you calling the film, King?
King *Apocalypse Dawn.*
Mags Cool.
King OK. Roll it.

The room is plunged into darkness. Flickering light on the projection screen, accompanied by moody music.

Here we go . . .

The light slowly fades.

Pause.

The end of the film. Lights are raised. The Ushers stand in silence.

King So what d'you think?
Geach It's got . . .

Pause.

King Yeah?
Elton The man asked you a question.
King Got what?
Geach . . . *artistry.*
Elton Fuck off.
Spike Been reading books again, Geach?
Geach No.
King But you liked it, yeah?
Mouse It was OK.

An ear-splitting silence.

Elton Say what?

An awkward silence descends on the Ushers.

Mouse I said it was OK.

Spotlight snaps on Dillon.

Dillon And shit, it was like . . . that was it. You know, that moment at the movies, when two tons of crap just kind of falls from nowhere . . .
Jo-Jo Interior. Boiler room. Night.

King is badly shaken.

Elton You want me to hit him, King?
Spike Mess him up a bit?
Elton Beat the crap out of him?
King What did you think of the film?
Spike Think?
King Honestly.
Spike Your best yet.
King Yeah?
Spike Bada bing!
Elton Bada boom!
Spike Numero uno.

Elton The cat's meow.
Spike The dog's bollocks.
King You're just yes-men, aren't you?
Elton What d'you want me to say?
Spike Shut the fuck up.

Snap cross-fade to the multiplex foyer.

Twiglet Interior. Multiplex foyer. Night.
Jay You twat. You stupid bloody twat.
Mouse What did I do?
Twiglet You don't quite get it yet, do you, Wonder Boy?
Fish It's simple.
Whizz Rules of the game.
Fish King comes up with an idea for a film. We like it. King storyboards the film. We like it. King makes the film. We like it. King shows us the film . . .
Jay We fucking love it.
Mouse I said. It was OK.
Jay No, not OK. *We fucking love it.*
Mouse But . . .
Fish *Love it.*
Twiglet Get it now?
Mouse Yeah.
Jay See?
Fish Not much to it. It's all about the pecking order, right? You've just got to understand the pecking order.
Mouse OK.
Tash Don't rock the boat, man.

Snap cross-fade to the boiler room.

King What if he's right, though?
Spike Right about what?
King What if the film's just 'OK'? What if I don't got it any more.
Spike The kid's a punk. Doesn't know shit.
Elton Reckon he'd bleed real easy, King.

King Do I *want* you to make him bleed? Did I *say* that?
Elton Did you?
Spike Reading between the lines . . .
King *No*. What if this kid's got vision? What if he knows stuff?
Spike About what?
King About film.
Spike So what if he does? He could never know as much as you, could he, Elton?
Elton He's right.
Spike I know I'm right. (*He massages King's shoulders.*) 'Cause you're the champ, King. What you don't know about film isn't worth knowing.
Elton Take it easy, King.
King That's it. There's only one way to sort this out.

Beat.

Spike Fuck.

Spotlight on Dillon. The Ushers gather downstage.

Dillon And whenever anything happens . . . whenever anybody questions King's authority, he does this quiz, right. But honest, a clean game. 'Cause say whatever you like about him . . . cocky shit . . . but honest to the core.
Fish The following evening.
Tash Interior. Canteen.
Twiglet Fasten your seat belts, it's going to be a bumpy night.

King enters, followed by Spike, Elton and Princess.

Spike How you feeling, King?
King Cool.
Spike Psyched up?
King Yeah.

The Ushers enter. A hum of nervous excitement.

Dillon So on the one hand you've got King. Head of the ushers. Hard as steel, confident. Then on the other hand, there's Mouse.

Mouse enters.

And to look at him you think, 'What the fuck do you know?' But there's something going on inside his head, and you can't work out what. Sparks in his eyes, like he's got a dynamo running. Fired up inside his brain . . .

Spike You gonna start this or no, Dillon?

Dillon Are you ready, gentlemen?

Spike They're here aren't they?

Dillon You know the rules?

Elton 'Course he knows the rules. He wrote the fucking rules.

Dillon I can only accept your first answer. No pauses or hesitations.

Spike A pause *is* a hesitation, you twat.

Dillon Yeah, right.

Princess Go *on*.

Dillon I've got to give them the rules. It's in the rules. Ten points for a correct answer. Minus ten for an incorrect answer. Incorrectly answered questions can be offered.

Princess That it?

Dillon That's it.

Spike Well, start then.

A moment of tension. A quiz-show buzzer rips through the cinema.

Dillon King. Your starter for ten.

King Fire away.

Dillon Who starred alongside Jack Nicholson . . .

Elton Here's Johnny . . .
Dillon . . . in the 1980 Stanley Kubrick film *The Shining*?
King Easy. Shelley Duvall.
Dillon Correct. Mouse. Name the four actors who star in the 1972 John Boorman film *Deliverance*.
Mouse Ned Beatty, Ronny Cox, Burt Reynolds . . .
Dillon I need all four names
Geach (*quietly*) Go on.
Mouse . . . Jon Voight.
Dillon Correct.
Fish (*in awe*) He did that alphabetically.
Jay Told you. He's got a photographic memory.
Fish How cool is that!
Dillon King. Name the director of the 1999 film *The Talented Mr Ripley*, starring Matt Damon, Gwyneth Paltrow and Jude Law.
King Anthony Minghella.
Dillon Correct.
King Complete the following film quotes. Mouse. *Jaws*. 'You're gonna need a bigger . . .'
Mouse 'Boat.'
King Correct. King. *A Hard Day's Night*. 'Tell me, how did you find America?'
King 'Turn left at Greenland.'
Dillon Correct. Mouse. *Doctor Strangelove*. 'Gentlemen. You can't fight in here . . .'
Mouse 'This is the War Room.'
Dillon Correct. King. *Star Wars*. 'You came in that thing?'
Elton Piss easy!
Dillon No conferring.

King squirms.

Spike King?
Dillon I'm going to have to hurry you.

Beat.

Time him.

Tash . . . ten seconds, nine, eight . . .

In unison, the Ushers count down the seconds.

Tash Zero.

Dillon I'm sorry, your time's up. I can offer it.

Geach Go for it, Mouse.

Jay Come on, my son.

Dillon Mouse? *Star Wars*. 'You came in that thing?'

Mouse 'You're braver than I thought.'

Dillon Correct. Minus ten to King.

King I knew it. I fucking *knew* it.

Dillon You didn't complete the question in time. I had to offer it.

Elton You don't have to do nothing.

Dillon It was too late.

Elton removes the power gloves. A gasp from the Ushers.

Elton The power gloves say he had plenty of time.

King Play by the rules.

Elton But . . .

King I told you. Play by the rules.

Dillon Next question. Mouse. *Citizen Kane*. 'Everything was his idea . . .'

Princess But he knows that. It's his favourite film.

Dillon Luck of the draw.

Spike This is a fix. It's a fucking fix.

Elton Better not be.

King Shut it.

Dillon I can repeat the question. 'Everything was his idea . . .'

Mouse 'Except my leaving him.'

Dillon Correct. King. *Titanic*. 'I'm King . . .'

King (*quietly*) Shit.

Dillon I can repeat it.

King I heard you.

Elton He heard you, you twat.

King Oh shit . . . *shit* . . .

Princess King? What's wrong?

King Stop talking. I can't think.

Dillon Start the clock.

Ushers Ten, nine, eight, seven, six, five, four, three, two, one . . .

Tash Zero!

Dillon I can offer it. *Titanic.* 'I'm King . . .'

Mouse 'Of the world!'

Dillon Correct!

King I knew that. I *knew* it.

Dillon Too late. Minus ten points.

King Fuck!

Elton You want me to sort him out, King?

Dillon I offered it. Nothing I could do. Mouse, your next question . . .

King is visibly stunned.

Spike King, you all right, mate?

Princess King?

King runs off.

Spike What just happened?

Jay What?

Spike I said, 'What just happened?'

Princess Who knows.

Snap to black. Spotlight on Dillon.

Dillon And that was it. A break in the space–time continuum. It was like. It was like . . .

Fish Montage.

Sharp lighting cuts from usher to usher.

Jay It was like he froze. Couldn't think of shit . . .
Elton Blank, yeah?
Spike I looked at his face and there was nothing happening. No spark in his eyes. Nothing.
Geach Like he knew he couldn't really fly.
Jo-Jo Fear. You could see it. See what was going on inside his mind.
Cass (*smiling*) Like he'd changed. Like fireworks in my head.
Mags Like something had gone wrong with his brain.
Fish Snapped, maybe?
Tash Dunno. Gone mad.
Whizz Lost it. Fruit loop.
Twiglet Non compos thingy.
Princess Like the lead had dropped out of his pencil. And suddenly Dillon looked sexier than I'd ever seen him look.

Dillon winks at her. Princess smiles back.

Dillon Cool.

Snap cross-fade. Lights up on the canteen.

Twiglet Interior. Canteen. Night.

King stands on his own. Enter Cass. Pause. Cass smiles.

King Yeah, what?
Cass You all right, King?
King All right? Do I look all right?

Pause. Cass reaches into her pocket.

Cass Chewing gum?
King No.
Cass Chocolate?

King What?
Cass Crisps?
King Look, can't you just piss off?

Pause.

Cass You can be a real knob-end sometimes, you know that?

Beat. She kisses King on the forehead and runs from the room.

Fish Interior. Store room. Night.

Small pool of light on the store room. Geach and Mouse sit huddled on the floor. Cass enters.

Mouse Who is it?
Cass It's me. Cass.
Geach You seen King?
Cass In the canteen.
Geach How's he look?
Cass Beautiful.

Beat.

Oh. Gutted.
Geach How about Elton?
Cass He wants blood.
Mouse Shit. What've I done?
Geach You're safe here, Mouse. They'll never find you here.
Mouse But I won. Fair and square.
Cass Don't make no difference. He's still gonna kick the shit out of you.
Geach Not if he doesn't find him he won't.
Cass But he will find him. Some time.
Geach Cass . . .
Mouse Cheers, thanks for that.

Cass But he *will*.

Pause.

Geach (*resigned*) Yeah.
Mouse What do I do now?
Cass Pray. Really hard.
Geach What you gonna do if you get through this alive?
Mouse Alive?
Cass You're freaking him out.
Mouse Don't know. You?
Geach Going to have a room full of autographs. You know, Hollywood stars. All signed and smiling at me.
Cass Why?
Geach Why not?
Mouse What you going to do with them all?
Geach Going to have them stuck to every wall, like a palace full of faces. And I'll invite people in, and they'll come in and, 'Shit,' they'll say, 'cause they can't believe what they're seeing.
Cass 'Daft twat,' they'll say.
Geach They won't. Will they, Mouse?
Mouse No. They'll say, 'Man with a vision, Geach is.'
Cass They won't. Will they, Mouse?
Mouse And they'll tell their friends. And their friends' friends. Until everybody in the world, they'll all know the name of Jimmy Geach.
Geach Shit.
Cass Something not quite right in your head, Elton says.
Geach He says that?
Cass He does.
Geach About me?
Cass Loose screw, he says.
Geach I've got vision, Mouse says.
Cass Piss off! Wouldn't know vision if it fell on you.
Geach Tell her, Mouse.

Mouse Tell her what?
Geach Tell her there isn't nothing wrong in my head. Tell her Elton got it wrong.
Cass He'll bloody brain you.
Mouse We're all like mice, Geach. Like fucking mice.

Pause.

Mice people, see? We're mice people.

Spotlight on Geach.

Geach I'm Buzz Lightyear, and I'm made out of plastic . . . and I'm strong. And I can fly and stuff, 'cause I've got rockets strapped to me back, and wings . . . great green plastic wings. And somebody says, 'Geach, I'm gonna fucking punch you in the head,' and I say, 'Not Geach, I'm Buzz Lightyear,' and before he can punch me in the head, I'm up and I'm flying, and I can see him way down below, like a little speck. And I wish I had huge great laser guns . . . not so I could kill him or anything . . . (*He thinks.*) No, actually I reckon I *would* kill him . . . if I had lasers. But only 'cause he was going to punch me in the head.

Beat.

Twat.

Lights revert to the store room. A noise.

Mouse Who is it? Who's there?
Elton I love the smell of napalm in the morning. Smells like . . . victory.
Dillon And sooner or later Elton catches up with his prey. In this case, sooner rather than later.
Fish Interior. Boiler room. Night.

Cross-fade to the boiler room. Spike keeps watch.

Elton Hold him, Geach.

Geach I don't want to.
Elton I said. *Hold him.*

Reluctantly, Geach takes hold of Mouse.

Anyone coming?
Spike Can't see anyone.
Geach Come on, Elton. Can't I go? Please, mate . . .
Elton Just shut up, Geach. You've got to ask yourself one question: 'Do I feel lucky?' Well, do ya, punk?
Mouse Not really. No.
Elton Oh, right. Good.
Spike Well?
Elton Sorry, that's thrown me.
Spike Just bloody hit him.
Elton Shit.
Spike What?
Elton I have to be in the mood.
Spike In the what?
Elton I have to be in the mood to hit people. I can't just turn it on and off . . .
Spike (*calmly*) All right, Elton.
Elton . . . like a tap or something.
Spike I said, 'All right.'
Elton I'm just telling you how I feel.
Spike Shit. I hate it when you get like this.
Elton Like what?
Spike You know.
Elton I don't, so you'll have to tell me.
Spike Like *this.*
Mouse Please, one of you, just hit me.
Spike Can't you just shut up?
Elton He's spoiling it now.
Spike Come on, mate. Pull yourself together.
Elton (*to Spike*) I walk through the multiplex and I see them all stood there. See the way they look at me. Like they're shitting themselves, right? Thinking,

'There's Elton, he's dead hard, hope to God he doesn't beat the crap out of me.'

Beat.

But do they think it's easy? To keep up the image. It's hard work, takes dedication. It's not just a nine-to-five job. There's the unseen preparation . . .

Spike Everybody appreciates the work you put in. (*He takes out Elton's power gloves.*) There you go.

Elton Cheers, Spike.

Spike You're very welcome.

Elton puts on the power gloves. Pause.

Elton Yeah, I'm with it now. In the moment.

Beat.

Think you're clever, don't you?

Mouse Don't know.

Elton Know what we do to twats like you?

Mouse No.

Elton Don't know much, do you?

Mouse Know enough.

Elton Know which fist's going to punch you first?

Mouse Right fist.

Elton Wrong. (*He punches him.*)

Mouse Didn't hurt.

Geach Why'd you say that, daft twat? Why'd you say that?

Spike Hit him harder. Till he screams. Hit him till he screams!

Elton Spike's got bloodlust.

Spike That's right. Got bloodlust.

Elton Guess again.

Mouse What?

Geach Leave him, Elton.

Elton I told you. Just hold him.

Beat.

Guess again.
Mouse Left fist.
Elton Wrong again. (*He punches him again.*)
Spike Harder! Hit him harder!
Geach Stop it. (*Geach lets go of Mouse.*)
Spike What d'you do that for?

Mouse runs from the room.

Geach You were hurting him.
Spike I think you've missed the point here.
Elton Missed the point, hasn't he?
Spike I think Geach is in need of a bit of education.
Elton Right.
Spike So let's educate him.

Elton raises his fist to punch Geach. Snap cross-fade. Geach screams, a blood-curdling yell.

Jay Interior. Multiplex foyer. Night.
Cass (*running in*) Anyone seen Geach?
Whizz Frankly, my dear, I don't give a toss.
Tash Thought he was with you.
Cass Shit, shit.

Mags runs in.

Tash Mags. What is it?
Mags It's Geach.

Elton enters, unseen.

Cass What's wrong?
Jay What's happened?
Mags I saw blood come puking out of him.
Fish Think he's sick?
Elton I only punched him light. Nothing heavy.

Geach stumbles in.

Cass (*to Elton*) You did this?
Fish Geach?
Geach I'm all right.
Elton Look, sorry, Geach.
Geach They call me *Mister* Geach.
Elton Do what?
Fish You heard him.

Geach begins to cough. He holds his hand to his mouth, it is covered in blood.

Cass Geach. What's wrong?

Geach staggers. He leans against the Ushers for support. They slowly lower him to the ground.

Jay Where does it hurt, man?
Geach All over.

Beat.

This is it.
Whizz What does he mean?

Geach slumps. Mags feels for a pulse. Beat.

Mags He's dead.
Tash (*to Elton*) You've killed him!

Snap spotlight on Dillon.

Dillon Geach was buried with a simple cross. Elton went to prison. And I copped off with Princess . . .

Lights up on Princess. She kisses Dillon, a full-on snog. She smiles. Spotlight on Dillon.

The multiplex. Palace of dreams, and all that crap. Fifteen screens, wall-to-wall entertainment. Close your eyes and tap your heels together three times. And think to yourself, 'There's no place like home . . .'
King And cut.

King enters, carrying his digital camera. He is followed by Mouse, who carries the clapperboard.

That's a wrap.

Princess (*wiping her mouth in her hand*) I thought we said no tongues?

Dillon I'd hate to take a bite out of you. You're a cookie full of arsenic.

Princess Get a life.

Geach rises from the floor, wiping blood from his mouth.

Geach OK, was I?

King Fucking ham.

Geach That good is it?

King Yeah. Great.

Snap to black. Lights are slowly raised on King, who sits on the ground looking back at footage on his digital camera. Mouse enters.

Mouse How's it look?

King shrugs.

OK?

Pause.

King I'm leaving. Given in my notice.

Mouse Leaving?

King Mum wants me to go on Jobseekers' Allowance.

Mouse Leave the multiplex?

King Says I'd get more money on Social.

Mouse But what . . .

King Half the time I'm here I don't get paid for it. Just hanging round. Nowhere else to go.

Mouse We were going to make more films. Only just started, you said.

King Time goes fast.
Mouse We can still do it, King. Make movies, yeah?

King shrugs. Pause.

King Remember real film? None of this super-cool shit you can plug into some computer. Real film.
Mouse Rough. Grainy.
King Yeah, right. Grainy. But everything's gone digital. Not the same.
Mouse No.
King I could have been a contender. I coulda been somebody. Instead of just a bum. Which is what I am.

Mouse laughs.

I sit there at home, watching the Oscars and shit. And some wanky ponce comes up in his tux, with some girl hanging from his arm, and I think, 'Fuck, I could do that.' I think, 'You cock, what've you got that I haven't got?'
Mouse Apart from the girlfriend?
King Yeah.
Mouse And the Oscar?
King (*sarcastic*) Yeah, right, cheers.
Mouse Sorry.
King Why can't I do that? And it's like I'm staring at black. Like the film's run through and there's just black. Sound like a complete wanker, don't I?
Mouse Yeah.

King smiles.

King I used to see everything, like a narrator, right? I woke up, and there it was, that voice in my head. Narrating. Like films running all round me. Everywhere I looked, there was film. But it's not like that, is it? Not really.
Mouse No.

King 'Cause no one gives a fuck what you're thinking, what you see around you. 'Cause everybody . . . they're all seeing their own films. And it doesn't matter if you don't share what's in your head with other people . . . they don't care, man. They don't give a fuck what's going on inside your brain. What you see. They don't care.

Mouse What d'you want me to say?

King Dunno. Don't say nothing I s'pose, just listen.

Mouse OK.

Fade to spotlight on Dillon.

Dillon That's the point about this place. It's about leaving, not about staying. Like some great fuck-off departure lounge on the way to someplace else. And the people that do stay, you feel sorry for them, right? Sad bastards that haven't got the courage to piss off and get on with their lives. Just stuck here. Man, if that was me, shit . . .

Lights up. The Ushers surge forward, expectantly.

Mouse Ready?

King Yeah. (*He shouts.*) OK, roll it.

The Ushers stand in silence as the film rolls. Flickering light from the projection room washes over the assembled group.

Dillon (*recorded voice over*) There's three types of ushers, right. There's Plankton . . . that's like the lowest of the low. Don't know shit. Then there's Dudes, they're, you know, cool. But they don't know movies. And top of the food chain, there's the Buffs. Know everything about every movie ever made, and to them, right, cinema . . . it's not just entertainment, it's life.

The flickering light from the projection room slowly fades to black.

Pause.

Lights are raised.

Elton Well, that's it.
Geach What?
Princess Mouse. He's upset the natural balance between cool and geek.
Jay The fundamental . . . *thing* . . .
Spike Power struggle.
Jay Yeah. That thing.

Pause.

Mouse I think this is the beginning of a beautiful friendship.
King Fuck off.

Mouse turns to King and smiles.

Dillon And cut to black.

Blackout.

End.

More Real than Reality

Christopher William Hill interviewed by Jim Mulligan

Christopher William Hill attended a 'fairly gritty comprehensive school' in Cornwall, a place he found trying, especially as he had an interest in drama and was not sporty. As a teenager he desperately wanted to be a comedy-sketch writer and an actor. In his last year at school an inspirational teacher allowed the students to mount productions of their own plays and this led on to Drama and Theatre Studies at the University of Kent, where he specialised in theatre direction. His first plays were performed at the Edinburgh Fringe, the others mainly in the West Country. He has worked as an actor and script editor for Bedlam Theatre Company of Cornwall. *Multiplex* is his second play written specifically for young people.

Multiplex is about the Planktons, Dudes and Buffs who work in the ghetto of the multiplex cinema. They have created a subculture where King is the top Buff and his henchmen ensure that his will is not thwarted.

> I wanted to have a rigid pecking order in the play. At one point King was going to be the violent character but in closed societies – like remand centres, for example – the person at the top does not need to throw muscle about in order to retain the position of seniority. The people immediately below the leader prop him up.

In *Multiplex* King, the *über-usher*, the undisputed master of the multiplex, is able to make his films and be assured of the grovelling approval of his followers.

> I'm not a hard-core buff. Some of my friends used to work in the local cinema and they had this story of an eccentric manager who actually lived behind the main screen. I found the buffs frighteningly technical. They had shelves stacked with videos and had all the vocabulary; some of them went on to work professionally in film.

The ushers are by no means uniform characters. Dillon sees himself as potential university material. Spike is an intelligent school drop-out. His father has left home, his mother drinks and he spends his time watching pornographic films. Elton is depressed, has no sexual charisma and takes his revenge on the weak by beating them up with his power gloves. The girls are also different from each other. Indeed, Jo-Jo is profoundly deaf. The one thing they have in common is their love of film and their ability to live part of their lives in terms of film.

> *Multiplex* is partly about whether dreams are attainable and partly about moving on and getting to a stage where you have to be realistic. There are, of course, a number of different types of reality. Some of these young people see films as more real than reality. They try to create stories or a screenplay around what is happening in their lives. Some people have told me they make their mundane jobs bearable by viewing the events unfolding in front of them as if they were moments in a screenplay.

The bizarre equilibrium is upset when Mouse arrives for a job as an usher. He really knows about film and becomes an innocent threat to King's regime. When he is asked for his opinion on King's latest filmic masterpiece he says it is OK and an awkward silence descends on the ushers. This is the beginning of the end for King, or rather the beginning of his enlightenment. The climax takes the form of a TV quiz show. Mouse defeats King and for that he must suffer at the hands of Elton's power gloves.

> At one point I was going to make the violence in the play very realistic. A lot of it is based on what happened to me. I used to catch a bus from my village to school and a boy we called Weasel always sat on the seat in front of me. He had what he called his power gloves – pathetic knitted things really – and when he put them on I knew he was going to punch me. Every day I experienced blind terror. So I used that, but I didn't want Elton to be a psychopath. There should be a cartoon knockabout quality to his performance, a touch of burlesque.

Interspersed between the episodes of the power struggle the ushers play their games, reveal their life stories, live out their fantasies and fancy each other, sometimes doing something about that. Occasionally reality intrudes. Cass fancies King, but the man of steel has a mother who wants him to go on the Jobseekers' Allowance. And Cass knows the tongue-down-his-throat sex won't last. It will all end in divorce, a bedsit, secondhand clothes, junk food and death. But we must not forget that Cass is a feisty woman with an ironic sense of humour. She talks tongue-in-cheek rather than tongue-down-the-throat.

> When you are growing up you feel there are limited life possibilities. You don't grasp the full potential until you are a little bit older. So yes, there is a darker side to their lives but the play is written with a definite sense of irony. If the production gets too caught up in the dark side it might be gloomier than I intended it to be. It's good to have a sense of realism but it's still tongue-in-cheek.

Christopher William Hill has made a comic play out of the lives of the wage-slaves. The ICL mission statement asserts that they have a duty to provide quality entertainment and to treat the customers as guests. 'No earrings will be worn, no smoking, no chewing gum on duty. No swearing . . . Happiness will be kept to a minimum at all times. We will not moan if our wage slips come through late. We will not grumble when we mop up sick, or cringe when we wipe shit from the floor. It is our duty. Part of the challenge – the ICL experience.'

Somehow, that casual visit to the cinema will never be the same again.

Production Notes

STAGING AND SETTING

The play is set beneath the dimly lit auditorium and candy-coloured foyer of a multiplex cinema. The stage should be as empty as possible. However, you might want to define the acting space by using a floor cloth, which could contain the multiplex logo, or be the sort of carpeting found in cinemas (but beware it's not too distracting). You might want to make use of existing exit signs and give them more of a movie-house treatment, or even light-up signs, 'To Cinemas 1–4', etc. Locations can be indicated through lighting and use of gobos (the sort used so effectively in real cinema foyers). Christopher William Hill has been very precise about the particular effects he imagines, so allow time to create a really good lighting plot, because the production depends on it. You'll need to create the flickering light of the projection screen: this could be placed on the floor, walls or wherever, the cast don't need to be looking at it when it occurs. The play should be performed in widescreen and glorious Technicolor.

You might be tempted to have the ushers dressing the stage as the audience comes in. If you decide to do this, make sure the cast are comfortable with the decision. Have them work at ushering the real audience, but make the ushers as neutral as possible – don't use this moment to give away too much about their characters.

Film sound, moody music and Dillon's repeated speech could work well prerecorded. The buzzer during the quiz should be a live sound. The customised uniforms should reflect the characters' personalities, for example, Princess is glamorous, with make-up and a short skirt.

The play has been written for eight males and seven females. But there's scope to add extra ushers if you wish.

EXERCISES

Have the cast visit a cinema to observe working ushers in action.

Get each cast member to talk about their favourite film and the reasons for their choice. Have them consider their character's favourite film and discuss what clues this gives to that character's personality.

King –The Third Man We hear a lot about King from the other characters. He is older and has been at the multiplex a long time. He does not try to acquire the henchmen Spike and Elton, but they acquire him. He has the confidence to make films but lacks a depth of knowledge. He gives up film and the multiplex, perhaps because of the appearance and influence of Mouse. The repeat of Dillon's introductory speech at the end of the play indicates that Mouse and King have arrived at an understanding. The film reflects King's departure. The phrase 'Aim low, avoid disappointment' is relevant to many characters. He reflects the idea that film can evoke aspirations – achievable or unreal.

Cass – From Here To Eternity This choice of film indicates a romantic personality. Cass is caring while looking after Geach, as she was for the moment when she kissed King. She seems to have low expectations for her life, but it still holds romance for her. This conscious confidence of her fate becomes ironical.

Geach – Toy Story He dreams of being Buzz Lightyear. He is vulnerable, gullible and a victim because he is sensitive and less bright than the others. He's slower but not backward. He exercises compassion by letting Mouse go when he's hurt. His other dream is much more attainable: collecting autographs from the stars. His 'They call me Mister Geach' dialogue can be likened to Sydney Poitier's speech in the film *They Call Me Mr Tibbs*. Geach becomes a hero as he stands up for himself, but dies for his beliefs at the end.

Princess – Something About Mary Princess aspires to being a celebrity. She is made vulnerable by King, who strips her of her persona and allows her to act another character (a directing technique Stanley Kubrick was renowned for). Her persistent questioning during the filming indicates a depth and intelligence that exceeds her preening concern over the way she looks. She is extremely proud of her performance and it spurs her on.

Jay – A Sex-Education Film He's good at looking after himself and preserving the status of those individuals at the top of the pecking order. He warns others of impending dangers. He occupied the victim position before Mouse.

Mags – Halloween She likes horror and cannot stand the pink, fluffy, 'girlieness' that her mother likes. She and her mother both think that the other is mad. The interest in horror could be a lever to annoy her mother.

Fish – The Sound of Music Possibly Fish is unsure of his sexuality: he seems asexual when he kisses Whizz. He's a character looking for an identity.

Jo Jo – Silence of the Lambs Jo-Jo is deaf. Her film choice is clever, sarcastic and macabre. Tash is her translator. There are a number of directorial choices around Jo-Jo. For instance, the cast might be onstage all the time, which would allow her to lip-read and observe all the action.

Dillon – Metropolis Dillon starts and closes the play. He speaks truthfully and convincingly. His role seems matriarchal: he umbrellas the group without disturbing the pecking order. He is the neutral, mature character who becomes the quiz-master. He is attractive to Princess when King is absent.

Mouse – Citizen Kane Mouse is the new boy. He isn't forthcoming about himself, but the other characters assume this means that his experience is extensive. He appears charismatic because of his knowledge. He prevents his tormentors from being violent towards him by challenging them verbally. Mouse knows who he is, and he affects the pecking order in the group. He uses a low-status name as a defence against the others; he pre-empts the bullies in this way.

Whizz – American Pie Whizz seems to kiss Fish for the sake of it. She seems to have appointed herself as the 'maneater'.

Have the cast improvise their experiences at the cinema. Have them give the scenes titles – here are some possibilities:

- Having your view of the screen blocked.
- Creating noise pollution with loud wrappings and mobile phones.
- Experiencing audience reactions such as sighing, groaning in unison.
- Intrusion of personal space.
- Still queuing for food and drinks when the feature has gone up.

Big changes in status occur as the play progresses. Break up the play into units and give each unit a title. Have the cast award their character a status number from one to ten (ten being the highest status) for each unit.

Suzy Graham-Adriani
March 2003
based on a workshop facilitated by David Prescott

PURPLE

Jon Fosse

in a version by David Harrower

Jon Fosse has been elected Best Foreign Playwright by the leading German-language theatre magazine, *Theatre Heute*. He has received several literary scholarships and prizes, and has a Master's Degree in Comparative Literature. Jon has written some thirty books, as well as volumes of poetry, essays, children's books and, increasingly since 1994, plays for the theatre. Last year over one hundred productions of his plays were seen around Europe. His plays are published by Oberon Books.

David Harrower lives in Glasgow. His plays include *Knives in Hens*, *Kill the Old Torture Their Young* and *Presence*, and adaptations of *Ivanov* and *Six Characters in Search of an Author*.

Characters

The Boy

The Girl

The Drummer

The Singer

The Bass Player

An unusually broad iron door opens and the Boy enters, holds the door open and the Girl comes in after him. He shuts the door and switches on the light by the light switch to the right of the door. The room is reminiscent of an air-raid shelter: darkened concrete walls, unpainted, no windows. There are some microphone stands, columns of loudspeakers and amplifiers, a black guitar and a bass guitar, each leaning on the loudspeakers, a drum kit and a spindleback chair; on the floor lie cables, empty bottles, debris.

The Girl (*looks around*)
This is where you rehearse
in here

Quite short pause.

I'm scared
just coming down here
I
and yeah
yeah it smells damp
And it's so cold in here
and

Cuts herself off.

The Boy
Yeah it is
but I told you
it was in a cellar
an air-raid shelter kind of

a small dark room
that's cold and horrible

The Girl
Yeah

Short pause.

but it's so far to come
down and down all those steps
in that creepy old factory

The Boy
Yeah

Short pause.

It's not very nice
no
but this is it
It was

Short pause.

the only place we could get hold of

Short pause.

The Girl
Can't we go back outside
It feels so shut up
in here

Short pause.

The Boy
But

Cuts himself off.

The Girl (*takes the Boy by the arm*)
Let's go
go back outside
or

yeah
yeah can we

The Girl lets go of his arm.

that creepy big factory
that's closed down now
I remember it from when I was a kid
I've always thought it was
thought it was so creepy
and then coming down into this cellar
down all those stairs
down and down
and

Cuts herself off.

The Boy
It's not that bad
here
is it
The Girl
Yeah
The Boy
It's somewhere for us to rehearse
The Girl
You sure
The Boy
Yeah

Short pause.

The Girl
C'mon
let's go back outside
The Boy
Now
The Girl
Yeah

The Boy
But we just got here
The Girl
I'm a bit scared
you
yeah
can't we go back outside again

The Girl takes him by the hand, the Boy is a bit embarrassed.

Imagine if we got trapped in here

Short pause.

If the lock got jammed
There's no windows in here
Nothing
The Boy
We won't
The Girl
It could happen
The Boy
Stop it

Short pause.

The Girl
Yeah let's go
It's so cold here

Short pause. The Girl lets go of his hand.

How can you play music in here
The Boy
We don't
Not music
it's maybe something else
but it's not music
The Girl
Why d'you practise here then

The Boy
It was
yeah like I said
we couldn't get anywhere else
only this cellar
this air-raid shelter
underneath the old factory

Short pause.

The Girl (*walks around a bit*)
What a place to rehearse
The Boy
It's not great
The Girl
And it's so cold
The Boy
Fingers are the worst
it's hard to play with frozen fingers
The Girl
How can you stand it here
The Boy
There's nowhere else
The Girl
No

Pause. The Girl looks at the black guitar.

The black guitar
that's your guitar
The Boy
Yeah
you remember it
The Girl
Yeah
yeah of course

A bit embarrassed.

that time
in your room

The Boy (*a bit embarrassed also*)
It's all right
it's not too bad
it's quite a good guitar

The Boy goes, picks up the guitar.

The Girl
Yeah

Short pause.

you haven't been playing very long

The Boy
No
not long

The Boy strums a couple of chords.

The Girl
It's a nice guitar

The Boy
Yeah

Short pause. The Boy plays part of a very slow, simple solo.

The Girl
That's nice

The Boy
It's OK

The Girl
Who wrote it

The Boy
I can play a bit
but not much
I'll never be good at it
never amazingly good

The Girl
But you've only just started playing
I think you're very good
I
The Boy
No

Pause.

I know
I'll never be good
It's like that
You know these things

Pause.

The Girl
You are good
The Boy (*messing about*)
No I'm not
The Girl
You are

Pause.

And the others
they've just started playing too
haven't they
they haven't been doing it very long
either
The Boy
They know almost nothing
It's hopeless
The Girl
None of them
The Boy
The drummer had never hit a drum
before he started
The Girl
And the others

The Boy
Same with the bass player
The Girl
And the singer
The Boy
Yeah
he must've sung before
like the rest of us
but he says
when they were singing at his school
he never sang
And he's not that great at singing either

The Boy plays a bit of the solo again.

The Girl
That's nice
The Boy
Yeah it's all right
The Girl
What is it
what's it called
The Boy (*a bit shy*)
I wrote it myself
It's called Grandmother

The Boy laughs a bit.

The Girl
Then you are good
aren't you
The Boy (*hesitating*)
No

Short pause.

I know a bit
I can play a bit
but not much

I'm as bad as the others
to be honest

Short pause.

There's no point practising
We sound awful
None of us can play anything

The Girl
But you've just started
you've bought the equipment and everything

The Boy
All our money's gone
I don't think we've any money left

The Girl
It's expensive
all this equipment

The Boy
We bought everything secondhand
we got some of it quite cheap
The bass player's father had a few
microphones
a PA
And a bass guitar
yeah he had a few things
There's so many people who've played in bands
everyone has
well almost everyone

Short pause. The boy begins to play his solo again.

The Girl (*in the middle of the solo*)
It's sad about your grandmother

The Boy
Yeah

Short pause.

it is

Pause.

The Girl
To die
The Boy
Yeah

The Boy continues playing.

The Girl
But it happens
The Boy
Yeah

Short pause.

She died
so suddenly
The Girl
Yeah

Short pause.

You'd lived with her your whole life
The Boy
That's how it turned out
The Girl
Since you were small
The Boy
Yeah
there was

Short pause.

yeah I think my mum came home one time
and then she left again
so I just kept staying there
at my grandparents
That's how things turned out

Pause.

The Girl
Your mother

Cuts herself off.

The Boy (*laughs briefly, stops playing, hits the open strings of the guitar*)
Yeah her yeah

Pause.

yeah her
I don't see her much
Can't remember the last time
The Girl
Didn't she sing
in a band
The Boy
Yeah a long time ago
or
yeah maybe she still does
They made a record apparently
years ago
But I've never heard it
I've never seen it
Just one record
I don't know where she is now
or what she's doing
I've no idea

Pause.

The Girl (*hesitating*)
No

Short pause.

she was very old
your grandmother
The Boy
Yeah

The Girl
But it happens to everyone
The Boy
It's always sad
though

Pause.

The Girl
You and her
you were good friends
The Boy
Yeah we were
The Girl
And your grandfather
he

Cuts herself off.

The Boy
Nothing changes with him
he's around
doing what he's always done
The Girl
In the pub drinking beer
The Boy (*hesitating*)
Yeah

Pause.

The Girl
But he wasn't your mother's father
yeah I think
yeah you said

Cuts herself off.

The Boy
No
The Girl
No one knows who it was

The Boy

No I don't think so
No one talks about it
It's just like that
Just like with me

Laughs briefly.

No one talks about it

The Girl

Just like with you

The Boy

That's how it goes

Short pause.

The Girl

That's the way it is

Short pause.

But you
yeah I
I think I'd like to
yeah like to go
Before the others come
I think

The Boy (*questioning*)

You want to go
It was you who wanted to come down here

The Girl

Yeah

Hesitates a little.

but I didn't know the others were going to come
You said nothing about that
until we were coming down here
on the stairs
You told me on the stairs

And before that you told me you weren't even going to practise today

The Boy (*as if he doesn't mean it*)

You can stay here if you want

The Girl

You sure

The Boy

Yeah
yeah the drummer said
he'd come earlier than the others

The Girl

It's so cold here
I'm going to go

The Boy (*a bit disappointed*)

On your own

The Girl

Yeah but

Cuts herself off.

The Boy

Yeah

The Girl

Yes I'm going to go

The Boy (*a little worried*)

Are you coming back later
this evening

The Girl

Maybe
Or

Laughs a little.

it's not much fun
being here
so
yeah

no
no I don't know

The Boy (*as if he doesn't want her to come back*)
You'll get to hear us play sometime

The Girl
I'd love to
But not today

The Boy
No

The Girl
Some other time
maybe

The Boy (*hesitating*)
Yeah
we're not very good

The Girl (*nervous*)
You haven't been playing long though

The Boy
No

The Girl
Maybe I

Cuts herself off. Short pause. The Girl goes towards the door.

The Boy
You're going

The Girl (*scared*)
Yeah

The Boy
Maybe

Hesitates, a bit embarrassed.

maybe we can meet afterwards
this evening
I mean

if you don't come back here
then we

Cuts himself off.

The Girl
When
The Boy
Around nine
maybe
after the rehearsal

Quite short pause.

we're not going to rehearse for very long
The Girl
Of course I'll meet you
The Boy
By the café
where we met last time
The Girl
Yeah I'd like to
I'll go over to the café
I
then
I'll wait there

The door creaks and opens and the Drummer stands there, holding it open. The Drummer looks at the Girl.

The Drummer (*surprised*)
You're here
The Girl
Yeah
The Drummer
What're you doing
The Girl (*embarrassed*)
I'm

Hesitates.

Nothing
The Drummer
Nothing
The Girl
No

Short pause. The Drummer leaves the door open behind him and goes towards the Girl.

The Drummer
Did you come to listen to us
maybe
or join the band
maybe
or be a chorus girl
maybe
We could do with a chorus girl

Looks towards the Boy.

couldn't we

The Girl doesn't answer, shrugs her shoulders.

Stockings and that kind of thing
That'd be good
wouldn't it
The Boy
I was only showing her where we practise
The Girl
Yeah

Short pause.

The Drummer (*to the Girl*)
That's why you're here
The Girl
Yeah

The Drummer goes towards the Girl, puts his arm around her shoulders, pulls her to him, kisses her on the cheek as she tries to get free.

The Girl
Stop it

The Drummer lets her go.

The Drummer
Stop it

Short pause.

what's the matter
what's wrong with you
The Girl
wrong with me
The Drummer
Yeah
why're you being like this

The Drummer tries to take her hand, she doesn't let him.

No

Long pause. The Drummer puts his arm round her shoulders again, pulls her towards him, and she unwillingly lets him do it.

The Girl
No stop it

The Drummer releases her.

I'm going to go
I'm going

The Drummer goes and sits behind the drums, sits and fiddles with the drumsticks.

The Drummer (*to the Girl*)
We could do with someone on backing vocals
so if you want to join in
then you

Cuts himself off. To the Boy.

That'd be good
wouldn't it

The Boy nods. The Drummer tries to play a bit. The Girl looks towards the Boy, waves slightly to him, walks towards the door. The Drummer stops playing. To the Girl.

Wait
I mean it
maybe you could sing
d'you not want to

The Girl
No

The Drummer
Are you going

The Girl
Yeah

The Girl remains standing holding the open door.

The Drummer
You're not even going to try and sing

The Girl
I can't sing

The Drummer
Doesn't matter
None of us can do anything

The Girl
I don't want to

The Drummer (*looks towards the Boy*)
Are we just going to let her go
like that

The Boy
What else do you want to do
The Drummer (*gets up, stands there, looks at the Girl*)
You can stay for a bit
listen to us play
since you're here
The Girl
No I have to go

The Boy looks at the Drummer, then takes off his guitar, stands with the guitar in his hand, looks at the Drummer.

The Drummer
Are you going too
The Boy
Yeah this's just a waste of time
The Drummer
No for fuck's sake
The Girl
I'm going now

The Girl goes out the door, shuts it behind her.

The Boy
This's going nowhere
It's a waste of time
None of us can play

The Drummer sits down again, begins to hit the drums and cymbals, getting more and more into it.

Cut it out

The Drummer continues and the Boy keeps looking at him.

Stop it
Will you stop it for fuck's sake

The Boy leans the guitar against the loudspeaker column.

I'm going
I can't stand this

The Drummer plays as the Boy walks towards the door, then the Drummer suddenly stops and looks towards the Boy, who stops.

The Drummer (*to the Boy*)
Where're you going
The Boy
I can't stand listening to that
The Drummer
Then give me the key
for fuck's sake

The Boy feels in his pockets, takes out a key from a pocket and throws it to the Drummer, who catches it.

You can't stand it
The Boy
No
The Drummer
So I don't get to play
The Boy
Yeah go ahead
play
The Drummer
It's just you who gets to play
The Boy
Play as much as you want
but I'm not listening to it
The Drummer
Do what you want
The Boy
I'm going

The Drummer
No
C'mon
You're making an idiot of yourself
You're being childish
C'mon
The Boy
Are we going to play together
or just you
The Drummer
We're going to play
The Boy
You're done then
The Drummer
Yeah yeah

The Drummer puts the drumsticks down, walks out onto the floor.

Of course we'll play
But the others aren't here yet
I wanted to practise a bit on my own
The Boy
Yeah of course

Pause.

The Drummer
What time are they coming
The Boy
They're coming soon I guess
I don't know
The Drummer
You don't know
The Boy
They're coming yeah
The Drummer
They'd better be coming

The Boy
I'm pretty sure they're coming

The Drummer goes and sits behind the drums again, picks up the drumsticks, looks at the Boy, who picks up his guitar, strums a chord, and the Drummer plays the best he can while the Boy strums another chord, fingerpicks a little and the Drummer plays on. They do this for a while. The Boy stops playing, stays standing, looking at the Drummer, who still carries on. The Drummer also stops suddenly.

The Drummer
What is it
The Boy
It's not right
The Drummer
What d'you mean
The Boy
It sounds terrible
bloody awful
The Drummer
And it's my fault
The Boy
Yeah partly yours

Short pause.

I think I'm going to go
The Drummer
No you're not going
The Boy
No
The Drummer
No you're not
The Boy
Why not

The Drummer
You're not going anywhere

The Drummer gets up, goes over to the door and the Boy begins to play his solo. The Drummer locks the doors, stands up straight and looks towards the Boy.

Do you never get bored of that song
is that the only song you know

The Boy (*continues playing*)
Yeah yeah

The Boy plays a bit more, then stops. Pause. The Drummer goes and sits behind the drums, hits the drums and cymbals and the Boy takes off the guitar, stands it up against the loudspeaker column, goes towards the door.

The Drummer (*calls to him*)
You can't go
You're not fucking going anywhere

The Drummer stops playing.

Or
just go
you
go whenever the hell you want
just go

The Boy
Yeah I'm going

The Drummer
Even though we're supposed to be practising

The Boy
It's a waste of time
You're just bashing away

The Drummer
And you play

Mimicking him.

so nicely
so softly

The Boy
I don't make the noise you make anyway

The Drummer
Just go
you
get out
what're you waiting for

The Boy
The others aren't even coming

The Drummer
How d'you know that

The Boy
I don't
But d'you see them here
then
There's no one here

The Drummer (*threatening*)
Fucking well go

The Boy (*a bit scared*)
I'll go when I want

The Drummer
No
you fucking won't

The Boy
So you decide if I'm going or not

The Drummer
Too fucking right

The Boy
I see

The Drummer
If you're not going to practise
then

The Boy
I want to
but it's all just a mess
The Drummer
So pick up your guitar
and we'll play
pick it up
then
for fuck's sake
The Boy
No
I don't give a fuck about this
The Drummer
Yeah you're going
Go on then for fuck's sake
Get out of here you fucking wimp

The Drummer begins to play again and the Boy goes over to the door, stands up straight and looks towards the Drummer, who stops suddenly.

You not going after all
I thought you were going to go
make your mind up
either you go or you don't
D'you understand
either you go
or you stay
The Boy
Unlock the door
The Drummer
No fucking way
The Boy
Do it
The Drummer
No

The Boy
Cut it out
This is stupid
the door's locked
And you locked it
The Drummer (*pretending to be scared*)
Then we're both locked in

Quite short pause.

in this cold rotten cellar
the door must have swung shut
the lock got stuck
when she went out

Cuts himself off, quite short pause.

fucking hell
hah
The Boy
You're scared now
The Drummer
Aren't you
The Boy
Give me the key
The Drummer
No
The Boy
Don't be stupid
The Drummer
I'm not being stupid
The Boy
Then stop messing about
The Drummer
What the fuck goes on in your head

The Drummer gets up and goes slightly threateningly towards the Boy.

Who do you think you are
you say you won't play
but who was it
who got me to buy
this fucking drum kit
was it you
maybe
course it fucking was

The Boy (*a little protectively*)
You wanted it yourself

The Drummer
It was you who made me buy it
Everything was going to be so great
We'd start a band
get gigs
And all the girls

Short pause.

and the only girl who turns up
yeah

Cuts himself off.

The Boy
I never said any of that

The Drummer
That's exactly what you said

The Boy
No

The Drummer
Fucking hell
You're lying
you lie all the time
You're always lying
and then you play

Mimics.

that solo of yours
so soft and nice
the only song you can play
you played it for her too
didn't you

Quite short pause.

play it softly and nicely
for me too
go on

The Boy
I can't be arsed with any more of this

The Drummer
No
So I'm stuck here
with this fucking drum kit
Maybe I should just keep it at home
in the flat
at my mum and dad's

The Boy
Keep it where you like

The Drummer
Fucking hell

The Boy goes and picks up the guitar, sits down on the chair, sits and holds it.

That guitar of yours
you can't even play it
only that one stupid song
you think you can play
you sit there holding it
like it's a woman
you're holding

The Boy
Give it a rest

Someone tries the door from outside, pulling it, then knocks hard on it.

Go and open the door then
for fuck's sake

The Drummer
Will I tell you something
I don't like women
I

The Boy
You don't like women

The Drummer
No

The Boy
All right
You do what you want

The Drummer
I do that too
yeah what else would I do

Long pause. Another knock on the door.

The Boy
Will you unlock the fucking door

The Drummer
OK then you wimp

The Drummer goes to the door, tries it, it's locked, takes out the key, unlocks it, the door opens and the Bass Player comes in, followed by the Singer. The Drummer shuts the door. Pause. The Boy remains sitting.

The Singer
We're a bit late
we were at the café
and forgot the time
and then she came in

Looks towards the Drummer.

the one you're going out with

Slightly hesitantly.

your girlfriend
and

Cuts himself off.

The Drummer
I'm glad you've come
The Bass Player
What was the door
doing locked

Quite short pause.

Why was the door locked
The Drummer
I locked it
The Bass Player
Why
The Drummer
So

Looks at the Boy.

he wouldn't run off
The Singer (*to the Boy*)
D'you not want to rehearse
The Boy
Yeah
The Singer
Why did you want to go
then
The Drummer
Because of the noise I make or
something like

Short pause.

or maybe he wanted to go
to meet some woman
or something

Short pause.

The Bass Player
We're all here now
All of us
We can rehearse now
The Singer (*to the Boy*)
Yeah c'mon
don't be pissed off
The Boy
No I've had enough of this
I'm going
The Drummer
You're not fucking going
The Singer
He can go if he wants to
The Bass Player (*to the Drummer*)
You can't force him to play
The Drummer
Can't I
The Singer
All right stop it
The Bass Player (*to the Boy*)
Let's play for a bit
It went well last time
We got a lot done
It was the best rehearsal we've had
You can't give up now
The Singer
We need to have a guitarist
The Bass Player (*to the Boy*)
You can't give up

The Drummer
He's not fucking going to quit
if he quits I'll fucking well

Cuts himself off.

The Bass Player (*to the Drummer*)
Calm down
The Singer (*goes over and slaps the Boy on the shoulder*)
C'mon
then
let's play
Don't be like this

The Boy just sits there.

C'mon
The Boy
The drummer locked the door
The Bass Player
What was the point of that
The Drummer
That bastard there
got me to buy a drum kit
and when I try to learn how to play
then
yeah fucking hell
The Bass Player (*to the Boy*)
He needs to practise
The Boy
But he can't play
he just batters it
bashes away
The Drummer
I have to practise
The Boy
Yeah yeah

The Singer (*to the Boy*)
C'mon
don't just sit there
can't you play your guitar and

Cuts himself off.

The Drummer
I'm fucking going to

Cuts himself off. The Drummer crosses and grabs the guitar neck, tries to take the guitar from the Boy, who holds tightly on to it.

The Singer (*to the Drummer*)
Cut it out

The Bass Player (*to the Boy*)
Why don't you join in
then
We can play for a while

The Drummer twists the guitar out of the Boy's hands.

The Boy
Give me the guitar

The Drummer
Yeah there you go

The Drummer hands the guitar to the Boy, who remains sitting with it in his lap. The Drummer goes and sits behind the drum kit and the Bass Player picks up his guitar, then plays a little bass line, then the Drummer tries to play as well as he can with the bass line and it goes well. The Boy sits as before. They stop playing suddenly.

The Singer (*to the Boy*)
C'mon
don't be stupid
don't just sit there
play with us

The Bass Player (*crosses to a microphone, speaks into it*)
On guitar the legendary Georg

The Drummer looks at the Boy, who remains sitting.

C'mon then

The Boy shakes his head. The Drummer gets up and goes over to him, takes hold of the Boy's hair, holds it up.

Get some scissors
and we'll cut this off

The Singer
No stop it

The Drummer
Do it

The Bass Player
There's no scissors here

The Boy
Let go

The Drummer pulls his hair harder and the boy stands up.

Ow
Let go for fuck's sake

The Drummer
C'mon
We'll give him a skinhead
His hair's too long

The Bass Player
Stop it

The Singer
Let go of his hair

The Drummer
Not before I've skinheaded him

The Bass Player
Stop messing about

The Drummer
I'm not messing about
get me a knife
or some pliers
doesn't matter what

Long pause. The Drummer lets the hair go and the Boy remains standing.

The Singer (*to the Boy*)
You don't want to play any more

The Boy shakes his head, touches his hair, straightens it out. To the Bass Player:

What'll we do then

The Bass Player shrugs his shoulders.

We'll have to get hold of another guitarist

The Drummer
No fucking way
He's going to play

To the Boy:

Why the fuck are you still hanging around here

The Singer (*to the Boy*)
You don't want to play

The Boy
I don't want to play with him

The Drummer
I don't care what you do

The Bass Player (*to the Boy*)
You have to
You can't give up

The Singer
C'mon

The Bass Player
We're starting to get it together
a little bit

we're getting quite good
we'll be able to perform soon

The Drummer (*to the Bass Player*)
Or maybe
maybe we should just throw him out
not give a shit about him
Find another guitarist
He just wants to go and see

Cuts himself off.

The Bass Player
Who

The Drummer
That girl he's messing about with

The Bass Player
Yeah

To the Boy.

Have you got yourself a girlfriend

The Boy
No

The Drummer
Are you sure

The Singer (*to the Boy*)
Why not just play anyway

The Boy
I said no

The Singer (*hesitating*)
Well if you don't want to

Cuts himself off.

The Bass Player
We can't force you

Short pause.

The Singer (*to the Drummer*)
D'you know any guitarists

The Drummer
The place is crawling with guitarists
And it's crawling with girls
Girls and guitarists
The Singer (*cuts him off*)
All right
The Bass Player
There's
yeah there's Fredrik
I think Fredrik plays guitar
The Singer
He does
He was at the café
wasn't he
She

To the Drummer.

yeah your girlfriend
she was with him
sitting at his table
The Drummer (*questioning*)
Can Fredrik play guitar
The Singer (*to the Boy*)
You sure you don't want to play with us any more

The Boy shakes his head.

The Bass Player
We'll ask Fredrik
I'll go over to the café
see if he's there
The Singer
I'll go with you
The Drummer
D'you think they're still there
The Bass Player
I'll see if he's there

The Boy
Yeah then I'll go
then
The Drummer (*to the Boy*)
Finally now you're going

Suddenly.

No you're not fucking going anywhere
The Boy
No
The Singer (*to the Bass Player*)
Will we go and see if Fredrik's there
The Bass Player
But has he got any equipment
The Singer
I don't know
The Bass Player
We can ask him
The Singer
We'll ask him
The Drummer
Yeah you go
go and ask him
The Singer (*to the Boy*)
You're sure you don't want to
The Drummer (*jokingly*)
Absolutely sure
The Bass Player (*to the Boy*)
Say something
D'you want to or not
The Drummer
He's stopped talking now
The Bass Player
We don't even know
if Fredrik wants to

The Drummer
He wants to
The Singer
I think he's only got an acoustic guitar
And he doesn't have an amplifier
The Drummer (*to the Boy*)
Then he'll have to use your guitar
The Singer
Can he
The Bass Player
It'll be OK

The Boy doesn't answer.

The Drummer (*to the Singer and Bass Player*)
Go over there
The Singer (*to the Bass Player*)
Will we go
The Bass Player (*to the Drummer*)
Yeah we're going
then
The Drummer (*to the Boy*)
Sit down for fuck's sake

The Boy remains standing. The Singer and Bass Player go towards the door. The Boy makes to go too but the Drummer stands up in front of him. The Singer and the Bass Player look at the Drummer and the Boy.

Sit down
I said

The Boy tries to go but the Drummer moves, blocks his way and then grabs his hair.

Sit yourself down
I said

Short pause.

Yeah

The Drummer drags the Boy by the hair, sets him down in the chair.

And now you can sit there
hah
sit there you bastard

Short pause. The Drummer pulls the Boy's hair to one side, looks at the Bass Player and Singer.

We'll give him a skinhead
C'mon

The Singer and the Bass Player go and stand around the Drummer.

C'mon
find something
a knife
or something

The Singer
Stop it
The Bass Player
Leave him alone
The Drummer
What the fuck
The Singer
Let go of his hair

The Drummer lets go of the Boy's hair.

The Drummer
You sit there until your grandmother

Hesitates.

yeah
the old one
till she
the one you live with

Hesitates.

lived with

Hesitates.

yeah

Cuts himself off.

or that mum of yours
until she

Cuts himself off.

wherever she is
or your dad
wherever the hell he is

The Singer *(to the Bass Player)*
Let's go

To the Drummer.

Come on
Leave him alone

The Singer and the Bass Player go towards the door and the Singer remains standing holding the door open while the Bass Player goes out. To the Drummer.

C'mon
then

The Drummer *(to the Boy)*
You can sit there
and play songs to your grandmother
as long as you like
you can play songs to her
or to that mother of yours
or that grandmother of yours
or whoever the fuck you play to

The Singer (*to the Drummer*)
C'mon
Let's go

The Singer goes out and shuts the door after him.

The Drummer
I'm coming

The Drummer goes quickly towards the door, turns off the light, goes out and closes the door, the sound of the lock turning. The door's locked and the Drummer pulls at the door to check it's locked. Pause. The Boy begins to play his solo, it turns slowly into a slow, torn improvisation, he stops playing, remains sitting, leaning forward over his guitar. Pause. The door's pulled at, then the sound of the lock turning, the door opens and the Girl comes in, leaves the door open behind her, turns on the light.

The Girl
You're sitting here in the dark

The Boy
Yeah

The Girl
But you

The Boy (*cuts in, gets up*)
Why are you here
what d'you want

The Girl
We were supposed to meet

Cuts herself off.

The Boy (*puts down the guitar, leans it on the loudspeaker column*)
Why are you here

The Girl
They asked me

Cuts herself off. The Girl goes towards him.

The Boy
What've you come here for

Short pause.

You shouldn't have come

Pause.

The Girl
We made an agreement

Cuts herself off.

Come on let's go

The Boy
Who said I was here

The Girl
They did

The Boy
Who

The Girl
The others
at the café

Pause.

The Boy
Why are you here

Quite short pause.

They said that
that I was locked in

The Girl
Yeah

Short pause.

The Boy
Who gave you the key

The Girl
They did
The Boy (*questioning*)
They did
The Girl
Yeah

Pause.

The Boy
You talked to them
The Girl
Yeah

Pause.

The Boy
With the drummer
The Girl
Yeah
The Boy
In the café
The Girl
Yeah
The Boy
And he gave you the key
The Girl
Yeah

Pause.

C'mon let's go
The Boy (*asks*)
Will we go

Short pause.

The Girl
C'mon then
The Boy
Yeah

Short pause.

In the café

The Girl

C'mon
before they come back
they're going to rehearse
they're coming here
Fredrik's on guitar
instead of you
c'mon
let's go

The Boy

Yeah

The Boy remains standing.

And you

Short pause.

are you going out with everyone

The Girl

Let's go now

The Boy

Are you

The Girl

No

Pause. The Boy crosses to the Girl, grabs hold of her hair, bends her backwards, by the hair.

No don't

The Boy

You're going out with everyone

The Girl

Don't
no
don't

The Boy
Going out with everyone

The Boy pulls her hair even harder.

The Girl
Don't do that
It hurts
No
no don't
Let me go

Pause. The Boy remains standing holding her hair.

Don't
No
Don't

Short pause.

You're scaring me
Let me go
Don't

Pause.

No don't do that
The Boy
Are you a slut
The Girl
No don't
The Boy
They say

Cuts himself off. The Boy pulls her hair.

The Girl
No don't
don't don't
The Boy
D'you go with everyone

The Girl
No don't
The Boy
Are you a slut
The Girl
No
The Boy
You're a slut
just like my mother

The Boy lets go of her hair. Pause.

The Girl
Why're you like this

Short pause.

Why're you being like this
The Boy
No

Short pause.

The Girl
Don't be like this
The Boy
No

Short pause.

The Girl (*looks towards him*)
Come here

The Boy goes over to the Girl and she strokes his hair and then he strokes her hair.

Let's go
The Boy
Yeah

Pause.

The Girl (*takes the Boy by the hand*)
it's going to be all right
wait and see
The Boy
Never
It'll never be all right
The Girl
It'll be all right
The Boy
Never
it'll never be all right

Short pause. The Boy lets go of her hand. Short pause.

The Girl
Did you love
your grandmother
The Boy
Yeah
I guess so
I did love her
The Girl
And me
d'you love me
The Boy (*hesitating*)
No
The Girl
A little
just a little
The Boy
No

Short pause.

The Girl
A little
The Boy
Maybe a little
No I don't think so

Cuts himself off.

The Girl

Even if you call me a slut
you love me
you love me a little
even if you call me a slut

The Boy

I don't know

Quite short pause.

I don't think I love you

Short pause.

The Girl

C'mon
c'mon let's go
yeah
yeah before the others come

Short pause.

But

Short pause.

yeah bring your guitar

The Boy picks up his guitar and goes out with it in his hand and the Girl turns off the light and the door closes softly behind them.

Seeing the World in a Different Way

Jon Fosse interviewed by Jim Mulligan

Jon Fosse started writing poems and stories when he was twelve years old and has gone on to be one of Norway's leading writers. He has received several literary awards, his novels and plays have been translated into thirty languages and his plays have been produced in almost every European country and outside of Europe.

> I don't quite understand what is going on in my plays and in my writing. I'm not an actor and I haven't worked in the theatre. It was a great surprise to me that I managed to write my first play and an even bigger surprise that it worked on the stage. My first novel was published in 1983 when I was twenty-three years old. I called it *Red Black* in homage to Stendhal's *Le Rouge et le noir*. It's hard to explain why I called this play *Purple*. All I can say is the Norwegian word covers purple, lilac and mauve but David Harrower, the translator, chose purple.

Purple could hardly be simpler. The action takes place in a cellar deep below a disused factory. At the start the Boy and the Girl enter the cellar and talk. The Drummer enters and after a while the Girl leaves. The Boy and the Drummer quarrel. The Singer and the Bass Player enter, stay for a while, then leave. The Drummer locks the Boy in the cellar. The Girl then returns and lets him out.

> My writing is a kind of extreme realism. If I am writing well with the pace well done it is realistic in a way that changes the realism into something else. Something behind the realism appears. In my plays

> I rarely use names and I don't describe appearances. The person only becomes a character when he steps onto the stage. They are more like fields of emotion and energies which are connected to one another.

This detachment makes huge demands on directors and young actors. The sparse dialogue contains seething emotions and nihilistic life stories. Jon Fosse has been compared to Harold Pinter, but he himself refers to Samuel Beckett as one of his influences, his favourite writer for 'the strength of his pictures and the force of his writing in a very quiet and humble way'. Indeed, Jon Fosse goes so far as to call Becket 'a literary father, someone to look up to and to rebel against'. In *Purple* very little happens on the surface but there is tension in the silences and between the people on stage.

> I never try to illustrate anything or use metaphor. I just write it directly. The cellar is a safe place but it is also a threat. The play is full of ambiguities. I do not quite understand what the message is. Is the Boy bringing the Girl down to the cellar or is she bringing him? How much has happened between the Boy and the Girl? Is she still in a relationship with the Drummer?

With care we can piece together some of the life stories of the Boy, the Girl and the Drummer. We know that the Girl remembers the black guitar from the time she had been in the Boy's room and she knows all about his family. We know that the Boy's family life is bleak. He doesn't know who his father is, his mother is never there, the grandmother he loved has died and his grandfather drinks. We know that the Drummer feels he has some rights over the Girl. Everything else has to be mined from Jon Fosse's frugal words.

> The Girl's in a transitional stage. She's moving on from the Drummer and she might move to the Boy.

> Later on there is mention of Fredrik the new guitarist and I think the Boy is imagining she is establishing a third relationship with Fredrik. Everything is insecure. It is moving on from here to there. It is the condition of being young that you are in between in so many respects. The Drummer goes into the cellar and sees the Boy with the Girl. He is jealous but he is not to blame for that. He gets a bit aggressive – that's understandable. One thing is clear, however, the Drummer had no intention of leaving the Boy locked in the cellar. In the end, when he gives the key to the Girl he proves that he doesn't hate. In the end the Drummer is setting the Boy free.

The tension between love and hate and violence in the final scene is almost unbearable. The Boy is torn. 'Are you everybody's girlfriend? Are you going out with everybody?' And he hurts her by pulling her hair hard. 'You're a slut just like my mother.' Then the Girl strokes his hair and he strokes her hair, tenderness before a reluctant, almost guilty admission of love. 'Even if you call me a slut you love me. You love me a bit even if you call me a slut.' And then the Boy goes as far as he is able, damaged as he is. 'I don't know. I don't think I love you.'

> There is violence and aggression in relationships from both sides. Men and women are connected for better or worse. In one way we understand one another. In another way we never do. When I sit in my cottage and write, that is all I can do, write. If people find something in it that can be useful to them, then it's great, but if not that's OK. In a way I am Quaker. There is something in me and in every human being that is a unique inner light. I try to point to it and if art becomes strong enough it pulls together a strong kind of identity. I believe in theatre and books. If you

can paint a picture in your own way it might be possible for people to see the world in a different way. The world does not look quite the same afterwards. Writing somehow changes the way we look at life.

Production Notes

STAGING AND SETTING

Purple is set in a cold, dank, underground room underneath an old factory. It begins when the Boy opens an unusually broad iron door for the Girl to enter the space. He shuts it and switches on the lights. The door might be real or imagined, but you might want to suggest its heaviness and creaking with sound effects. Doors come into Jon Fosse's work a lot, open or closed, whether someone is about to enter or not. The room is reminiscent of an air-raid shelter. It has darkened concrete walls, unpainted, and no windows. There are some microphone stands, columns of loudspeakers and amplifiers, a black guitar (or any other colour if you don't have one) and a bass guitar, each leaning on the loudspeakers, a drum kit and spindleback chair. There are cables, empty bottles and debris on the floor. Whenever a play calls for 'debris', keep it to the minimum and make sure it's fire-proofed. As far as set is concerned, less is definitely more – a black square would suffice. The use of space and light is of equal importance. The use of space is of prime importance in the staging of Jon's work, in particular the relationships between the actor and the space, the actor and fellow actors and the actor and the audience. In this respect, space is far more important than scenography.

When the Drummer appears – the boyfriend of the Girl – there's immediate tension in the air. Who is she with now? After she leaves, the rest of the band appear (the Singer and the Bass Player) and we discover that the Boy wants to leave the band, despite the fact that it was his initial enthusiasm that got them all started: it was he who persuaded them to buy the equipment. The Drummer is furious with the Boy for abandoning the band and, his anger turning to violence, he refuses to let him leave the room. Grabbing the Boy's hair, he says he wants to cut it off. Finally the whole band leave the Boy in the room, locking the door as they go. The Girl appears at the end and the Boy, frustrated and humiliated, copies the Drummer's action and grabs the Girl by the hair. They reach a form of understanding and the Boy and the Girl leave the room together.

Jon writes in New Norwegian. He tells us: 'It's a synthetic language, a collection of different dialects, New Norwegian has three genders. It's a theatrical language because of its inherent artificiality but there's something earthy about it. New Norwegian belongs to reality but it is also at one and the same time theatre.' David Harrower, a significant playwright in his own right, worked from a literal translation and adapted the play published here. He says: 'A literal translation, by its nature, flattens out the language, robbing the play of its poetry. The play is left quite stilted and brittle. You then have to find a way of translating it into English.'

The two writers talked to each other a lot throughout the process. David wanted to understand the colloquialisms within the language. David is Scottish and has put the play into 'Scots English', incorporating the particular rhythms of this language. You may wish to make some fine adjustments to the colloquialisms within the text to suit your cast's regional dialect, but be careful not to seriously affect or alter the overall rhythm of the lines. Jon is a poet as well as playwright and chooses every word with great care; the poetic quality of the language is in the colour and sound of each of these distinct choices. The play has the rhythm of normal conversation but with a certain strangeness to it. You might find the actors are tempted to add additional words or punctuation but this should be avoided because it will cloud the piece. Urge the actors to speak the lines as cleanly as possible whilst avoiding artificiality or stylisation. Adding words, however inconsequential, will alter the overall meaning and rhythm of the dialogue. Form and structure must somehow be present when it's acted out. Play it seriously and the humour will come through.

CHARACTERS AND CASTING

Characters in Jon's plays are often not all they appear to be. None of them is inherently bad or overly speculative. They don't have great aims or goals in life, they simply want to have a dream. It makes them very modern characters. Usually he prefers not to give his characters names. He doesn't want to describe a specific human being in a 'real' way. He only uses names when it can't be avoided, for practical purposes.

The Boy is a real challenge. If he's played as a victim it will soon become boring. He must find his force and be an equal to the Drummer. The Boy exposes himself willingly to the treatment he receives at the hands of both the Drummer and the Girl. He has the opportunity to escape many times but he doesn't do so. He's the driving force within the band, he persuaded the Drummer to buy his drum kit. By the end of the play the Boy has taken on and adapted many of the Drummer's characteristics – he pulls the Girl's hair, etc. – and we see the Boy slowly discovering the Drummer in his own character, and vice versa.

There is a latent eroticism in the relationship between the Boy and the Drummer. When the Boy accuses the Girl of being a whore, it is meant both as a means of distancing himself from her and as a warped declaration of love. The actor playing the Boy doesn't have to be very proficient on the guitar. If there is a 'victim' in the play it's the Drummer. The focus of the play is the triangular relationship between the Boy, the Girl and the Drummer.

Purple has a cast of five: four male, one female. They're roughly the same age.

EXERCISES

Every line in the play embodies new action, new feeling and new potential. Every second comes the feeling that something completely different might happen. The characters don't have great plans. Take your time to work through the script to find out moment by moment how the characters feel about one another. Pay attention to those things that are left unsaid. This is of equal importance to what is actually being spoken by the characters. Look out for the recurring stage direction: '*Cuts him/herself off.*'

Hold some of the rehearsals in a small, enclosed space to get a sense of the claustrophobic setting.

Work out the plot of the play in depth. Ask questions such as: 'Does the Drummer really lock the door?' (he does); 'Why does he later give the key to the Girl?' In giving the key the Drummer is effectively giving the Boy to the Girl.

Break the play into scenes. Look at them in detail. For instance, there is big potential in the Boy and Girl's first entrance – what are these two going to do down in that room? This beginning is less about what they say to each other and much more about the central relationship. The drama of Jon's writing is what happens beneath the surface, and that's what you've got to find.

Look at this exchange on page 461:

The Girl

. . .
The black guitar
that's your guitar

The Boy

Yeah
you remember it

The Girl

Yeah
yeah of course

A bit embarrassed.

that time
in your room

Have the actors work out what went on between the two of them previously. Decide what motives the Boy had for inviting the Girl to this isolated spot. Decide too if the Girl is happy down there.

Look at the section when the Drummer makes his entrance. You could call this scene two. Decide if the Boy has invited the Girl to the rehearsal space in order to confront the Drummer.

Look at the passage of time between the Boy being left by the Drummer and the Girl coming for him. This is indicated by a lengthy stage direction on page 499. This could be achieved by having the Boy sit alone in the dark, playing his guitar. It could represent a break or shift in time. When the Girl returns the Boy could wait before acknowledging her, to indicate that the play has passed into another 'landscape'.

Suzy Graham-Adriani
March 2003
based on a workshop facilitated by Kai Johnsen

THE QUEEN MUST DIE

David Farr

David Farr is a writer and director who has focused on international work. He was the Artistic Director of London's Gate Theatre from 1995 to 1998 and won the Writers' Guild Best New Play Award for *Elton John's Glasses* in 1997. His other written plays include *The Danny Crowe Show*, *Night of the Soul* and *Crime and Punishment in Dalston*. He is presently Artistic Director of the Bristol Old Vic Theatre.

Characters

THE GIRLS

Shannon, fifteen

Lisa, fifteen

Sandra (also known as 'Ronnie'), fifteen

THE BOYS

Darren Simpson, sixteen

Billy Simpson, twelve

Mad Mike, fifteen to eighteen (age can vary)

Shaun Digby, fifteen

The Queen
(a silent role for large papier-mâché statue)

Place

A town in the middle of England
Alleyways in the town
The living room of Margaret Chivers

Time

The night of 1 June 2002,
the eve of the Queen's Golden Jubilee

SCENE ONE

A bit of wall somewhere in the rich part of town. Three girls stand in front of wall. They are Lisa and Sandra and Shannon. Lisa is small, mousy. Sandra is a little overweight possibly. Shannon is the most glamorous of the three. All three are standing in simply horrendous home-made union-jack dresses.

Shannon We can't wear these.

Sandra I look like a flag.

Shannon I don't care if she's fifty years on the throne, or five hundred, we can't wear these.

Lisa Just think of it. Us dancing . . .

Sandra With a massive papier-mâché statue of the Queen . . .

Lisa On a motorised float . . .

Sandra Through the middle of town . . .

Lisa In front of the whole population.

Shannon I'll die.

Sandra You'll die! You're gorgeous and you still look like a dog. What must I look like?

Shannon Look at my tits, Lise.

Lisa What about them?

Shannon Is my point! I've got the best breasts in year ten. (*searching the folds of the dress*) Where are they?

Lisa I've got tassels. Why did your mum give me tassels?

Shannon She said you were the tassels type.

Lisa I hate your mum.

Sandra Maybe we can blend into the background.

Lisa Ronnie, there is no background. It's us three, a papier-mâché Queen, and half a ton of bunting.

Sandra This is all your fault, Shannon Dobson.
Shannon Is not!
Sandra It was your idea to do a dance.
Shannon Was not!
Lisa Was.
Shannon Was not!
Sandra And then you roped us in because we weren't as good-looking as you.
Lisa Yeah, that's right, Shannon. If it wasn't for your vanity . . .
Shannon I was told we would be dancing in glamorous gear to popular tunes of the five decades. I was told I could choose my costume.
Sandra I don't think your mum reckoned on a halter-neck bikini.
Shannon That bikini was gorgeous.
Lisa You just wanted to show your arse off to Adam McEwan.
Shannon Christ, he's going to be there. This is worse than suicide.
Sandra He's going to get a right hard-on with you wearing that.
Shannon That does it. I'm not wearing this. We are not wearing this!
Sandra So what do we do?

Pause.

Lisa Burn them!
Shannon Won't work.
Lisa Why not?
Shannon If we burn them, my mum will know it was us, and we'll be grounded for three weeks.
Lisa It's worth it, isn't it?
Shannon Three weeks, Lisa.
Lisa So?
Shannon When is Britney at the NEC?

Lisa Two weeks tonight. (*Beat.*) Oh.

Shannon Thank you very much.

Lisa We're screwed.

Sandra Hold on a minute. You only got two tickets for Britney and you've promised Lisa the other one. So what's stopping me burning mine?

Shannon One, because you're first reserve for the concert. And two, because if you burn your dress and make us do the jubilee parade alone, we'll tell your mum about Mitchell Figgis and the bottle of cider.

Sandra You wouldn't do that. (*Shannon would.*) You bitch.

Lisa So what do we do? Because I am not wearing this abomination in front of the whole town!

Shannon That's why I called the meeting. I've got a plan of action.

Lisa Go on.

Shannon First we go back to my mum and tell her how much we love the dresses.

Sandra That will be the biggest lie ever told by man or woman.

Shannon Second, free from all suspicion, we eliminate the Queen.

Pause.

Sandra Don't you think that's a bit extreme?

Shannon Not the Queen in Buckingham Palace. The Queen that is currently sitting in Mrs Chivers' living room in Penthall Gardens.

Lisa You mean . . .?

Shannon I mean if we can get in there without being noticed and destroy the statue, then there will be no Queen, no float, no procession, and no ritual humiliation.

Sandra Wow.

Lisa But it's by an artist. He won a prize or something.

Shannon Who says?

Lisa It was in the paper. He's bringing art into the community. He's funded.

Shannon So what?

Lisa And he's staying with the Chivers because they're great supporters of the liberal arts.

Shannon So what?

Lisa He made the Queen in their garage. It's taken him four months.

Shannon I don't care if it took him twenty years, I'm not wearing this dress.

Lisa And anyway the Chivers will be there . . .

Shannon They're not there. Mr and Mrs Chivers are at a pre-Jubilee hoe-down in a barn four miles outside town. They've taken the artist with them.

Lisa The house is empty?

Shannon Not quite.

Sandra They've got a kid.

Shannon Which is being baby-sat.

Lisa By who?

Sandra By who?

Shannon By Shaun Digby.

Lisa Shaun 'the lips' Digby?

Shannon 'The lips' is all that stands between us and fashion safety.

Sandra How do we do it?

Shannon Lisa goes in, makes out like she fancies him and gets him upstairs. Then we sneak in and deface Her Majesty. When we're done, Lisa makes out like she had nothing to do with it, and he can't even say she was there, 'cos it would look like he was having girls in the house on the sly.

Pause.

Sandra That is brilliant.

Lisa Excuse me. Why am I the one kissing Shaun Digby?

Shannon Everyone knows he fancies you.
Lisa He only fancies me because he knows he hasn't got a chance of getting you. He's just being realistic.
Sandra Don't be down about it, he's all right is Shaun.
Lisa He's a minger! I'm not doing it.
Sandra I will.
Shannon He doesn't fancy you.
Sandra Oh.
Lisa I'm not doing it.
Sandra Go on, Lise.
Lisa No way.
Shannon Sandra, do you like Britney Spears?
Lisa That is blackmail.
Shannon She's playing the NEC, did you know that? I've got two tickets.
Lisa I'm not doing it, so don't even try it.
Shannon I think I've got the ticket here.
Lisa I'm growing out of Britney anyway.
Shannon Yeah, here we are.
Lisa Don't try it, girl!

Shannon slowly moves the ticket towards Sandra.

Lisa All right I'll do it! You're a bitch though. And I'm not kissing him.
Shannon You don't have to. Just use your charms.
Lisa He oils them lips, I swear he does.

Pause.

Sandra So, while she's upstairs necking Digby . . . what exactly are we doing to the Queen?

SCENE TWO

A wall in the poor side of town. Three boys. Darren and Billy Simpson and Mad Mike Atkinson. Darren is lean, dissatisfied with life and very intense. Billy, his younger brother, is in awe, and rather grubby. Mad Mike is Mad Mike.

Darren He said what?
Mad Mike He said he was busy.
Darren Busy doing what?
Mad Mike He didn't say, did he?
Darren Three months we've been thinking about this. Three months of precise planning. And now Les is busy. What would have happened to the French Revolution if the night before Danton had told Robespierre, 'Sorry, I'm busy.'
Mad Mike I don't know. What would have happened?
Darren There would have been no French Revolution, that's what. France would be like England, ruled by a sovereign no one has voted for, responsible to no one, accountable to no one, supported by centuries of privilege and living in five massive palaces for no reason that anyone can possibly understand. You know what? Les did this on the anti-globalisation march as well. Remember what he said when he found out it was Macdonald's we were protesting against?
Billy 'But I like the apple pies at Macdonald's.'
Darren 'I like the apple pies.' That's not the point, is it? Try and get our useless generation to understand that politics requires commitment. It requires a level of sacrifice. We're talking about global slavery, extortion of the weak, we're talking basic human rights. So what if you can't get a frigging apple pie! Buy a Cox, and boil it! Try to understand we're not little consumers in our little consumer worlds, we can't just pick and choose beliefs like we're in a sweet shop. Well, we'll show him. We'll do it on our own. Us three and Mary. That's all we need.

Billy Daz, about Mary.
Darren Now Mary understands passion.
Billy Daz.
Darren Mary is a flame, a beacon.
Billy About Mary.
Darren Where is she? I thought we agreed four-thirty.

Pause.

What?
Billy Mary's not coming.
Darren What do you mean, she's not coming?
Billy She left a message.
Darren Why didn't you say?
Billy I was gonna tell you but then you got all upset about Les.
Darren Why isn't she coming?
Billy She said . . . she said it was because of last night.
Darren What about last night?
Billy You and her went out.
Darren What if we did?
Mad Mike Oh Christ, what happened?
Darren Nothing! We had a discussion about expressions of individual freedom in a post-romantic age, that's all.
Mad Mike Oh no.
Billy She said you got a bit intense, Daz.

Pause.

I think you scared her a bit. Calling her Rosa Luxembourg and all that.

Pause.

Darren She's not coming?
Billy She said maybe you should just leave things to cool for a while. She really likes you. But she's got GCSEs and everything. She hasn't got time for terrorism.

Pause.

Darren OK, OK. Well, it's just us three. Or are you going anywhere Mike? Am I too 'intense' for you? Billy, check the alley.

Billy All clear.

Darren Then I declare the meeting open. Firstly, as chair, I want to say something. The Popular Republican Front has been in existence for six months. Its stated aim: to offer protest against the imperialist and anti-democratic institution of the English monarchy, in this the Jubilee Year. Our actions have so far been largely secret, involving discussion, and debate, and resulting in a series of resolutions as agreed at the last meeting. Billy, read the resolutions:

Billy One. That the monarchy is an anti-democratic institution existing only because of generations of privilege and injustice. Two. That the nation must be encouraged to debate the validity of said institution and to be given the opportunity to vote on its continued existence. Three. That the impending jubilee celebrations are an imposition on the freedom of every individual, funded as they are and as are all royal activities directly from the pockets of every British citizen. Four. That direct action of protest is a justifiable response. Five. That the said action may justifiably involve violence against capitalist property and symbols of establishment power but no violence against humankind is justified.

Mad Mike Or animalkind neither.

Darren Or animalkind neither. And now I ask you, Billy, as secretary, to countersign this statement, which shall act as a manifesto for the group in the future.

Billy Where do I sign?

Darren Just here. OK?

Mad Mike So what are we gonna do? 'Cos my finger's getting itchy.

Pause.

Darren Tomorrow a procession will make its way through the town. This procession will celebrate a tyranny that to this day keeps the British people in its vice-like grip. That makes us subjects where we should be citizens. That owns our executive, our lawmakers, that owns our church, our post, our theatres and opera houses. Even our government rules at Her Majesty's pleasure. And we sit like dogs lapping it up. Well not any more.

Mad Mike What are we gonna do?

Darren We're going to stop tomorrow's procession.

Billy Are we going to chain ourselves to one of the floats, Daz?

Darren No, Billy. That action, though ideologically sound, is practically flawed.

Mad Mike Pigs'll cut us out.

Darren Like they did at Newbury. No, our action must be something that we can say with absolute confidence will stop the chariot of privilege in its corrupt tracks. Have either of you studied tomorrow's procession?

Mad Mike Tossers on floats, i'nt it?

Darren Six floats. The Mayor has one, with some photographs of the town through the last fifty years. The Women's Institute have a small float celebrating the role of women in the Commonwealth. Mainly photographic material again, but they have a wreath of some kind. Following that are three of the primary schools, who are showing drawings and paintings that the children have contributed. Note how time and again the young are manipulated into collaborating with the established powers. And then . . .

Billy Then what?

Darren Then there is the final float. A giant-sized statue of the Queen sculpted by an artist commissioned from taxpayers' money, will parade on a truck through the streets accompanied by young female dancers dressed in the Union Jack in a glorious and rousing tribute to Elizabeth Regina.

Pause.

Or rather it won't.

Billy What do you mean, Daz?

Darren The Queen will not be in a state to parade tomorrow morning. Because tonight, the Popular Republican Front will have conducted a ritual beheading of the sculpture, in the living room of Margaret Chivers, a middle-aged arch-royalist who lives on the posh side of town.

Pause.

Mad Mike We're gonna cut off her head?

Darren The execution will echo the beheading of Charles I by the great revolutionary Oliver Cromwell. It will be filmed and we will deliver videos through significant letter boxes over the next few weeks.

Mad Mike Significant?

Darren Local press, local council, national press, the BBC, 10 Downing Street, the House of Commons, the UN Council for Human Rights, and Nelson Mandela.

Billy Wow.

Mad Mike How we gonna do it?

Darren Leave that to me. Meet here at six tonight in dark clothing. Oh, one thing, Mike. I'm counting on you for the axe.

SCENE THREE

The living room of Margaret Chivers. Well kept, tidy. A three-piece suite dominates the room. Lots of china, etc. French windows to the garden. A door to the hall and the front door just visible. A canary in a cage chirps away occasionally.

On the sofa sits Shaun Digby. He may be slightly overweight, and he may have unusual lips, or he licks them a lot. He is watching TV and eating crisps. Next to him is the giant statue of the Queen, covered by a cloth. Shaun is watching the TV, which has football on. The phone rings.

Shaun Hello? Is that Mrs Chivers? How's the party? Everything's fine here. No I haven't heard a peep from her. (*Looks at Queen.*) I haven't heard a peep from her either. No, I'll make sure I don't spill anything on her. I know how important she is to you. Is the artist enjoying the hoe-down? That's good. About eleven? All right.

He puts the phone down. Sits down. The phone rings again.

Mrs Chivers?

Beat.

Yeah, it's me (*Beat.*) It's OK, Dad. You don't have to say that. (*Beat.*) I know you love me. I know you didn't mean it. (*Beat.*) Forget it, will you? (*Beat.*) Listen, the kid's crying, I better go. (*Beat.*) Love you too.

He puts the phone down, returns to couch. Eats some crisps. There is a knock at the French windows. Shaun goes to see who it is. Opens. It is Lisa, nicely dressed up.

Lisa All right?
Shaun Yeah.
Lisa Great.
Shaun What you doing in their garden?

Lisa I was just passing. Can I come in?

Shaun I'm baby-sitting.

Lisa I'll help you. (*She enters.*) Swanky place. (*She sees the Queen, covered up.*)

Lisa (*innocent as you like*) What's that?

Shaun It's the Queen.

Lisa Oh right.

Shaun It's for the procession tomorrow. The artist put a cover on it to protect it.

Lisa What's he like?

Shaun I think he may have a condition. He nodded a lot when I spoke to him.

Lisa I brought some alcopops.

Shaun What you doing here?

Lisa I was just on my way to Simon Miller's party, and I knew you were here so I thought I'd just pop in. Pop in to say hello. (*this a little alluringly*) You got a bottle opener?

Shaun I don't drink alcopops.

Lisa Nor me. But I thought, seeing as it's just us. We could try a few out. It's always worth trying something new, isn't it?

She waltzes into the kitchen and fetches a bottle opener. She comes back and as she is opening the bottle . . .

Lisa You look really handsome in that top.

Shaun Do I?

Lisa You should wear that colour more often.

Shaun I always wear this colour.

Lisa Oh. Must be the light. It really suits you anyway. *Really* suits you. You want some?

Shaun All right.

Lisa What you watching?

Shaun The World Cup.

Lisa Oh, I love the World Cup. Who's playing?

Shaun I dunno. I don't watch it for the football. I just love South Koreans.

Lisa You what?

Shaun I'm going to emigrate to South Korea. I've sent off for the papers.

Lisa Why?

Shaun Because when they win a game they have this massive party in the streets and squares, a million people getting drunk and dancing and hugging each other, and then at midnight, someone blows a whistle, and they all pack up, tidy the litter up after them, and go home on excellent public transport. I think that's a kind of Utopia.

The phone rings.

That'll be Mrs Chivers. She gets nervous being away.

Lisa From the kid.

Shaun From the statue. (*He picks up the phone.*)

Shaun Mrs Chivers?

Pause.

(*quietly*) What is it now? You've already said that. (*Beat.*) Dad, this really isn't the time. (*Beat.*) Of course I believe you. (*Beat.*) I swear I believe you. I've got to go, the kid's crying. (*Beat.*) Love you too. (*He puts the phone down.*)

Lisa Is your dad not at the hoe-down?

Shaun He's at home.

Lisa With your mum?

Shaun No, she's gone away for the weekend. She's not really a fan of the royals.

Lisa And him?

Shaun Oh yeah. Yeah, he is.

Lisa Do you like my dress?

Shaun Yeah.

Lisa Do you really?

Shaun What you doing?

Lisa I've always really liked you, Shaun. I mean I've always admired you. From afar.

Shaun Listen, maybe you'd be better off at the party.

Lisa I thought you liked me.

Shaun You know I do.

Lisa Well then, relax.

Shaun I just think you'd be better off at the party. If you want a good time, I mean.

Lisa I'm having a good time here.

Shaun It's just I'm not in a very 'good time' kind of mood. No, honest, Lisa, I think you should go.

Lisa You haven't shown me round yet.

Shaun What do you want to see?

Lisa I don't know, I just fancy a quick tour. To the other rooms. Downstairs and . . . upstairs . . .

Shaun I'm not supposed to go into the rooms.

Lisa Live a little, Shaun.

Shaun I find living quite hard as a rule.

Lisa Come on, it'll be fun. No one's going to catch us. (*Pause.*) Listen. My dad said something to me once: 'You only ever regret what you didn't do.'

Shaun OK. Wait there.

Lisa What you doing?

Shaun Shutting the windows.

Lisa No! Leave them. I might need to make a hasty exit if someone comes back. Don't want to take any risks, do we?

Shaun Lisa. If I ask you something, will you tell me the truth?

Lisa Of course, Shaun.

Shaun You're not taking me for a ride, are you?

Lisa What do you mean?

Shaun I just don't think I could cope if you were taking me for a ride.

Lisa Well you'll have to find out, won't you?

They exit. Immediately Shannon and Sandra appear through the French windows. Shannon has a pot of paint.

Sandra Give her credit. She didn't hold back.

They stop at the foot of the covered statue.

It's enormous.
Shannon Get a chair.

While Sandra gets a chair, Shannon pulls off the cover to reveal the statue. It is very lifelike, if oversized. Sandra returns.

Sandra Oh my God. It's her. It's really her.
Shannon Sshhh! Quick!
Sandra I mean it's really her. Our sovereign. I don't know if I can do this. I can't do it, Shaz. She'll be in my dreams.
Shannon Then hold the chair and I'll do it.

Sandra holds the chair and Shannon stands up on it. Shannon opens a pot of green paint and takes out a brush. At which point the doorbell rings. Pause.

Sandra What do we do?
Shannon I don't know.
Sandra Do it quick and we'll run for it!
Shannon They'll see us.

Enter Lisa.

Lisa (*loudly*) I'll get it! (*quiet*) Who is it?
Shannon I don't know. Where's 'the lips'?
Lisa He's in the bedroom.
Sandra He likes you.
Lisa I'm gonna have to snog him in a minute, so you better get a move on.
Shannon Go back and say it was a Jehovah's Witness. We'll text you when we're done.

Lisa Well hurry up, I'm dicing with a greasy death up there! (*She returns up.*)
Shannon (*to Sandra*) You answer it. Pretend to be the baby-sitter and get rid of them.

Shannon leaps down and hides behind the Queen. Sandra goes to answer the door.

Billy Hello.
Sandra Hello, I'm the baby-sitter. What do you want?
Billy I've lost my dog. Would you come and help me look for it?
Sandra Wait there. (*She closes the door.*)
Sandra It's just a kid. He wants me to help him look for his dog.
Shannon Go on. I'll paint her while you're gone.
Sandra See you back at base.

Shannon hides again. Sandra opens the door.

Sandra All right then, but we must be quick, I have a baby to look after.
Billy Thanks.

We hear the door shut. Shannon once again climbs on the chair and gets out her pot of paint. She is about to smear green paint over the Queen when Darren runs through the French windows into the room with an axe. In his shock, he falls over the sofa, and she falls off the chair and ends up painting her own face.

Darren Aaah!
Shannon Aaah!
Darren Who are you?
Shannon Don't kill me! I'll do what you say. Just don't kill me.
Darren I'm not going to kill you.
Shannon You look like you are.
Darren Who are you? What are you doing?

Shannon I was . . . just giving her some finishing touches.
Darren Who?
Shannon Her. I'm the artist's assistant. I mean, I come from round here but I was given a placement . . . to assist. So I'm just . . . assisting . . . Getting her really peachy for tomorrow.
Darren With green paint.
Shannon It's an art thing. You have to study to understand. What are you doing with that?

Pause.

Darren I was chopping wood.
Shannon Oh right. Why?
Darren I was in the next-door garden, when I saw you through the window and I didn't recognise you so I . . .
Shannon Oh, you're a neighbour.
Darren That's right. We operate a vicious Neighbourhood Watch scheme and I was down the log pile when I saw this stranger with a paintbrush . . .
Shannon Why were you chopping wood in June?
Darren I like to prepare for winter.

Enter Mad Mike, in Oliver Cromwell dress, with a video camera on a tripod. On seeing Shannon he falls flat to the ground.

Mad Mike Who's she?
Darren It's all right, Mike, she's just the artist's assistant.
Mad Mike What's she doing here?
Shannon Who's he?
Darren Mike is . . . my brother. He was . . . he was videoing me chopping wood. Weren't you, Mike?
Mad Mike I'm saying nothing!
Shannon Why's he dressed like that?
Darren Mike, why don't you go back home and I'll see you there.
Mad Mike I think we should kill her.

Darren No, that won't be necessary.
Shannon He was filming you chopping wood.
Darren Yeah.
Shannon In that get-up.
Darren OK. The truth is we were doing a low-budget horror movie in the style of *The Blair Witch Project* in our back garden. And that's when we saw you through the window.
Shannon You make movies?
Darren Yeah. But I don't want everyone knowing.
Shannon I want to be in the movies. That's if I don't become an artist, of course.
Darren I reckon you could be in movies.
Shannon (*showing her good side*) Do you?
Darren Yeah. If you don't become an artist.
Shannon How many movies have you made?
Darren Quite a few.
Shannon Can I audition?
Darren Maybe not right now . . .
Shannon But soon?
Darren Yeah, I reckon.
Shannon How will you find me?
Darren Which school you at?
Shannon Lee Bridge. You?
Darren St Peter's.
Shannon That's in the shit bit of town, isn't it?
Darren Yeah. So you've been working on the Queen, have you?
Shannon Oh yeah, yeah, for ages. I really want her to look brilliant.
Darren You like the Queen, do you?
Shannon Don't you?
Darren 'Course we do. We think she's amazing. We think she's a true one-off. Don't we, Mike?
Shannon Yeah, I mean I would really hate it if anything were to happen to her tonight.

Darren Me too. I'd be furious. I'm a massive royalist. You are too, aren't you, Mike?

Shannon Give me more royal stuff, I can't get enough of it.

Darren I mean, if I had my way, they'd have more power than they do now. But there are some people who see it really differently . . .

Shannon Really? I don't know anything about that.

Darren Some people, for example, think it's weird that the Queen takes millions of taxpayers' money to live in massive houses that could be in the public domain, hoarding thousands of gardens, rooms, paintings and sculptures that should in reality belong to the British people.

Shannon That's just so blind of them, isn't it?

Darren I know. Some people think it's strange that the Queen still technically owns all the land of this country, including rivers, beaches – even the sea's hers. They think it's a bit odd that homeowners the country over don't actually own their houses at all, they're just owning it in her name.

Shannon I don't find that strange.

Darren Nor me. But there's no telling with some people. Personally, I just love the feeling of being a royal subject. And tomorrow will be the crowning moment of that.

Shannon You watching tomorrow, are you?

Darren Isn't everyone?

Shannon Yes, I suppose they are. Well listen, I think I'm done really.

Darren You sure?

Shannon I was just touching her up. I'll be off now. I'm going. Maybe see you tomorrow, yeah?

Darren God save the Queen.

Shannon Yeah. (*She leaves and closes the front door.*)

Darren Collaborator!

Mad Mike We should have taken her out.

Darren And how would we do that?

Mad Mike She's seen our faces.

Darren Resolution number five. No violence against humankind is justified.

Mad Mike Or animalkind.

Darren Or animalkind.

Mad Mike You fancied her.

Darren I did not.

Mad Mike You fancy a royalist.

Darren Are we going to sit here chatting or are we going to set up the execution? Billy can't keep that girl looking for his dog all night.

Mad Mike Where do I go?

Darren On the chair.

Mad Mike takes a stocking out and puts it over his head, then replaces his Cromwellian hat on top. He climbs on the chair with the axe, as Darren places the camera in the middle of the room.

Have you got the script I gave you?

Mad Mike Who wrote this shit?

Darren John Milton, the great republican poet and supporter of Cromwell.

Mad Mike Why can't he write plain English?

Darren It was plain in 1650. Get on the chair. Turn towards me. No, you're blocking the Queen. Hold on.

He covers the canary cage and the bird stops singing.

Mad Mike What you doing?

Darren Stopping it singing.

Mad Mike That's cruel.

Darren It's only for a minute! OK, now do the whole arc of the swing without actually decapitating her, just for angles.

Mike does so, stopping just before the neck.

Darren And once more. Good. OK, I'm recording. Read it slowly and clearly and then perform the execution.

Mad Mike (*reads*) 'It is lawful, and hath been held so through all ages, for any, who hath the power, to call to account a tyrant, or wicked king, and after due conviction to depose and put him to death.' (*He raises the axe to behead the sculpture.*)

Darren Stop.

Mad Mike What is it?

Darren You should say 'wicked king or queen'.

Mad Mike It doesn't say that.

Darren But you should say it. Go again, please.

Mad Mike 'It is lawful, and hath been held so through all ages, for any, who hath the power, to call to account a tyrant, or wicked king or queen, and after due conviction to depose and put him to death.' (*He raises the axe.*)

Darren Him or her to death. You should say him or her.

Mad Mike I'll put you to death in a minute.

Darren OK, one more time. And this time, think about what the poor have suffered at the hands of this vixen, and mean it!

Mad Mike (*with sudden and great simple power*) 'It is lawful, and hath been held so through all ages, for any, who hath the power, to call to account a tyrant, or wicked king or queen, and after due conviction to depose and put him or her to death!'

Mike takes a huge swing, and is about to decapitate Her Majesty, when Lisa enters.

Lisa Will you get a move on? I'm virtually shagging the bastard. Aaaah!!

Mad Mike Aaaah!

Mike swings, misses the Queen and falls, embedding the axe in the sofa. A plume of duck feathers rises up around the room.

Darren Who are you?

Lisa I'm . . . I'm the baby sitter.

Darren You're what? You can't be. Who are you?

Lisa Who are you?

Mad Mike (*to Darren*) Don't say anything. Don't say anything! (*to Lisa*) Now you listen to me. You say nothing about this, you understand me? You came down, you tripped, and you split open the sofa. You never saw us, you never heard us. We do not exist. Is that clear? Or do you want an axe in your skull?

Lisa It's clear.

Mad Mike Let's go.

Darren What about . . .?

Mad Mike I said let's go. (*to Lisa*) And remember. I know where you live!

Mad Mike and Darren gather their stuff and leave, Mike just having time to lift the cloth off the canary cage. Lisa looks around for a second.

Shaun (*from off*) Lisa?

Lisa Oh no.

She runs out of the French windows into the night. The stage is empty for a second, and then Shaun comes down.

Shaun Lisa what are you . . .? (*He sees the mayhem. He sees she is not there.*)

Shaun Lisa?

Silence. He sits down and with a terrible quiet sadness puts his head in his hands. Then he starts to put the feathers back in the sofa . . .

SCENE FOUR

The wall on the poor side of town . . .

Darren Why pull us out?

Mad Mike The operation was in danger.

Darren But we hadn't achieved anything!

Mad Mike We were at risk!

Darren She was just a girl!

Mad Mike I felt it was my responsibility, given the lack of rational leadership in the room, to order an immediate retreat.

Darren And now we haven't done anything! Yet again we've achieved nothing!

Billy Forty minutes I spent looking for a dog that doesn't exist. And all for nothing.

Darren (*to Mad Mike*) What did you say?

Mad Mike What about?

Darren Lack of rational leadership. Is that what you said?

Mad Mike What if it was?

Darren Are you saying I lacked leadership?

Mad Mike I'm saying you were too busy eyeing up that artist girl to pay attention to anything.

Billy What artist girl?

Darren That is not true.

Mad Mike This girl was in there, painting the Queen, when we arrived. You should have seen him. Giving her the eye. Telling her how much he loved the royals . . .

Darren That was cover!

Mad Mike He was so busy with the charm offensive, he forgot why we were there in the first place. So when the other girl came down . . .

Billy Other girl?

Mad Mike He was in no position . . .
Billy What other girl?
Mad Mike This other girl. Another baby-sitter. How do I know? The point is someone had to take control!
Darren I do not fancy her. She is a royalist, toe-sucking bitch!
Billy Three girls all looking after the house. That's a bit weird.

Pause.

Darren Just what I was thinking.
Mad Mike What does it mean?
Darren They've been hired to protect the Queen. Of course! Why didn't I think of it earlier? They must have suspected something like this might happen. Well, they're not beating us. Not this time. I am sick and tired of every one of our efforts coming to nothing.
Mad Mike Since when did my efforts come to nothing?
Darren Excuse me? Who organised the march against the nuclear power station? Who didn't check whether it was actually a nuclear power station and not a water-cooling plant? Who tried to throw plant pots at Margaret Beckett and smashed the health food shop window? Useless! Pathetic! Well, not any more. We're going back, and boys, we are going to chop that royal head off if it kills each and every one of us. Who's with me?
Billy I'm with you, Daz.
Darren Good boy, Billy. Mike?

Pause.

Mad Mike It was Claire Short.
Darren Mike.
Mad Mike It was Claire Short and she ducked!

Pause.

Mad Mike I'm with you.
Darren OK, OK! Let's do it. Up the Republic!
All Up the Republic!

SCENE FIVE

Another bit of wall.

Sandra What happened?
Shannon I was interrupted!
Sandra Forty minutes I spent looking for that dog. We didn't even find it. The kid was distraught. He had tears rolling down his face.
Lisa I come down, she's not even in the room. This bloke's standing on a chair with an axe and the other one's filming him.
Sandra You what?
Shannon They're making this movie.
Sandra What are they doing making it in Mrs Chivers' living room?
Shannon They saw me while they were making the film next door. That's why I had to get out.
Sandra You were caught? We're going to get done.
Shannon We're not going to get done.
Sandra We could go down for that. Entering and trespass.
Shannon Will you chill out? I told him I was the artist's assistant. He completely fell for it.
Sandra (*to Lisa*) What were you doing all this while?
Lisa I was keeping Shaun busy.
Shannon (*to herself*) I reckon he's a really good film director.
Sandra (*to Lisa*) Were you now? Did you kiss him?
Shannon (*to herself*) He might be the new Spielberg.
Lisa I had to!

Sandra What was it like?

Lisa It was . . .

Shannon . . . and I could be like Laura Dern in *Jurassic Park*. (*Mimes being afraid of a dinosaur.*)

Lisa It was . . . really . . . really . . . it was . . . I mean it was horrible, obviously . . .

Sandra You loved it.

Lisa Did not!

Sandra You fancy Shaun Digby.

Lisa I do not!

Sandra How long d'you kiss him for?

Lisa I'm not the one fancying anyone. Listen to her waxing lyrical about Alfred Hitchcock. Doing a bloody screen test when she should have been getting the job done!

Shannon I was not waxing anything!

Lisa I would never have kissed Shaun if you hadn't taken so bloody long.

Shannon He came in as I was about to paint her green. What was I supposed to do? Just carry on smearing Her Majesty in Dulux gloss?

Lisa So what now?

Shannon We go back.

Sandra What if they're still there?

Shannon They won't be, they've got a filming schedule to keep to. Lisa can take Shaun upstairs for a bit more hot action . . .

Sandra . . . seeing as she enjoyed it so much . . .

Lisa Did not . . .

Shannon . . . and this time we'll get it done. What do you say?

Sandra I'll give it one more go.

Shannon Prepared to snog Shaun for another twenty minutes or so?

Beat.

Lisa All right.
Sandra That was hard.
Lisa I'm doing this for you, slag!
Sandra Sure you are, Lise. Sure you are.
Shannon And if the film director is still there, I'll deal with him.

Pause.

Sandra I give up with you two, I really do.

SCENE SIX

Shaun Digby is carefully replacing individual feathers into the sofa. The phone rings. He answers.

Shaun Hello? (*Beat.*) Is that you, Dad? (*Beat.*) Dad, you're drunk. Stop shouting at me. (*Beat.*) Dad, I'm not coming home if you're gonna be like that. (*Beat.*) I don't know where I'll go. (*Beat.*) Dad, stop it. I said stop it! Shut it! Shut it, will you!!

He slams the phone down. It rings instantly. He picks it up.

I said shut it, you pisshead!! (*Beat.*) Oh, hello, Mrs Chivers. No, everything's fine. I just had a hoax caller, that's all. Everything's great here. She's fine. She's fine too. How's the hoe-down? Strip the willow? Cool. OK, then, 'bye now.

He puts the phone down and continues his feather-packing. He stops to swig more of the alcopops that Lisa left. I believe it's known as drowning one's sorrows.

The bell rings. Shaun sighs. The bell rings again. Shaun goes to answer. As he opens, three masked men push him back into the room.

Darren Get down on the floor!

Mad Mike Down! Down! Down!

Darren Get down and you won't be hurt.

Mad Mike Down! Down Down!

Darren Who are you?

Mad Mike Down! Down!

Darren Who are you?

Mad Mike Down! Down!

Darren (*to Mad Mike*) He is down! Will you shut up! (*to Shaun*) Who are you? Where are the others?

Shaun What others?

Mad Mike Don't fuck with us!

Shaun There are no others.

Darren Billy, check the house! (*Exit Billy.*) So who are you?

Shaun I'm just the baby-sitter.

Darren Don't mess me around!

Shaun I am! Honest!

Darren I've already met two other baby-sitters here tonight! Which organisation do you belong to? You're trying to stop us, is that right?

Shaun I don't know what you're talking about!

Mad Mike I say we kill him.

Darren Shut it! (*to Shaun*) There were three girls in this house earlier, and no sign of you. So don't fuck with me, OK?

Shaun Three girls?

Darren One claimed to be the artist's assistant and the other two baby-sitters. Now unless this is an exceptionally difficult toddler, I think three baby-sitters is a bit excessive, don't you?

Enter Billy.

Billy All clear.

Darren Tie him up.

They tie Shaun up and blindfold him.

Darren You're just lucky you've fallen into the hands of an ethically responsible protest organisation.

Mad Mike You royalist scum!

Darren Now sit there, keep quiet, and nothing will happen. Billy, get the chair.

Billy I've seen you before.

Darren Billy!

Billy Do you work in Asda on Saturdays?

Shaun Yeah. On dairy.

Billy That's it!

Darren Get the chair!

Shaun is tied and blindfolded. Billy gets the chair, Darren rushes outside the front door, fetches the camera and sets up, and Mad Mike dons his Cromwellian uniform and axe and climbs up.

Shaun (*blindfolded*) What you doing?

Mad Mike None of your business.

Darren You don't know it, but you're witnessing history. You're witnessing the beginning of the end of one of the most oppressive regimes in the dismal record of man.

Shaun What do you mean?

Darren Just listen. You'll figure it out. OK, I'm recording. Read it slowly and clearly and then perform the execution.

Shaun What you doing?!

Darren Will you calm down!

Shaun Don't kill me! Please, don't kill me.

Darren We're not executing you, you tosser.

Shaun Sounded like you were.

Mad Mike We will if you don't shut your mouth!

Darren covers the canary cage and the bird stops singing.

Darren OK, I'm rolling.

Mad Mike (*reads with terrific and dramatic conviction*) 'It is lawful, and hath been held so through all ages, for any, who hath the power, to call to account a tyrant, or wicked king or queen, and after due conviction to depose and put him or her to death.'

He raises the axe to behead the sculpture. The doorbell rings.

Darren Cut!

Mad Mike Who is it now?!

Darren How should I know?

Mad Mike (*to Shaun*) Who is it?

Shaun I don't know.

Mad Mike Talk!

Shaun I don't know, honest!

Mad Mike (*cry of frustration*) Aaaah!! We should have carried on with the execution!

Darren The doorbell was on the tape. You can't send that to Kofi Annan!

Mad Mike I don't give a shit about Kofi Annan! I just want to take that head off!

The bell rings again.

Billy Get him to answer it. Like in a movie, he has to act dead normal and entice the person inside. Then we can deal with them too.

Darren Brilliant. (*Grabs Shaun.*) Do it.

Mad Mike And listen to me. One false move, and you can forget Resolution 5, you'll be dead meat. Because I have had enough!

Shaun is untied and goes to the door. Darren and Mad Mike hide behind the door. Billy hides behind the Queen. Shaun opens. It is Lisa.

Lisa Hi.

Shaun Hi.
Lisa I'm sorry I disappeared earlier.
Shaun That's OK.
Lisa Can I come in?
Shaun Well . . . maybe now's not . . .
Lisa Don't be upset.
Shaun No, I really don't think now's the time . . .

But Lisa pushes him in, and starts to kiss him passionately. Billy, Darren and Mad Mike all come out from their hiding places. Lisa and Shaun kiss madly for a while more, then Lisa sees the three men.

Lisa Oh my God.
Shaun That's kind of what I meant.

Billy and Mad Mike grab Shaun while Darren grabs Lisa and covers her mouth. Both are blindfolded.

Darren Don't move. You are in the hands of the Popular Republican Front. If you do not resist, no damage will come to you or your boyfriend.
Shaun (*extricating himself*) I'm not her boyfriend.
Mad Mike Shut it!
Darren Billy, let's get them upstairs and if you hear so much as a squeak out of them, kill them. (*He mimes to Billy: 'Not really.'*) Get on the chair, Mike!

Billy and Darren march the two, blindfolded and tied up, upstairs. Mike gets on the chair.
Darren rushes down.

Mad Mike Come on!
Darren OK, rolling. Go go go!
Mad Mike (*reads with fast fury*) 'It is lawful, and hath been held so through all ages, for any, who hath the power, to call to account a tyrant, or wicked king or queen, and after due conviction to depose and put him or her to death!'

He raises the axe to behead the sculpture. Shannon and Sandra burst through the front door, paint in hand.

Shannon Let's do it!

Mad Mike falls off the chair and his axe goes through the mantelpiece, smashing a fair amount of crockery.

What are you . . .?

Darren (*grabs axe*) Don't move! You are in the hands of the Popular Republican Front! If you try to resist us, we will kill the two hostages we have upstairs! Now sit down!

Shannon Is this in the movie?

Darren This is not a movie! This is very VERY REAL!

Billy appears.

Billy What was the noise? Bloody hell.

Sandra That's the kid with the dog.

Darren Get upstairs and guard the hostages!

Billy They don't need guarding. They're quite happy, actually.

Shannon Aren't you film-makers?

Darren Do we look like film-makers? We're an action group, and if only you would stop interrupting us, we are here to behead this symbol of class corruption and societal decay that has held Britain in its icy grip for the last thousand years!

Shannon You want to destroy the statue?

Darren Yes, your beloved little statue, your little Queen, whose face you were trying to make so perfect – I'm afraid that, come tomorrow, she won't have a face!

Shannon But that's what we want to do.

Darren What do you mean?

Shannon We're here to destroy the statue too.

Pause.

Darren Don't even try it, 'artist's assistant'.
Sandra She's telling the truth.
Mad Mike I think we should kill them.
Shannon Why else would I have a pot of bright green paint? I was going to deface her, but then you came in pretending to be neighborhood vigilantes so I had to make something up.
Mad Mike Don't believe them.
Darren Shut it! (*to Shannon*) And the one upstairs?
Shannon She's part of it too! Her job was to get 'the lips' out of the way. Go on, behead away, we won't stop you!
Darren Billy, go and untie the girl.
Mad Mike I say we kill them!
Darren And I am head of this organisation! Billy, go!

Exit Billy

Sandra Where is she? What have you done with her?

Pause.

You tied her up!
Darren We thought she was against us!
Sandra That's our mate that is!
Darren How was I supposed to know? This is a major political operation, I had to make a quick decision! So what, you're not a royalist?
Shannon No way!
Darren And you really wanted to destroy the Queen?
Shannon Yeah!

Pause.

Darren I thought we were alone! I thought no one felt as we did. It's unbelievable. Two groups, fighting for justice, for equality, for the end of privilege . . .
Sandra Well, not exactly . . .

Shannon kicks Sandra.

Shannon (*to Darren*) Yeah, exactly.
Darren What's the name of your group?

Pause.

Shannon Women Against the Monarchy. Or WAM for short.
Darren And you're the leader?
Shannon Of course.
Darren How long have you been preparing this?
Shannon Oh, ages.
Darren Months . . .
Shannon If not years. We've been completely focused on it, haven't we, Ron?
Sandra Uh . . . yeah . . . completely.
Shannon We're like totally underground. No one's heard of us at all.
Darren But this is amazing. I thought we were alone. I thought no one understood . . . no one felt . . . no one in the whole country . . . and all this time, on my own doorstep . . .
Shannon I believe in a world without class, a world without privilege, a world where men and women are free to live equally and in peace.

Sandra coughs.

Darren A world without corruption.
Shannon A world without sleaze and scandal.
Darren A world of honesty, unstained by money, where men and women can live with each other . . .
Shannon Love each other . . .
Darren And be at one with the beautiful world we've been given.

Pause. Darren and Shannon are close.

Billy (*entering*) I've untied her, but she doesn't want to come down.

Darren Billy, meet . . .
Shannon Shannon.
Darren Shannon is the head of Women Against the Monarchy.
Billy What's your manifesto?
Shannon We think manifestos are old-fashioned. We believe in action and action alone.
Darren So do we.
Billy But what about the resolutions . . .
Darren OK, listen. (*to Billy*) Shut it. (*to Shannon*) I have a proposal. I propose that the two movements unite in one action group, and that together we behead the Queen as a statement of unified protest. Together we're stronger. What do you say?
Shannon Sounds good to me. I'd better ask my fellow sisters first, though. Ronnie?
Sandra Whatever.
Darren Billy?
Billy I spent three days learning that manifesto.
Darren Billy!
Billy Together we're stronger!
Darren Good boy. Mike?

Pause.

Mad Mike What will the group be called?
Darren I don't know. People Against the Monarchy.
Mad Mike PAM.
Darren We can decide that later! I want to propose a joint execution of Her Majesty the Queen by the Popular Republican Front and WAM.
Shannon Seconded.
Mad Mike How will the execution be joint?

Pause.

Darren I want Shannon to do it.
Mad Mike She's not touching my axe.

Darren In the name of equality between groups . . .
Mad Mike It's my axe!
Darren You can stand next to her and read the words! But she has to do it! I film it. She does it! You read the words. Is that clear? Or do I have to question your allegiance?

Pause. Mad Mike hands her the axe.

Mad Mike This is strictly a lend.
Darren OK, let's do it. Get on the chair, Shannon.
Shannon You're going to film me? I haven't put any make-up on.
Darren You'll have a stocking on your head.
Shannon Oh.
Mad Mike We're sending this to world governments. Do you want to be identified by the CIA, KGB and MI5?
Shannon Only asking.
Darren Have my stocking.
Shannon Thanks. (*She puts it over her head and climbs the chair. She stands, very aware of her appearance.*)
Darren Oh, that looks great.
Shannon You don't think I should get a shorter skirt?
Mad Mike Is this a fashion show or an execution?
Darren Rolling! Mike, read it.

Pause.

Mad Mike (*reads with grim determination*) 'It is lawful, and hath been held so through all ages, for any, who hath the power, to call to account a tyrant, or wicked king or queen, and after due conviction to depose and put him or her to death.'

Shannon raises the axe to behead the sculpture. Lisa runs in.

Lisa STOP!!

Shannon swings, misses the Queen, swings right round and knocks Mad Mike off the arm of the sofa. He smashes into a glass cabinet that falls on top of him.

Darren What are you doing?!

Lisa You can't touch her! You mustn't!

Darren What are you talking about? Carry on with the execution!

Lisa I won't let you! (*She runs in front of the camera.*)

Darren Get out of the way.

Shannon Get out of the way, Lise, this is my great moment!

Darren Mike, pull the intruder out of the way!

Billy I think he's unconscious, Daz.

Darren Billy, pull her out of the way.

Lisa You have no idea what damage you will be causing if you go through with this!

Darren Are you a member of WAM or not?

Lisa What are you talking about?

Darren I thought you were supposed to be against the monarchy, not protecting it! What's going on here?

Lisa Shaun, come in!

Enter Shaun, nervously.

Darren Who untied him?

Lisa I did.

Darren Are you insane? Why did you do that?

Lisa Because I love him.

Darren You what?

Lisa Shaun, tell them what you told me. About your dad.

Shaun I don't think I want to.

Lisa Tell them!

Shaun Lise . . .

Lisa How many reasons does your dad have for being alive?

Shaun Three.

Lisa Name them.

Shaun Leicester City (*changeable*), the Queen, and beating the shit out of Mum and me.

Lisa What's happened to Leicester City?

Shaun They're relegated.

Lisa What's happened to your mum?

Shaun She's left him. Yesterday.

Lisa But she didn't take you with her.

Shaun No, I think she forgot that bit.

Lisa So, if the Jubilee parade is cancelled, what will your dad have left?

Shaun Beating the shit out of me.

Lisa How much alcohol has he drunk so far this weekend?

Shaun Six bottles of beer, three bottles of wine and a quarter of whisky. That's when I left to come here.

Lisa How many more days off has he got for the Jubilee?

Shaun Three.

Lisa So you'll be alone with him for three days . . . That's why you can't touch her. If that parade goes ahead, Shaun's dad will be able to focus on the glory of Empire and Shaun will be spared. But if you execute her, you are condemning this boy to a living hell.

Pause.

Darren Go ahead with the execution, Shannon.

Lisa You can't, Shaz . . .

Darren I'm sorry about Shaun and his dad, OK. But the fate of individuals cannot deter us from the wider aim.

Lisa What aim?

Darren The freeing of a whole country! Every liberating movement has caused suffering to individuals. You have to look at the greater good.

Billy What about Resolution 5?

Darren That's different.

Billy Why is it different? If he's gonna get leathered for the next three days because of us, how is that different . . . ?

Darren Because it's different! We won't hurt anyone ourselves. But we cannot legislate for every consequence of our actions . . .

Billy That's not how I saw it.

Darren I don't care how you saw it! We're going ahead! We've been planning this for months, we're not stopping now for one sad bastard with a juiced-up father! We're action groups, not agony aunts!

Lisa Action groups?

Darren Before you came down it was agreed that the PRF and WAM should come together . . .

Lisa What are you talking about?

Shannon Shut it, Lise!

Lisa What's WAM?

Darren What do you mean, what's WAM? You're in it.

Lisa What did she tell you?

Shannon Shut it or the Queen's a goner.

Darren She told me about Women Against the Monarchy . . .

Lisa What, that's us, is it?

Shannon I mean it, Lisa Edwards! If you want to spare your lover a beating . . .

Darren What? What?

Pause.

Lisa We're not members of Women Against the Monarchy.

Pause.

Shannon You're dead.

Darren What do you mean?

Lisa We're not members of anything! We were going to do a dance on the motorised float with the statue and then we discovered we had to wear these really dog dresses and so we thought we'd come and deface her so the parade would be cancelled. That's the only reason we're here!

Shannon That is not true!

Lisa Is that true, Ron?

Pause.

Sandra Yeah, that's true.

Shannon OK, maybe that's true for them, but I am a fully paid-up member of WAM. I'm politically motivated, I'm worthy of you and your group, and I will show you how much I believe in it now. (*She grabs the axe and the paper and reads triumphantly.*) 'It is lawful, and hath been held so through all ages, for any, who hath the power, to call to account a tyrant, or wicked king or queen, and after due conviction to depose and put him or her to death.'

Shannon makes to swing, but then stops. Pause. Lisa is holding up something in her hand.

Lisa Do it and I tear them up.

Shannon Where d'you get them from?

Lisa Nicked them from your wallet so you couldn't use them to blackmail me any more.

Darren What's going on?

Lisa Well go on, then. You give it to the Queen, and I'll give it to Britney.

Shannon You won't do that, that's your ticket too.

Lisa Try me.

Shannon You worship her. You spend almost every day trying to be her.

Lisa I don't care.

Darren Britney?

Lisa Oh yeah, we're big on Britney.

Darren But she's . . . she's appalling . . . she's the sickening epitome of US-led globalisation, as perpetuated through the exploitation of young innocent children, turning still-growing kids into rabid consumers demanding ever more impossible levels of satisfaction.

Lisa And we're seeing her in concert in two weeks' time.

Darren (*to Shannon*) You cannot love Britney Spears and be who you say you are.

Shannon I don't love her. I think she's shit.

Darren Then what are you waiting for? Kill the Queen.

Lisa Go on, Shaz. Kill the Queen!

Darren Show me your beliefs, Shannon. The Queen must die!

Lisa Do it, Shaz. Go on.

Darren Shannon, the Queen must die!

Pause. Shannon slowly lowers the axe down by her side. Pause. Darren sits.

Darren How could you . . . how could you say all that?

Shannon I'm sorry.

Darren Men and women . . . free to live in a world without class, without money . . .

Shannon I'm sorry, OK. But Britney's just so cool.

Shannon remains standing on the chair with the axe by her side. Billy approaches Darren.

Billy It's all right, Daz, we'll find someone else to join us.

Darren No we won't.

Billy 'Course we will.

Darren We won't! (*Beat.*) I'm disbanding the group.

Billy You can't. We're still together! We're still strong!

Darren Strong? Look at us, Billy. Mary and Les have left. Mike's unconscious. You're eleven and I'm just a sad loser. Face it. No one cares any more. Nothing's gonna change. Politics is dead.

Mad Mike suddenly stands, still in his Cromwell gear, his head bleeding heavily. He screams a cry of great vengeance.

Mad Mike Don't ever say that! Don't ever say that nothing's gonna change!

Mike hurls himself, grabbing the axe, at the Queen. Shannon, Lisa, Sandra grab him. A great fight. Mike makes one big swing and smashes the bird cage that was hanging from the ceiling. Pause as bird feathers fly everywhere.

Look what you made me do! Look what you made me do!

Mad Mike drops the axe and collapses weeping on the sofa. A brief tableau. Cromwell lying on the sofa. Duck feathers. Broken crockery. Broken glass. The Queen, untouched, serene. Shaun goes over and looks at the Queen.

Lisa Is she all right?

Shaun Amazing. All around, destruction and chaos. And not a scratch on her.

The sound of a baby's cry. Pause. A key in the lock. The door opens. A fruity woman's voice.

Woman We're back!

They all look at each other. Blackout.

End.

Desperate Stories about Desperate People: It's Enough to Make You Laugh

David Farr interviewed by Jim Mulligan

As a student at Cambridge University, David Farr and two actresses set up a company, Talking Tongues, to write and devise their own plays. The style was not naturalistic but visual in the style of Theatre de Complicite. One of their plays won *The Guardian* Award at the Edinburgh Festival and did well at the Gate Theatre in London. Since then David Farr has covered a wide range of writing and directing, including *Great Expectations* and *Coriolanus*. He has written monologues and plays and directed over thirty plays and operas. He will shortly be taking up the post of director at the Bristol Old Vic.

The Queen Must Die is a comedy set in a small English town not unlike Guildford, where David Farr grew up. He regrets that he did not have a more exciting teenage experience, but feels: 'That's probably why I've ended up writing and directing, because it is continually exciting and unpredictable.'

> All my comedies are set in small closed communities where people live frustrated lives. I call them desperate comedies. They are formed around a desperate idea with desperate people trying to achieve something in a world that does not quite allow them to do what they want. It's not a farce, although it uses farcical techniques. In farce you have to be dispassionate and have an almost callous view of your characters. I love my characters. You feel sympathy for them, but they are nonetheless undergoing torture and you cringe for them.

The Queen Must Die is subversive in intent. A crucial character is the papier-mâché statue of the Queen. At the end of the play she remains serene, not a scratch on her in the carnage and chaos that she has caused. The title is both literal and ironic, and the symbolism at the end will not be lost on the audience.

> I see the play as a staunchly republican piece. It is a genuinely political play about England and its attitude to change. The English have an extraordinary tolerance and put up with the most bizarre things. Their attitude to the royals is a good example. They don't have the power they used to have, but they create a mind-set whereby we feel we are subjects, not active citizens. I think we would be better off as a republic and I think it is inevitable. Until that happens the royalty will continue to have a grip on the national consciousness.

Darren is a frustrated but dogged revolutionary whose ideas are not yet clearly formed and who has to cope with people not turning up to his meetings and being let down by the girl he fancies because she wants more than revolutionary rhetoric when she goes out with him.

> Darren has to be a hero. He can't be a weirdo. When you look at him you have to be sympathetic towards him. He has to be intelligent and eloquent enough to be aware of his situation. And he has to be good-looking enough for Shannon to fall for him when she thinks he is a film-maker. Mad Mike, on the other hand, is a comedic creation and can be whatever you want him to be. He's wildly psychopathic taken to a ludicrous extreme, but he's not as mad as he thinks he is and he's only mad in a small-town situation.

Shaun is at the emotional heart of the play. In the midst of all the political ideas there is a simple, rather sad relationship between a father and his son. The fact that this is only revealed in the last few lines of the play is important. The abuse does not dominate but is a way for the characters to investigate issues.

> I don't want to portray Shaun purely as an abuse victim because the play is not about that. The boy is being given an incredibly rough time by his father and it's important for the other characters to recognise that. In all plays people learn things and Lisa learns a huge amount. She learns that this boy she has always mocked is weird for a very good reason and in accordance with the comic genre she falls madly in love with him. He is totally unable to defend himself, so Lisa does it for him, and beautifully. She will wear that dog dress in public rather than see him take an extra beating.

There is a range of characters in the play from the utterly realistic Billy and Shaun to Mad Mike, a rebel without a cause, and Darren, an embryonic demagogue who sees the futility of his dreams. The girls are much more realistic and young people will probably be able to identify easily with them, but the actors will still have to figure out the politics of their relationships: who is the leader, who is worried about being excluded and why hasn't Ronnie got a ticket for Britney when the other two have?

The Queen Must Die is primarily intended to be funny, but part of it is about the loss of any kind of real political idealism. The market looks on the young as consumers and they have become single-issue activists picking and choosing issues as they pick and choose their clothes and CDs. They are the victims of US-led globalisation exploiting innocent children and 'turning growing kids into rabid consumers demanding ever more impossible levels of satisfaction'. Of course the audience will laugh when Darren analyses the effect of Britney Spears in these terms, but they will also have an uneasy feeling that there is some truth in it.

> All good comedy should make you laugh and think. If it's really good it also makes you feel. I hope when they look at the untouched Queen at the end they will think that it is more than just a bit of fun. The central yearning of the characters, the sources of their desperation, must be understood. If the actors think this is just funny it won't work.

Production Notes

STAGING AND SETTING

The Queen Must Die is a farcical comedy starring seven teenagers (3 f, 4 m) and a giant papier-mâché statue of Queen Elizabeth II. The story takes place in a medium-sized British town the night before the Queen's Golden Jubilee in 2002. There is a procession planned through the town. The highlight will be a large motorised float boasting three young female dancers and a specially commissioned papier-mâché statue of Her Majesty. However, two very different groups of adolescents are determined that the statue will never make it to the procession.

One group, calling itself the Popular Republican Front, is an anti-monarchist action group that comprises Darren (our deeply flawed hero), his twelve-year-old brother Billy, and their unhinged comrade Mad Mike. This hopeless crew wants to execute the statue of Her Majesty, film the beheading, and send video tapes to the United Nations.

The other group intent on destroying the Queen is made up of the three girls who have been chosen to be the dancers on the float. Led by Shannon (our heroine), their reasons are less ideologically heroic: they can't stand the dresses they are being forced to wear for the procession.

But for both groups, one fact remains: this night, the Queen must die. All that stands between them and success is Shaun 'the lips' Digby, who happens to be baby-sitting in the house where the statue is being kept.

There are three locations and things need to move quickly to keep the momentum of the action. Avoid blackouts. The living room needs to be a permanent fixture. Try not to move the furniture. It needs to be as realistic as possible to let the comedy work. Make the room as small as possible in order that entrances and exits can be achieved quickly, thereby keeping the pace of the farce. Feathers flying out from the sofa can be effected by having a technician behind it propelling them with the help of a CO_2 fire extinguisher. Things really do need to be broken in front of the audience's eyes. A real axe might be a liability but you could cheat by fixing a latex head to the handle. The doors are essential to drive the physical momentum of the play. The effigy of the Queen needs to be as recognisably her as it can be, and she needs to be smiling serenely. You might use a commercially made mask or a photograph, and carve out a polystyrene base. The effigy should be larger then life but could be standing or sitting, possibly next to Shaun on the sofa. The girls' dresses have to be plausible but badly made – certainly they should be baggy or ill-fitting. The three masked intruders might wear balaclavas, or better still, Prince Charles masks.

Avoid the temptation to 'ham up' the action; avoid caricature. To get the best from the script the characters must be played straight and believable. Keep things simple. Remember that many plays are extended argument. Try not to blur the clarity of the argument with unnecessary emotion. The more passionate the line the more important it becomes to deliver it 'straight'. For instance, if the line suggests nervousness, don't do over-nervous acting. Let the line speak for itself.

EXERCISES

The energy of the performance will need to feel over the top to the actors, otherwise it will feel flat for the audience. Beware of long pauses; they will make the action sag.

Encourage the actors to play the energy right through to the end of each line. In real life the energy might drop but it must not in performance. Check that the next actor to speak is picking up the energy of the previous line and keeping the energy 'in the air'. In comedy you need to 'ride the laugh' – that is, catch the laugh as it begins to fade and come in with the next line just before the laugh finishes. Use the energy of the laugh to keep the pace going. Don't let the actors anticipate the laughs from the audience. The dialogue is not realistic, it's heightened naturalism. However, the actors need to understand their motivation from moment to moment. Get them to work out the intention behind every line by expressing it as a verb. Have them ask, 'How am I trying to change other people in this scene?'

Here is an example of 'actioning' you might want to introduce to the actors. Look at Shaun's speech on page 529 (the 'actions' below are in square brackets):

> **Shaun** Hello? [*soliciting*] Everything's fine here. [*reassuring*] No, I haven't heard a peep. [*satisfying*]

All this is additionally humorous and has extra depth because Shaun hasn't really got his mind on what's happening.

> I'll make sure I don't spill anything on his . . . [*pleasing*] Is the artist enjoying the hoe-down? [*diverting*]

Shaun's father phones. (How often does that happen?)

> Yeah, it's me. [*downbeat and embarrassed because Shaun is upset. He's tried to get away from his dad but Dad is pursuing him. Dad drunk and feeling bad. Shaun has to go back home after baby-sitting, possibly to another beating*] It's OK, Dad. You don't have to say that .[*distancing*] I know you love me.

[*enduring*] I know you didn't mean it. [*placating*] Forget it, will you? [*distancing*]

Have the actors script the Father's conversation at the other end of the line.

Love you too. [*dismissive/embarrassed*]

Decide at which point he puts the phone down and so on.

Storyboard the moments of chaos. The audience can only take in one action at a time, so make sure these scenes are carefully broken down action by action. On page 539–40, for instance:

1. Mike builds his Milton speech to a reasonably high climax.
2. Lisa enters the room, says her line, 'Will you get a move on?' before seeing Mike.
3. There is a moment (a beat) as they see each other.
4. They scream, Mike topples and falls.

The bursting in of the intruders towards the end of the play must be carefully choreographed to give the appearance of chaos. As before, each speech and movement must be clearly delineated so the audience is able to follow the action. Consider how they all react. They have not seen Shaun before, Shaun has no idea who they are or what they want. Consider Billy's reaction to what is happening. How Darren asserts himself over Mad Mike and Mad Mike's reaction to this.

All these actions should be rehearsed as separate sections, then run together very quickly so they appear chaotic but are all clearly identified stages.

We don't meet Mrs Chivers on stage. Nevertheless, she's an important character. Give her a persona. Decide what relationship she might be having with the artist who made the sculpture. How does her personality affect her taste in living-room furnishings? Also, the baby is never seen but the sound of it wailing might add another dimension to chaos at the end of the play.

Look at the section on page 545 when Shaun is on the phone to his dad. Script the whole conversation to use in rehearsal to help Shaun build up to the climax of the section when he calls Mrs Chivers 'pisshead'. The build-up is important for the pay-off of the gag.

Suzy Graham-Adriani
March 2003
based on a workshop facilitated by Lindsey Posner

TOTALLY OVER YOU

Mark Ravenhill

Mark Ravenhill's first full-length play, *Shopping and Fucking*, was produced by Out of Joint and the Royal Court Theatre, and opened at the Ambassadors in 1996 prior to a national tour. He has since written several more plays that have received productions around the world and are published by Methuen Drama Ltd.

Note

This play was suggested by a one-act play by Molière. In *Les Précieuses ridicules*, two young women reject their suitors because they do not have courtly manners, manners which Molière believed were affected and stifling of humanity. Like Molière's play, mine is written to be played on a bare stage. The scenes are not set anywhere and need no scenery or furniture – nothing to suggest a location. Which sounds abstract on the page but plays very naturally. And makes sense of Molière's humanism. It's the person that counts not the illusions – be it courtly manners or celebrity – they fool themselves with.

A mark in the dialogue like this / is the cue for the next actor, creating overlapping dialogue.

Characters

Kitty
Rochelle
Hannah
Sinita
Letitia
Donna
Rachel
Indu

Jake
Dan
Tyson
Framji
Victor
Michael
Rubin

and members of a drama class

ONE

Enter Kitty and Jake.

Kitty Don't laugh, Jake, don't laugh at me.

Jake I'm sorry, Kit. But when you talk about celebrity. When you tell me that you and Roche and H and Sin are going to be famous –

Kitty We are.

Jake I have to laugh.

Kitty Because . . . ?

Jake Because . . . In six months – six months when I thought we'd told each other all our secrets – six months and you've never told me that –

Kitty And when I do you laugh at me.

Jake I'm sorry, Kit.

Kitty I choose to share my dream with you and you mock.

Jake I shouldn't but . . . I just never knew. Tell me. Tell me what you dream about.

Kitty You musn't laugh.

Jake I won't.

Kitty Even a giggle and I'll stop.

Jake I promise. I want to understand girls. I want to understand what goes on inside their heads I want to know what you talk about. You and Roche and H and Sin. Tell me. Tell me about your dream.

Kitty OK. We're going to be celebrities. Pretty soon, you're going to see us everywhere. Huge billboards with our faces on a thousand feet high. TV screens with us talking, moving, dancing, laughing. The front pages will tell you what we're up to every day. If we choose the swordfish over the caviar in a restaurant they're going to analyse it live on CNN. You go to buy a can of Coke – they'll have our faces on the side. Whole coachloads of Japanese schoolkids are going to dress like us. Your screensaver, your desktop, your mobile's welcome screen – all of them will be me and Roche and H and Sin.

Pause. Then Jake laughs.

Oh piss off, Jake. Just piss off.

Jake I'm sorry, Kit. I just – you know.

Kitty What?

Jake Look at us. This town, this school. It just seems such a fantasy.

Kitty An ambition. That's the trouble with you, Jake. You don't want anything.

Jake I want –

Kitty I am so fed up with you.

Jake I'm sorry I'll –

Kitty I don't want to see you any more.

Jake What you're –?

Kitty I'm ending this relationship. Here. Now. Goodbye.

Jake No. Kit. Wait. You can't just walk away.

Kitty Why not?

Jake Because I love you.

Kitty That's nice.

Jake And you love me.

Kitty Do I? Do I really, Jay? I don't think so. No. I think I used to. But I'm growing up fast. Six months ago I was a kid and now . . .

Jake Now you're a celebrity.

Kitty Now I'm ready to be a celebrity. And I don't need you any more. So – there. I'm freeing you.

Jake Kitty, please.

Kitty You're a nice guy. You're good-looking. Ish. You have a sense of humour. Someone else will go out with you.

Jake No.
Kitty Goodbye. I'm not your girlfriend any more.
Jake I've still got the photo of you up beside my bed. The photo I put up the day I asked you out and you said yes.
Kitty You have to go now. Rochelle's on her way over and we've got a lot to talk about.
Jake Plans for the future?
Kitty Sort of.
Jake So what now? Talk to your stylists? Talk to your PR people? Sort out a few shoots? A few interviews?
Kitty Piss off, Jake.
Jake Or maybe you're just going to sit here with *Heat* /and *Hello* –
Kitty No, actually, no.
Jake Sit here and waste your time with pointless, pointless dreams?

Enter Rochelle.

Rochelle Hi, guys.
Jake What are you going to be?
Kitty How do you mean?
Jake In five years, ten years, twenty years. What are you two going to be?
Kitty I told you, Jacob. Celebrities.
Rochelle That's right.
Jake Are you going to be in a band?
Kitty Maybe. I don't know.
Jake Or act?
Kitty Yeah. Could do.
Jake Or model or present on MTV or –?
Kitty Yeah, yeah. Jake –
Jake Well – which one? What's going to make you famous?
Kitty I don't know. I don't care. / It doesn't matter.

Jake You've got to have a talent. You've got to have a gift. An achievement.

Kitty Of course, yeah.

Jake And I hate to break this to you girls but you can't sing, you can't act, you're OK-looking but you're not models –

Kitty We'll find a way.

Jake Dreaming, the pair of you.

Kitty You reckon?

Jake Yeah. Silly, silly girls.

Kitty OK. You want to know? You want to know what's gonna make us famous?

Jake Yes. I want to know what's going to make you famous.

Kitty OK. We're going to date celebrities.

Rochelle That's right.

Jake Oh really?

Kitty Not boys, not children, not the kids we have to hang around with here, but proper, A-list, friends-of-Elton-John-and-his-partner-David-Furnish celebrities.

Rochelle That's right.

Jake Ridiculous.

Kitty To you. To you. You boy. You infant. But to us. Have you any idea how frustrating it's been, going out with you when you know you should be going out with a star?

Jake Fantastic. Sleep your way to the top.

Kitty No, Jake. Love my way to the top. And the top is going to love me. Now can you please go? Roche needs to talk to me, don't you, Roche?

Rochelle That's right.

Kitty Roche is majorly upset, aren't you, Roche?

Rochelle That's right.

Jake And where are you going to meet him? Where are you going to meet your celebrity?

Kitty I don't know.

Jake Just gonna bump into him at the 7–11?

Kitty Maybe.

Jake He spills his Fanta over you and the next week you're snogging on a secluded beach on page four of *Heat*?

Kitty Possibly, yes, possibly.

Jake You're pathetic, Kit.

Kitty I hate you, Jake. Freak off. Go on. I don't want you here. It's gonna happen. Today. By the end of a day I'm gonna be dating a celeb.

Rochelle That's right.

Jake By the end of today? That's a promise?

Kitty That's a promise.

Jake Ha. Ha. Ha.

Exit Jake.

Kitty Loser. We're gonna show him.

Rochelle Maybe he's right, Kit. Maybe we're never going to make it.

Kitty No. You know what that horoscope said.

Rochelle I know.

Kitty 'Cast off old attachments and prepare to live your dreams.' And that's exactly what we've got to do. Did you stick to the plan?

Rochelle Yeah. I did it just like you said. Only . . .

Kitty I need you with me, Rochelle. We've got to stick together. Everybody else in this stupid school, this stupid town, is gonna laugh at us, but you and me and H and Sin, we've got to keep on going for each other. OK?

Rochelle OK. Just . . .

Kitty Yeah?

Rochelle Dan cried. When I said, 'I don't want to be your girlfriend any more,' he burst into tears. Like great big sobbing tears. And I wanted to say, 'Dan, Dan. Stop. I didn't mean it. I still love you.'

Kitty But you didn't.

Rochelle No, Kit. I didn't. Select All. Delete. Just like you said.

Kitty You had to do it, Roche. Dan's a nice guy . . .

Rochelle He's a really nice guy.

Kitty But can you imagine him with David Beckham or Sting or the Queen?

Rochelle No. No I can't.

Kitty He'd say all the wrong things. And what about his skin?

Rochelle It is a bit zitty.

Kitty Exactly. 'Rochelle and her acne-covered boyf welcome you into their new luxury home.'

Rochelle Yuck. No way.

Kitty We're gonna find you a nice Calvin Klein model.

Rochelle Oh yeah. Skinny but toned.

Kitty And a tattoo like a barcode on his bum.

Enter Hannah.

Hannah Oh God. I feel like such a bitch. 'Tyson, this is the end.' He just kept on repeating in this really pathetic voice: 'Why? Why? Why?' Over and over again. 'Why? Why? Why?' And now he wants back everything he ever gave me: CDs, videos, T-shirts. Everything. And I'm going to miss them so much. This better be worth it, Kit.

Kitty Worth it? H. What's Tyson when you are gonna have your pick of film stars, singers, footballers, models? You want Brad Pitt?

Hannah I'd love Brad Pitt but –

Kitty Then work it, girl. We are gonna be so famous he won't resist.

Hannah But isn't he with –?

Kitty You'll be all over the papers for days. Your publicist will have to work overtime. 'I regret all the hurt I've caused,' you'll say. 'But Brad and I are so happy together.'

Hannah Yes. An intimate wedding. Brad. Our families. And a few friends.

Kitty That's it. And where's Tyson gonna be? Stacking shelves? The call centre?

Rochelle Car-park attendant maybe.

Kitty Let him read about it in the papers.

Hannah Brad and I are gonna meditate for an hour together every morning.

Rochelle And have tantric sex together for four hours every night.

Hannah Tantric sex? What's that?

Enter Sinita, crying.

Sinita I hate you, Kitty. Why did you make me do that? I love Framji, I do. And now. And now. I finished with him. (*Cries.*)

Rochelle Come on, babe.

Sinita He says he never wants to see me again. Or walk down the same street as me. Or take the same bus as me. Or use the same search engine as me. Totally – gone. For ever. And what am I gonna do without him?

Kitty Do without him? Do without him? You know what you're gonna do without him. Same as me without Jay, same as Roche without Dan, same as H without Ty. Be a celebrity.

Sinita And are you sure about that, Kit?

Kitty Yes of course. Totally sure. Aren't you?

Sinita Well . . .

Kitty Sin. You can't give up this easily. I know this is hard. But think of the reward. Think of waking up in this totally fantastic house next to your totally buff boyfriend.

Rochelle And there's a TV crew already there as you open your eyes. They're making a documentary about you 24/7. (There's a whole cable channel that shows it all totally live.)

Hannah And then you exercise with your buff personal trainer.

Kitty Take some conference calls with Japan as you eat your breakfast – they're planning this Barbie-type doll of you to launch in markets right around the world.

Rochelle The morning: photo-shoots – a calendar. Some fittings for your bridal gown. *Hello* is sponsoring your wedding. Only fourteen months to go.

Hannah Lunch with Donatella, Beoncye and Madonna. Chatter, chatter. You debate: is hatha yoga now passé? Then cameras: flash, flash, flash.

Kitty The afternoon: a massage and a meeting with the team from LA who want to turn you into an animated series for TV. You tell them: nice idea but you're holding out to see what happens with the movie rights.

Rochelle Then off to a gallery. You've done a painting for charity. Just a fun thing. 'I'm no artist,' you tell the waiting press.'But I do care about sick children and I just wanted to do whatever I could to help.'

Hannah And then up the red carpet at a film launch. 'Is it true they're making you into a musical?' 'No comment.' Then party, party. 'Hi, Nicole! Hi, Ewan! Hello, Uma!' Then driven home.

Kitty And as you fall into your bed you say: 'I did it. This is me. My dream, my hope, my destiny. Celebrity. Today was hard. I know that, girls. 'Cast off old attachments,' that's hard. But now it's time, time to live your dreams. Are you gonna do that, Sin?

Sinita Will I have a stalker?

Kitty Maybe.

Sinita I'd like a stalker. Someone who fills their house with pictures of me. Goes through my bins. Names all their children after me. Who can't get me out of their head.

Kitty Of course you'll have a stalker.

Sinita And threatens to shoot himself if I don't return his calls.

Kitty Yes. Absolutely.

Sinita Oh wow.

Kitty Are we sticking together, girls? Are we sistas?

Rochelle/Hannah/Sinita Yeah.

Kitty Then come on. New *OK* out today. New *Sugar*. See what our horoscopes say today.

Kitty produces magazines from her bag and hands them round.

Kitty Oh my God. Can you believe that? OOPS I ATE IT AGAIN. BRITNEY PILES ON THE POUNDS.

Rochelle She often does that when she's under stress. It's her flaw.

Sinita My uncle e-mailed me this video-clip of Britney and Justin doing it.

Rochelle I think actually in her heart she still misses Justin.

Sinita But maybe it was just look-alikes or something. It was a bit of a shaky camera and the lighting wasn't so good.

Hannah I bet it was, though. I bet Britney's done it.

Rochelle Do you think chocolate's a carb?

Kitty OK. Horoscope time. Oh my God. Oh my God. Look at this. 'A stranger will show you the way to future happiness today.' What does that mean? Keep your eyes peeled for a stranger, girls.

Enter Letitia, Donna, Rachel, Indu, Michael and Rubin.

Kitty Ugh, look.

Hannah Do I see the most uncool people on the whole planet?

Sinita The whole universe.

Rochelle Oh no. The drama class.

Indu Hey, girls, you missed a great drama class today.

Kitty We've got no time to talk to you guys. We're waiting for a stranger.

Rachel We all had these numbers and that was the status you were. Status is like a power, yeah a sort of power, influence, status sort of thing.

Sinita Right.

Rubin So – say you're a king. Then you're like a ten. Unless you're a low status, sort of nervous king. Then you're like a three or something.

Hannah Wow. Sounds amazing.

Letitia And I got a two. Which is really, really low. Like a really awkward, stupid, clumsy sort of person.

Rochelle Wow, Tish. That must have been hard.

Letitia Yeah. That's what I thought at first. But then – when I got into it. Wow. I was like this total two.

Kitty Tish. You're sad.

Donna Not as sad as you, bunking off so you can –

Sinita Drama's for losers, Donna.

Michael But if you wanna be celebrities –

Hannah And what do they teach us? Improvisation? Theatre games? *Romeo and Juliet?* No thank you. That's not the stuff we need to know.

Rochelle Yeah. We wanna know how to make love to the camera.

Sinita How to make the camera love us.

Kitty How to use a microphone. When to listen to your stylist and when to listen to your instincts.

Hannah How to handle the press. What dress to choose for a première.

Sinita How to mime in videos, voice-over for an ad.

Kitty And whose the best agent if you're gonna be a star. But do they teach us that? No.

Rochelle This is the twenty-first century. Drama's for losers.

Letitia But I just think it would be so great.
Sinita What would?
Letitia To lose yourself. Become another person.
Kitty That's not the way it works any more, Tish. You're a brand. You sell yourself. You don't become another person.
Letitia But that's what I wanna –
Kitty Then you keep going to drama classes. You keep wasting your time with silly games. But me and the girls aren't doing that. Are we, girls?
Rochelle/Hannah/Sinita No.
Kitty Come on, girls. Let's find a stranger to show us the way to future happiness. Enjoy the acting, Letitia.

Exit Kitty, Rochelle, Hannah and Sinita.

Letitia Status ten. Status ten. Status ten. Status one. Status one. Status one.

Exit Letitia.

Donna Tish? Tisha? She is so upset.

Exit Donna, Indu, Rachel, Michael and Rubin. Enter Jake and Victor.

Jake Victor. Will you stop following me? I want to be alone.
Victor But we said we'd go to a movie.
Jake Yeah. Well. I've changed my mind.
Victor There's a sci-fi thing. Which sounds good. Or an action thing. Which sounds OK. Or a CGI thing. Which sounds cute. Or a comedy. Which sounds hilarious. Which do you fancy?
Jake None of them.
Victor I've got some DVDs if you wanna –
Jake No.
Victor Or games. My mum left pizza and some oven chips –

Jake Vic. I want to be by myself. Please.
Victor But – why?
Jake Kit finished with me.
Victor No way.
Jake Yeah. She chucked me. So –
Victor I'm sorry.
Jake And I just want to go into my room and play Korn and be alone.
Victor But surely a movie would –
Jake No, Vic. I'm sorry.
Victor Or a pizza or just hanging out at Burger King.
Jake Victor. No.
Victor OK. But maybe if we just talked –
Jake This isn't freaking Oprah or Rikki OK? It's not: JAKE – MY GIRLFRIEND JUST DUMPED ME. Then talk, talk, talk and out she comes from behind a freaking screen. And she talks and Oprah talks. And the crowd goes 'Ooo' and then we hug and I cry. And it's the end and Oprah says: 'When you talk the hurt begins to heal.' OK?
Victor OK.
Jake Why does everybody want to talk? Confess? To kiss and tell? I hate this freaking world we live in.
Victor I know you do, Jay.
Jake These freaking superficial boybands and models and movie stars confessing everything just so they can fill up magazines. It's all shit.
Victor That's right, Jay.
Jake Well, I'm not talking. Because no one understands what's happening inside me. No one knows and there's no way I can make them know. And I don't want to make them know.
Victor But I'm your friend.
Jake I know and . . .
Victor All the things we've done together. Things I've done for you.

Jake But Vic – you're a dork. You've never been out with a girl.

Victor I'd like to.

Jake And I don't want to talk to someone who doesn't know anything about girls.

Victor You know Letitia?

Jake If you haven't been out with a girl you're a child, Vic.

Victor She did the Nurse in that scene from *Romeo and Juliet*.

Jake That's the difference between us, Vic.

Victor I like Letitia. I keep on having dreams about her. I want to ask her out.

Jake You're a child and I'm a man.

Enter Dan.

Dan I don't believe it. I just don't believe it. Roche finished with me.

Jake She chucked you?

Dan Just sat me down and said: 'I don't want to see you any more. We're finished. Over.' She wants to be a celebrity, Jay.

Jake Oh my God.

Victor Do you want to see a movie?

Dan Where do you get Prozac from? Do you have to go to a doctor?

Victor I think the action movie could be good.

Dan Or is it an over-the-counter thing? She's going to be famous and she doesn't want to be seen with a boy like me. Would you call me zitty?

Enter Tyson.

Tyson Bitch. Bitch. Bitch.

Jake What's that, Ty?

Tyson Hannah. What a freaking bitch. Chucked me. I've never been chucked. Never. Sure – I've chucked a few times. But I've always done it sweetly. I'm a good chucker, but Hannah – freaking horrible.

Jake Did she say she wanted to be –?

Tyson A celebrity. Can you believe that? I told her: no freaking way, baby. And then she got mad at me and chucked me. I'm just so angry.

Victor Maybe going to a movie would help?

Tyson What's he doing here? What are you doing here?

Victor There's a sci-fi movie –

Tyson Shut up, Victor, shut up.

Victor I'm just trying to –

Tyson Victor!

Victor OK. OK.

Enter Framji.

Framji Guys. You'll never guess. Sin finished with me.

Jake We know.

Framji She wants to be a celebrity and –

Jake We know.

Framji She says I'm holding her back.

Jake We know. Same for all of us, Fram. Me and Kit. Dan and Roche. H and Ty. You and Sin. We've all been chucked.

Dan On the same day.

Tyson At the same time.

Framji But – they must have planned this.

Jake That's right.

Framji I don't believe it. What a bitch.

Tyson Yeah. Total bitches. All of them.

Enter Kitty, Rochelle, Hannah and Sinita.

Kitty Oh hi. We didn't know you were here.

Jake Yeah. That's right. We're here.

Hannah We're looking for a stranger. To show the way to future happiness.

Tyson Right.

Rochelle Like it says here. You seen a stranger?
Dan No. Don't think so. No.
Kitty Come on, girls. They're not gonna help us.

Exit Kitty, Rochelle, Hannah and Sinita.

Framji Did you see that? Didn't even look at me.
Jake We need to show them, guys.
Tyson Yeah. We need to punish them.
Dan We need to hurt them.
Framji To teach them a lesson.
Jake To show them how stupid they are.
Dan But how?
Victor Maybe if I –?
Dan What's the best way to make them suffer?
Victor Can I –? I've got an idea.
Tyson Victor. You don't know anything about girls. You go off to the library and let us figure this out.
Framji They're coming back. They're coming this way.
Dan Run.
Jake Stay.
Tyson Hide.
Victor Guys. I'm going to show you – Can I show you? Guys.

Jake, Dan, Tyson and Framji hide as Kitty, Rochelle, Hannah and Sinita enter. Victor conceals his face.

Victor The future. The future. I see the future.
Rochelle Ugh. Look. A loony.
Sinita A loony homeless person.
Hannah Ugh. Gross. They don't wash. And they really smell.
Sinita And they get aggressive if you don't give them money.
Rochelle Well, I'm not giving him anything.
Kitty Girls. Listen for a moment. Just listen to what he's saying.

Victor

The mortal man walks backward
His face towards what's gone
The future is a mystery
But still he travels on.

Sinita It's like mad person's talk.

Kitty No. It makes sense if you listen.

Victor

But I am not as other men
Who only see what's done
My brain is burnt with future lives
I see the world to come.

The future. The future. I see the future.

Kitty Who are you?

Hannah Kit, I think we ought / to be going now.

Kitty No, no. We've got to talk to him. / Find out –

Rochelle He's really creepy, Kit.

Sinita Yeah. I think he may be Dangerous.

Kitty But girls – if he sees the future –

Victor I know you. I know you. I know you. I know you.

Sinita Oh my God. He's going completely mental.

Rochelle I want another Diet Coke. Let's all go and buy another Diet Coke.

Sinita Yeah, Roche. Good idea.

Kitty Girls. We've got to ask him. We've got to make him tell us. What happens to us? How do we get to be celebrities?

Hannah There's no point asking him. He's a spazza.

Kitty Stick together, girls. We've got to stick together.

Victor I know you. I know you. I know you. I know you.

Kitty Me?

Victor Everybody knows you.

Kitty In the future?

Victor You are famous in the future.

Kitty Oh my God. That's amazing.

Victor Your picture is everywhere in the future. A hotel in Bangkok, an iMax in New Mexico, a hologram in Times Square – it's you.

Kitty I knew it. I knew I was right.

Victor You are a line of clothes, a cola drink, a fitness video, a salad dressing, a dress-me doll, an arcade game, a mouse mat, a bumper sticker, a syndicated column, a talkshow, an infomercial, the most hits in a day on AOL, a remix, beauty tips, a goodwill ambassador, an eight-page pull-out supplement, a diet plan, a chain of restaurants, a literacy campaign, a sex symbol, role-model superstar. You are live action, animation, computer-generated, holographic, CD ROM, exclusive pictures, pay-to-view. All of them are you and you are all of them. Oh yes I know you. In the future I know you. In the future everybody knows you.

Kitty And Roche and H and Sin as well?

Victor And Roche and H and Sin as well.

Rochelle Oh my God.

Hannah Oh my God.

Sinita Amazing.

Victor The bedrooms that you live in now will be musuems – a shrine for all your fans to come and worship. Coaches will pull up outside your school: 'That's the place. That's where she studied.'

Rochelle That is so cool.

Victor Everybody who ever knew you will auction every gift you ever gave them. 'This item personally touched by Kitty.' And everything bought – instantly.

Sinita What will we be famous for?

Victor Do you know the band Awesome?

Sinita No.

Victor Four boys. The finest voices. Best dance routines. Best power ballads. The four most famous faces of the future.

Kitty And we're . . .?

Victor You date them. And they bring you fame.

Hannah And when do we meet them? Where do we meet them?

Victor You've already met them.

Kitty We have?

Victor They are here in your town, your school right now. Awesome are amongst you. The four most famous faces of the future, the biggest celebrities the globe has ever known are Jake and Dan and Ty and Framji.

Sinita But we just . . . oh no . . .

Victor Yes?

Rochelle We just chucked them.

Victor You . . .? Oh no. Then you must unchuck them fast. You can't meddle with the future. You have to date them or the future's empty: blank videos, blank ads, blank T-shirts, blank covers on the magazines. Without your faces, everything's a void. Quick, quick. Find your friends. Oh God. It's hurting. When time is bent like this it hurts me. Ugh. Ugh. Put the future right. Go out with Jake and Dan and Ty and Fram. Date Awesome! Agh! Agh! Back on the path or I'll die!

Kitty Oh my God!

Victor Before it's too late! Aaaaaagggh!

Exit Kitty, Rochelle, Hannah and Sinita.

Framji Woah! Yes! Yes! Yes! Excellent, Victor!

Tyson Yeah! Fantastic! Excellent! That was / so cool.

Jake Brilliant! You are such a / good actor.

Victor Thank you.

Dan Yeah. You were totally convincing. Amazing.

Jake And now. Now we can get our own back.

Tyson Yeah!

Jake Now we're going to turn the tables. 'Cos we know what it's like to want someone, need someone, love someone and be pushed aside. We know that feeling, don't we, guys?

Dan Oh yeah.

Jake Well now it's their turn. They are gonna beg us guys. They are gonna cry and plead and do anything they can to get us back. But we are gonna say: no way. Agreed?

Framji/Tyson/Dan Agreed.

Jake Come on then. Let the fun begin.

Jake, Framji, Tyson and Dan start to exit.

Victor Listen, guys. I've got another idea. Make them look really stupid.

Jake What's that, Vic?

Victor Let's play with their minds. These girls want to meet celebrities. Then let's arrange for them to meet a few. Let's make them think they've made it. Then destroy them.

Tyson Yeah.

Victor You're going to see those girls looking so stupid. Follow me.

Enter Letitia.

Letitia Hey. What you up to?

Victor We're sort of . . . we're gonna do some acting.

Letitia Acting? I love acting.

Victor I saw you in that scene. The Nurse.

Letitia Oh yes. The Nurse. I wanted to be Juliet but . . .

Victor You want to do some acting with us?

Tyson Vic. This is a boy thing.

Dan Yeah, Victor. This is us against them.

Letitia Who against who?

Jake Sorry, Vic. But we don't want her involved. No girls.

Exit Jake, Dan, Tyson and Framji.

Letitia What do they mean, us against them?
Victor They just – they've sort of gone off girls.
Letitia And what about you? Are you off girls?
Victor Oh no. I'm on girls. I mean I like girls. I like a girl.
Letitia Yeah?
Victor Listen, if you wanna do the acting with us.
Letitia OK.
Victor I'll try and persuade them. I'd like to give you a big part. And we'll need the drama class as well. We'll need lots of people.
Letitia Are we putting on a play?
Victor A sort of a play. Well, more a sort of a concert. A play-concert-media-event sort of . . . you'll see.
Letitia OK. Victor –
Victor Yeah?
Letitia Nothing.

Exit Victor and Letitia.

TWO

Enter Hannah and Tyson.

Hannah Ty. Just listen for a moment. One moment – please. I made a mistake. I made the biggest mistake of my life. But we all make mistakes. And I was mad to finish with you. I don't know why I did that. Some sort of fever in the brain. But now – I miss you so much. I want you back so much. Ty, please –
Tyson H. I don't got time to talk about this now.

Enter Letitia, in disguise.

Letitia (*on mobile*) Yeah. He's here. Yeah he's right here in front of me. Is he OK? I don't know? (*to Tyson*) Excuse me, sir. Are you OK?

Tyson Yeah, sure. I'm OK.

Letitia (*on mobile*) He's with a girl. Yeah. No. Not so pretty. Well I don't know. I don't know if she's bothering him. (*to Tyson*) Is she bothering you, sir?

Tyson No. That's OK.

Letitia (*on mobile*) Of course I'll pass that on. Five minutes. OK. Bye now. Bye. (*to Tyson*) Sorry about that, sir. The stylist is ready for you, sir. Is that OK with you, sir?

Tyson That's fine. Are the rest of the guys –?

Letitia On their way, sir.

Tyson I'll be through in just a minute.

Letitia Certainly, sir. Sorry to interrupt, sir.

Exit Letitia.

Hannah Ty – who was that?

Tyson My PA. It's kinda embarrassing. But essential. You get used to it.

Hannah And the stylist?

Tyson You don't know? H, so much has happened since we split. Me and the guys formed a band. Awesome. Like the name?

Hannah I love it. It's brilliant.

Tyson And we've signed to a major label. And the record company have invested a lot of money and today's the day they launch us. Meet the press. Photo-ops. Promote our first single. 'So Totally Over You.' I think you're gonna like it.

Hannah Yeah. Sounds great.

Tyson We weren't sure at first whether we wanted the whole celebrity thing, you know? I think that could really play with your mind.

Hannah Oh definitely, yeah.

Tyson We talked about it for a long time. How are we going to handle being totally massive? But then we decided to give it a go. Have a laugh. Get rich. Can't be so bad, can it?

Enter Letitia.

Letitia I'm sorry, sir. The stylist?
Tyson On my way.

Exit Letitia.

Tyson Don't do anything I wouldn't do.

Exit Tyson.

Hannah Tyson. Tyson. Just you freaking come back here.

Enter Sinita and Framji.

Sinita No, no, no, please. Listen to me. Listen. Just give me a chance. One date. And if that doesn't work out –
Framji Sin – I've got no time for this. I have a career to launch. Have a good life. Ciao.

Exit Framji. Enter Rochelle and Dan.

Dan I'm late. I'm late. I'm late. Call me. No don't. I changed my number. Mail me. No don't, I've changed the address.
Rochelle Dan, we have to talk.
Dan Leave a message with Mum. My manager talks to her once a week. She passes on the messages. Most of the time.
Rochelle Dan –
Dan The stylist is gonna kill me.

Exit Dan. Enter Jake and Kitty.

Jake Kitty. Join the fan club, visit our web page. Have you any idea how busy our schedule is? Buy the single. It rocks.

Exit Jake.

Kitty Bastard. God. They are such bastards. Some people just can't handle celebrity. When we're famous we're really gonna stay in touch with our roots. We are gonna keep it real. Why can't they keep it real?

Hannah Maybe if you hadn't made us chuck them in the first place.

Sinita Yeah, Kit. I would still have been with Framji if it weren't for you.

Rochelle And I'd have Dan.

Kitty But the horoscope –

Rochelle Shut up about that freaking horoscope, Kit. We've lost them, Kit.

Kitty No.

Sinita Yeah. They're great big megastars and we're just schoolkids hanging around.

Kitty No way.

Enter Letitia.

Letitia I'm sorry. You girls are going to have to move. We have a press launch here in a few minutes.

Kitty We're with the band.

Letitia Oh no. If you're with the band I have you on my list here. See? Hair Stylist, Make-Up Stylist, Style Stylist, Personal Shopper, Personal Trainer, Press Aide, Vocal Coach, Dance Coach, Runner. You have to be on the list.

Kitty What about girlfriend? Is that on the list?

Letitia Girlfriend. No. Their management won't let them have girlfriends.

Kitty But they have to have girlfriends. Whose gonna sit beside them on their *Hello* cover?

Hannah Whose gonna help them out of the Met bar when they've drunk too many vodkas?

Sinita Whose gonna have their babies? Winter-Storm and Hawaiian Breeze?

Letitia You're thinking of a more mature market. These guys are for the pre-teens. The pre-teens want them single. Look at the focus groups.

Enter Michael, disguised as a stylist, with several assistants carrying clothes.

Michael Blinding. These boys look blinding. You wanna see the Polaroids? (*Michael passes some Polaroids to the girls.*) Hip and yet High Street, Now and yet For ever, Sexy and Yet Clean, More Than a Boy Not Yet a Man. Great, yeah?

Rochelle Oh my God, that's Dan. Look.

Sinita And Framji. Wow. Amazing.

Hannah Brilliant.

Letitia They're here. They're here. The press are here. You're going to have to go.

Exit Letitia.

Kitty Can we borrow some clothes from you? We have to blend in or they'll throw us out.

Michael They're due back with Donatella in an hour.

Kitty Just half an hour. Please.

Michael All right. Half an hour and I'm taking them back.

Kitty Thank you. Thank you. We are gonna look fabulous.

Exit Michael, Kitty, Rochelle, Hannah, Sinita and stylist's assistants.

Enter Jake and Dan. They have been 'styled'.

Dan So you're saying . . . ?

Jake I'm saying . . . that Kitty looked really sad.

Dan Which is kind of the idea isn't it?

Jake Which is kind of the idea, yes.

Dan Your idea.

Jake My idea. Yes. Just . . .

Dan Yes?

Jake I didn't realise . . . she looked so . . . lost.

Dan Jay. Think how much she hurt you. You can't go back now. Kitty is a bitch, OK?

Jake Yeah. Kitty is a bitch. Kitty is a bitch. Kitty is a bitch.

Enter Letitia.

Letitia What are you doing here? You should be backstage.

Exit Jake and Dan.

Enter Donna, Rachel, Indu, Rubin and others disguised as the Press: reporters, photographers, TV crews. Letitia organises them.

Enter Victor in disguise.

Letitia Ladies and gentleman, we have a very special new brand for you today. A brand for a multi-market environment. A brand with fantastic synergistic potential. Ladies and gentlemen, brand manager Karl Watkins.

Victor You know, when I started out in this business it was easy. You found a few boys who could sing. Or looked good. And you gave 'em a few songs. And you bought them a place in the chart. And they went massive. And we all got very rich. Nowadays, of course, it's all a lot more complicated. The market's fragmented. There's video games and web sites and Class A drugs competing for the kids' pocket money. Some mornings I wake up and I say: 'Victor, this is a young man's game. And you're a fat old bastard.' But every now and then, once in a decade, something happens and I get excited about Pop all over again. And my life has meaning. Ladies and gentlemen, does your life have meaning? It does now. Here's Jay, Dan, Ty and Framji. Here's Awesome.

Applause. Enter Jake, Dan, Tyson and Framji, with several big security guards (again members of Letitia's drama class in disguise) standing by them.

Jake Hi. This is our first single. Hope you like it.

Music. They sing: 'So Totally Over You'.

Used to feel this pain would never end
Used to think my heart would never mend
Used to pray that you'd come back to me
The nights were long
But now I'm free
'Cos I grew strong
And baby can't you see?

Chorus:

I'm so totally over you
(Never want to see your face again)
I'm so totally over you
(Don't need a lover, don't want a friend)
You said goodbye when I was true
Found breaking up was hard to do
But I'm totally over you.

Enter Michael, Kitty, Rochelle, Hannah, Sinita and stylist's assistants. The girls have been dressed in the most impractical high-fashion clothes imaginable.

We both must go our separate ways
You'll hurt another boy someday
And maybe I will love again
And learn to trust but girl till then

Repeat Chorus to fade.
Applause.

Victor Any questions for the boys?

During the press conference hands are raised and Victor chooses whose questions get answered.

Donna Where did the band begin?

Jake Well it actually began when my girlfriend chucked me.

Donna Really?

Jake Yeah. I'd been going out with this girl. And . . . this is really difficult to talk about. But. I loved her so much, you know? I couldn't stop thinking about her all the time. I couldn't imagine living without her. And then one day she finished with me. Just like that. Over. And I had all this hurt inside me. And it wouldn't come out. And it kept on hurting and hurting and it was growing bigger and bigger inside me like this great big ball of hurt. And then one day I started to hear this tune. And then I got these lyrics. And I wrote them down. And I started to feel better. And that's when I wrote 'So Totally Over You'.

Dan And Jay came to me. Because I'd just had the same experience. This girl I totally adored had dumped me. And he said he'd got this song. And he sang it to me. And I really related to it. 'Cos that's how I felt. All that hurt. And I heard like all these harmonies and I wrote them down.

Framji And then they sang me the song. And it made me want to dance. Because I'd been chucked too – by this girl who I thought was the most amazing thing to ever walk the planet. And I found if I danced it sort of let all the hurt out. And so I worked out all the choreography.

Tyson And the guys came over to mine. Because I was really hurting too after my break-up. And they sang the song, the harmonies, did the dance, and I was like 'Awesome'. And that's how we got the name.

Sinita What would you say to those girls if they were here today?

Dan Thank you.

Sinita Really?

Dan Yeah. I'd thank them. Because if we hadn't been chucked like that we wouldn't have had anything to write about.

Hannah And what about the lyrics of the song? Would you say they're true? Could you honestly say to those girls 'So Totally Over You'?

Tyson Oh yeah. That's our message to those girls. If she were here now I'd say: 'Hannah, I'm Totally Over You.' And I'd say: 'Thing is, H, even if I did still love you – even if, deep in my heart, I was still in love with you – I couldn't go out with you. I mean, I'm a celebrity now, right? I have to date other celebrities. And you're not.' I'd say: 'H, you're a wannabe. I can't date a girl like that. You're a nothing to me now.' That's what I'd say if she were here today.

Hannah Bastard. Freaking freaking bastard.

Exit Hannah.

Framji Yeah, me too. If she was here now I'd be like, 'Stop crying, Sin. Crying's not gonna change anything. Because I don't feel anything. I feel nothing for you. Totally Over You.' That's what I would say to Sinita. If she were here today.

Sinita Fram, no.

Sinita exits in tears.

Dan And Rochelle. I'd like to say: 'Had a few good times. Had a few bad times. Used to be hopes. But now it's all memories. Roche – I'm Totally Over You.'

Rochelle I'm not listening to this.

Kitty Roche. Stay.

Rochelle No.

Kitty But Roche –

Victor And now Jay.

Rochelle Why do we always listen to you, Kit? Why do we always do what you say?

Victor What's your message to your ex, Jay?
Rochelle We were happy. Me and H and Sin were happy with what you had.
Jake I . . . Listen I don't . . .
Kitty No. But you wanted –
Rochelle Don't tell me what I wanted. I wanted Dan. And I lost him and it's all your fault.
Victor Come on, Jay. Don't be shy.

Exit Rochelle.

Victor And what about you, Jay? What would you say?
Jake I don't know. I . . .
Tyson Jay . . .?
Jake If I was honest . . . I think I still miss her.
Kitty Really?
Jake So I suppose . . . no. I'm not over her.
Dan Jay – that's not what we –
Kitty So would you go out with her again if you had the chance?
Victor All of the boys are single. Can we have another question?
Kitty I wanna know. Would you like a second chance?
Jake Maybe. I don't know.
Victor Let's move on. Can we have another question?
Rubin If you were a fruit what kind of fruit would you be?
Kitty I want an answer to my question.
Victor What kind of fruit are you?
Framji Guava.
Dan Apricot.
Kitty Jay. Jay. Answer my question.
Victor I'm warning you. You'll be thrown out. Fruits. Tyson.
Tyson Blueberry.
Kitty Take her back, Jay.
Victor If you were a fruit.
Jake I. I . . . don't know.

Victor What kind of fruit?
Kitty Let him answer my question.
Victor OK. That's it. That's enough. Get her out.

Frenzy. Security guards descend on Kitty. She struggles.

Kitty I just want to talk to Jay. Jay – please.
Victor Get her out of here.
Kitty Jay. Listen to me. This is Kitty. Will you take me back? I was wrong. How was I to know you were gonna be famous? Take me back, Jay, please.
Jake Kitty. I can't –
Victor Out. Out. Out. I want her out.

Finally, the security guards get the better of Kitty and she is dragged out.

As soon as Kitty goes the mood of the room changes. Everyone stops playing their roles. (The press, security and stylists become Letitia's drama class).

Tyson What the freak you doing, Jay?
Jake I don't know.
Framji That's not the deal, Jay.
Jake I know.
Tyson Punish them. Hurt them. Teach them a lesson. That's what we said.
Jake I know.
Tyson So what the freak are you doing . . .?
Jake It just came out like that.
Framji What is this? You want Kitty?
Jake I think . . . Yes. I do.
Dan But she doesn't want you, Jay.
Jake She's chasing after me.
Dan Because you're in Awesome.
Framji She doesn't want the real you, Jake.
Jake The real me?
Framji You know. The one who goes to school and Burger King and listens to Korn.

Jake Oh yeah, him.

Dan The one who's not a celebrity.

Jake But maybe if she thought I was a celebrity for a bit longer –

Tyson No.

Jake Oh come on. Just a bit more.

Framji No way.

Jake Maybe if she thinks I'm a celebrity and we get back together and then I tell her. Maybe then she'll see that –

Dan Jay. We wanted to punish them. We've punished them. The story's over, OK?

Jake Vic – please. Listen everybody. Just keep on pretending. Just keep on imagining, OK? It was great wasn't it ? Didn't you like it? Didn't you love it? Wasn't it better than school? Wasn't it better than drama class? You were all great. Freak me. You were fantastic. I totally believed you. Like you were the press and security guards. And the stylists – great. Brilliant. Yeah. Oh – and Victor. That manager. Do that manager again, Victor.

Victor We're finished, Jay.

Jake I want to see you do the manager again. And Letitia?

Letitia Yeah?

Jake Brilliant.

Letitia Really?

Jake I totally believed you. You want to be her some more?

Letitia Well . . .

Jake Go on. Everyone wants to do some more.

Victor No. The play's over. The boys win and the lights go down. Thanks, everybody.

Jake But what about me? I didn't win. I want Kitty. I want Kitty back.

Dan Jay –

Jake I love Kitty and I want her back.

Dan Jay, you're embarrassing.

Jake You've got to help me. All of you. You've all got to help me get Kitty.

Framji She's not worth it, Jay.

Tyson It's her put all these ideas in their heads in the first place.

Jake I know.

Dan It's her who told them all to chuck us.

Jake I know.

Framji It's her who only wants you 'cos she thinks you're in a boyband.

Jake I know. But I still –

Dan You tell her, Jay. You tell her what's really going on. And then you'll see what she's like.

Jake OK. OK I will

Framji No boyband. No celebrity.

Jake OK. OK.

Tyson You'll tell her the truth?

Jake I'll tell her the truth.

Tyson Good luck.

Everyone exits apart from Jake, who is left alone for a moment. Then Letitia re-enters.

Letitia I want to be my character again. Just a bit longer. It was so exciting. I mean, she's a boring person but still . . . I made up a whole biography and everything. Like I lost myself. I never had that happen before. I mean, I've been in plays and that. But I was always like, 'Look at me.' Or sometimes, 'I look terrible. Don't look at me.' And I'd always be looking over at my dad with the camcorder. But then, just now, I was gone. Like if I'd look in the mirror I wouldn't have recognised myself. Did you feel like that? When you were up there singing and you were pretending to be in that band? Wasn't pretending exciting?

Jake Maybe. But – pretending. Isn't that lying?
Letitia No. It's acting.
Jake Which is lying.
Letitia No. It's different.
Jake How?
Letitia I don't know. But it is.
Jake I'm not gonna pretend or lie or act. I'm not gonna do any of that bullshit. I'm gonna tell her the truth.

Kitty enters.

Letitia I better – I've got a lot to do. Check on the tour bus. They're very demanding. Videos, games, drinks. It all has to be right.
Jake Stop it. Stop.
Letitia We're doing a twenty-one-city tour. Europe. America's next month. But that's the music business. Ninety-nine per cent promotion. You can have the product –
Jake Don't.
Letitia But if you're not promoting you might as well not exist.
Jake Shut up.
Letitia I've got a lot of calls to make. Don't forget – *Smash Hits* at 3.30.
Jake Please –

Exit Letitia.

Kitty Do you have a stalker yet, Jay? Girl who doesn't sleep because she's thinking about you. Cries every time she sees your picture because she wants you so much. Some girls are like that.
Jake So I hear. Kitty –
Kitty Yeah. Some girls are really stupid.
Jake Kitty –
Kitty Did you mean that stuff?
Jake What stuff?

Kitty At the press conference. Jay. Will you go out with me?

Jake I don't know.

Kitty Let's be famous together, Jay. Let's wear the same clothes. Let's have matching tattoos. Let's be on the front pages together.

Jake Kitty, listen I don't wanna –

Kitty Let's have an amazing wedding and cute kids and raise money for charity and –

Jake Kit. There's something else I have to tell you.

Kitty Yes?

Jake I'm not . . . there's not . . . I sort of . . . I'm considering . . . I'm thinking about leaving the band.

Kitty What?

Jake I want to leave the band.

Kitty Why?

Jake Because we're not allowed girlfriends. So I have to make a choice. Drive around in the bus. Millions of girls screaming. See my face everywhere. Get very very rich. Be a celebrity all over the world. Or choose you. And then I saw you at the press conference and you were calling out to me – I've made a choice. Who wants freaking celebrity? I want Kitty.

Kitty Is that true?

Jake Yeah. That's totally true.

Kitty But Jake. These people – parents, the kids at school, the teachers. They're all so boring. Do you want that?

Jake S'pose not.

Kitty When life could be exciting. I don't want to fit in, Jay. I want to stand out. Does that sound stupid to you?

Jake No.

Kitty And celebrities. They're not like us. Everything they do counts. When I read about that I'm so jealous. You can't just turn your back on celebrity.

Jake But I've got all these feelings for you. And you've got all these feelings for me. That's more important. Will you go out with me, Kit?

Kitty But I want to be famous. And I want you. I want both.

Jake Choose, Kit. Decide.

Kitty I can't choose.

Jake You have to.

Kitty But if I have to, I choose . . . celebrity.

Jake OK. Then – goodbye. I really – you know – really thought we were so like each other. But you're . . . we're so different, Kit. Goodbye.

Kitty Did you really write that song?

Jake Yeah, 'course.

Kitty That song's gonna be huge. It's gonna be number one in markets all over the world.

Jake You reckon?

Kitty And Awesome are gonna fly everywhere, be everywhere, do everything, say everything. There's gonna be Pepsi, there's gonna be Cola, Macdonald's and then there's gonna be Awesome.

Jake Yeah.

Kitty You drive out into the bush or the jungle or the desert or something and show them pictures. What do they recognise? – Mickey Mouse, Madonna and Awesome. Jake – they're gonna be so famous it hurts. You've got to be part of that, Jake. You've got to sing the song.

Jake But Kitty –

Kitty Sing the song. Sing the song – and I'll love you.

Jake Kitty –

Kitty Yes?

Jake I'm going back.

Kitty You're – ?

Jake I'm going back to the band. I'm going back to Awesome. I'm singing the song. I'm touring the world. I'm making the video. I'm going to be freaking famous.

Kitty That's it, Jay. That's it. And me . . .? Am I . . .?

Jake And you . . . and you're . . . and you're there with me, Kit. Every step of the way.

Kitty Yes. Yes. Yes. Everywhere you go. Who's that girl? Who's that beautiful girl he's with? Of course we're going to have to handle it carefully. Your fans –

Jake Want me single.

Kitty But your management, your PR –

Jake Will have to handle that.

Kitty Because we love each other.

Jake Yes. We love each other. And the fans will learn to accept –

Kitty Will learn to love that.

Jake Then we can be launched – rebranded – resold –

Kitty A new start. Two dolls in the box. 'Kitty and Jake.'

Jake Two faces on the covers. 'Kitty and Jake.'

Kitty Two faces on the invites. 'Kitty and Jake.'

Jake We're going to save the rainforests.

Kitty We're going to save the planet.

Jake We're going to shop for ever.

Kitty We're going to love our fans.

Jake But need our privacy.

Kitty We'll sell shares in our future happiness.

Jake We're going to promote, promote, promote.

Kitty And spin and spin and spin.

Jake Here and there and everywhere.

Kitty And somewhere and nowhere. We're gods.

Jake We're superstars.

Kitty We're everything.

Enter Rochelle and Dan.

Rochelle Has he told you yet, Kit? Has he told you the truth?

Kitty What is this, Jake?

Jake Kitty. Maybe we should –

Rochelle It was all a trick, Kit. It was a game. To get us back.

Enter Hannah and Tyson.

Hannah Weren't they brilliant? They worked out the song and everything. Totally convincing.

Enter Sinita and Framji.

Sinita Excellent. So romantic.
Kitty Was this your idea?
Jake No. Victor's.

Enter Victor and Letitia.

Victor 'The future. The future, I see the future.'
Kitty Oh my God.
Letitia And I was playing the PA. That was me. Totally amazing. And this is the drama class.

The press, security and stylists all enter, wave and exit.

Letitia Fooled you. Isn't acting great?
Sinita Shall we all go to the movies? Who wants to see a film? Let's eat lots of popcorn and drink Coke.
Rochelle Diet Coke.
Sinita Diet Coke and watch a movie. Who's coming? Everybody? Come on.

Exit everyone apart from Jake and Kitty.

Kitty I always thought everyone else was thick. And I was clever. And I had to organise everyone. And if I didn't nothing would happen. But it was me. I'm the thick one.
Jake No.
Kitty Yeah, stupid freaking stupid freaking idiot bitch to believe –
Jake Kitty – don't –
Kitty I just wanted to believe so much, so much – that stupid band, that song –

Jake It's kind of funny. You could laugh.

Kitty Yeah. I could laugh.

Kitty cries. Jake holds her.

Kitty You lied to me, Jake.

Jake No. It was acting, pretending. Something.

Kitty Why do boys never tell you what they feel? All the time I was going out I'd say, 'How you doing, Jay?' and you'd just be, 'OK.' Tell me what you're feeling, Jay. Scared of a girl?

Jake No.

Kitty Then come on. Tell me the truth about how you feel.

Jake The truth about how I feel. OK. I feel everything for you, Kitty. I feel love. I feel kissing and cuddling and all that kind of love. But also like sex kind of love. Like I want to see you naked.

Kitty Yeah?

Jake And I feel hate. Like I want to scream and shout at you. Like I want to find all your weak points and really make you hurt.

Kitty Really?

Jake I feel like I want to spend the rest of my life with you. I feel like I never want to see you again. I feel like you're a supermodel. I feel like you're my sister. Or my mother. I feel like I want to tell everyone you're my girlfriend. I feel like I want to pretend I never knew you.

Kitty God. Jacob.

Jake What do you call it, Kit? When someone makes you have all these feelings? Is that love?

Kitty I don't know.

Jake Neither do I. What are you feeling now?

Kitty I don't know.

Jake Tell me. Scared of a boy? Tell me.

Kitty I love you. I hate you. I want to kiss you. I want to scream at you. I want to stay with you. I want to run away from you. I – so much stuff.

Jake It's bad, isn't it?

Kitty It's terrible.

Enter Victor.

Victor You coming to see the film?

Jake I suppose. Kit. Do you wanna . . .?

Kitty I suppose.

Victor Letitia asked me out.

Jake That's nice.

Kitty Great, Vic.

Victor Aren't girls amazing?

Jake Yeah. Amazing.

Kitty What's the movie?

Victor It's a comedy.

Jake/Kitty Good.

End.

Obsessed with Celebrity

Mark Ravenhill interviewed by Jim Mulligan

Mark Ravenhill was nearly thirty when he started writing. Before that he had been successful at his Hayward's Heath comprehensive school and then at Bristol University, followed by work as a director. His first full-length play, *Shopping and Fucking*, was produced to great acclaim by Out of Joint and the Royal Court Theatre and opened at the Ambassadors in 1996 prior to a national tour. Five successful plays followed, the latest being *Mother Clap's Molly House*, which opened at the National Theatre in 2001 and transferred to the West End in 2002.

Totally Over You is a comedy based on a half-hour, one-act curtain-raiser by Molière, *Les Précieuses ridicules*. In the original play two young women are engaged to be married but they become infatuated by a servant who is affected and aspires to be a member of the Court. They then decide to finish with their fiancés because the young men are not courtly or mannered enough. The women are horrified when they find out what the audience has known all along.

> I've always liked that play and the idea that a character can put on a disguise and very easily trick other people who have known them for years. It's not something we use much in drama today but it was a common device when Molière was writing. As I started to write *Totally Over You* I started to recall what my schooldays were like. Emotions are heightened and it is important that you are seen to be going out with someone. How up-and-down you are can be dependent on your popularity or status.

Totally Over You is a play about a group of teenage girls who are obsessed with celebrity. Led by Kitty, they decide to dump their boyfriends convinced that they will be instant stars even though Jake tells Kitty, 'You can't sing, you can't act, you're OK-looking but you're not models.' The boys' revenge is swift and effective. They turn the tables when Victor organises the drama class and convinces the girls that the boys they have just abandoned are in fact the celebrated band Awesome.

> When I sit down to write a play it is to tell a story and explore a situation. In this case I wanted to write about the obsession with celebrity and a media-led culture. Love and the affirmative power of pretending and acting turn out to be very important in the play. Jake and Kitty make a journey from an early teenage kind of crush to find they are closer to something like adult love. I didn't see that coming – plays tend to creep up on you when you are writing them and surprise you. The idea of taking on roles and playing parts is something everyone enjoys but there is a particular pleasure when you are at an age and you are making choices or are scared about who you could be and what you could do. The excitement and thrill of taking on different personae and pretending to be different things is great. I think there is a basic pleasure in seeing the twists and turns of the plot – people pretending to be someone else, somebody wanting to get back at somebody else, seeing a character fall for a trick.

The girls are familiar with every nuance of celebrity: sleeping in the totally fantastic house next to the totally buff boyfriend, the breakfast conference calls to Japan, the lunches, the red carpet at the film launch and the stalker.

> Celebrity is an addiction and the girls are obsessive about it. It has become more and more important for people and now an interest in fictional characters has been replaced by people who are borderline real/fictional such as Madonna, J-Lo or Eminem. And now with *Big Brother* it is possible to attain celebrity without having much talent. One of the things that worries me is that I am so attracted to it. I like celebrity TV shows like *Pop Stars* and *Big Brother*. I understand the appeal. We have created adolescent adults, people who are refusing to leave adolescence.

One of the pleasing sub-plots is the way Victor, insecure and desperate to go to the movies with anyone, and yearning for Letitia, finds himself through acting. He takes on the part of director with relish. He convinces the girls he is a visionary who can see the future where they will be megastars. The only problem is their fame comes from being associated with the band Awesome. Shame they've just dumped the boys. Victor wins the approval of the boys and Letitia asks him out.

At the beginning of the play Kitty is the leader of the gang and has been used to that position for some time. She is humbled and matures during the play. When she threw Jake over it was a very significant act. They had been going out for six weeks and in adult terms it was the equivalent of a divorce. At the end, Sinita, Rochelle and Hannah have been embarrassed but are not unduly damaged. Kitty, however, has been profoundly changed, calling herself, 'Stupid freaking stupid freaking idiot bitch to believe. I just wanted to believe so much.' Jake finds the courage to express his feelings. 'I feel everything for you, Kitty. I feel love. I feel kissing and cuddling and all that kind of love. But also like sex kind of love. Like I want to see you naked . . . And I feel hate.' Kitty too realises that love is terrible. It will take some doing for young people to get this kind of honesty into their performance.

> I think they'll have a good time enjoying participating in a story that takes them on a journey. They'll talk about the celebrity culture. They will see Jake and Kitty on a journey towards maturity and this may be part of their own process of finding out who they are. *Totally Over You* may be their step towards maturity.

Production Notes

STAGING AND SETTING

Kitty dreams of becoming a star, but first she and her 'sistas', Rochelle, Hannah and Sinita, have to date some A-list celebrities, and that means dumping zitty boyfriends Jake, Dan, Tyson and Framji. Kitty eggs on her reluctant friends with promises of fame to come: photo shoots, opening nights and much more. Meanwhile, Jake, Dan and Framji swap stories of getting chucked and decide to teach the girls a lesson, but how? Geeky friend Victor has the answer. Posing as a wacky visionary, Victor convinces the girls that the boys are the biggest stars of the future, the ultimate boyband, 'Awesome'.

With the help of his drama classmates, disguised as personal assistants, stylists and the press, Victor stages a phoney concert to launch the band's debut single, 'So Totally Over You'. Desperate to win the boys back, the sistas sneak in but Dan, Tyson and Framji tell them where to go. Satisfied that the girls have learnt their lesson, the boys and their mates return to normal. But Jake wants the play-acting to continue; if only he can persuade Kitty to see beyond the celebrity, he thinks, maybe he can win her back. The two meet and Jake momentarily gives in to the fantasy of his pop-star life. The other couples, reunited at last, turn up and reveal the truth and Kitty and Jake finally have to face up to their true feelings for each another.

Inspired by Molière's *Les Précieuses ridicules*, Mark Ravenhill's play examines the world of instant celebrity. In Molière's text a group of women decide to dump their respective male partners because the men aren't courtly enough. A manservant, pretending to be a gentleman, fools the women. There's little disparity between the dated notion of courtliness and modern-day celebrity. Mark's play began as an exploration of celebrity but developed into a piece about the power of pretence and theatrical illusion. The notions of love and emotional growth are also major themes in the play.

Totally Over You has no particular dialect but the linguistic patterning is intentionally formal for theatrical reasons and should not be resisted. Certain geographical and cultural variances might justify very minor textual changes, but avoid changing the character names.

You might want to compose music to accompany the boyband's song. It could be performed live or pre-recorded, or a mixture of both. Music was commissioned from Simon Webb for the *Shell Connections* programme, and details of how to obtain it can be found on page vi.

There are fifteen characters in *Totally Over You*: eight girls and seven boys, aged between fourteen and sixteen. There are opportunities for larger casts to play the various members of the drama class, disguising themselves as reporters, photographers, TV crews, etc. The play was written to be performed on a bare stage. The scenes are not set anywhere specific and need no scenery or furniture to suggest location. Only the lightest forms of disguise need be used to fool the other characters. Play the piece as seriously as possible to enhance the comic potential. The action plays in real time, although dramatically condensed up until the second section. The textual break is significant: it signals that a short amount of time has passed, perhaps a few days. A couple of bars of music could be used to divide the two parts if desired.

EXERCISES

Discover the back histories of the characters (months and years before the play begins as well as just before the play begins). For example, decide how long Jake and Kitty have been going out. How long have the girls been interested in celebrities? When did they start reading horoscopes?

Take a pack of playing cards. One character attempts to convince another character to dump her boyfriend. Both characters are given a card to reflect the level of their want. One represents a minor motivational want whilst ten represents an intense motivational want. The actors should improvise a simple scene that acknowledges these wants. You can repeat this exercise giving the numerical value of the card to represent the extent to which Jake wants to hurt and ridicule Kitty.

Read through the script, looking at the narrative in small units. Then name each unit in accordance with the character's motivation, making sure the whole cast reach a specific group verdict on this. For example, the opening unit could be named 'Kitty wants to test whether Jake takes her seriously'.

Read through the script to explore varying status hierarchies. The hierarchy between Kitty and Jake, for instance, should be very broad to increase dramatic potential. Kitty might be a 9 and Jake a 6 in the first unit. Initially the love between Jake and Kitty is an adolescent crush. By the end of the play, however, their relationship is edging towards a mature form of love, and for this reason it is dark and scary. They are not the same characters or the same people they were at the start of the play. They begin as fourteen-year-olds and finish as sixteen- or seventen-year-olds. Their status will change as well.

Within the second unit is an extended speech by Kitty. With this and other extended speeches follow the punctuation very carefully and pause only when indicated. Sentences should be spoken in full as whole sentences, without pausing. Explore and discuss each section of the speech as a discrete and separate want or intention. For example, read through all of the lines spoken by Rochelle. This is a simple exercise that will help to illuminate the various characters.

Get the cast to form a large circle. Ask them to represent a number of drama archetypes: the fool, the innocent, the hero, the trickster, the mother, the king. Have the actors walk across the circle and greet another member of the group using one of the characters. Think about how each of the characters in the text would be defined using the archetypes. Bear in mind that they may be different characters at once – for example, Kitty could be the king but also a trickster and an innocent. Look at the other characters as well. With these distinctions in mind, get the group to repeat various lines from the play.

Explore how groups of fourteen-year-old boys and girls behave socially, both in terms of how they are in boy- and girl-only groups and how the genders interact. Look at the relationship that exists between Jake and Victor. Victor appears to be an unlikely friend of Jake's. In this hierarchical structure, Victor appears to have lower status, so why is he accepted by the others?

Suzy Graham-Adriani
March 2003
based on a workshop facilitated by *Max Stafford-Clark*

Participating Schools and Companies

Albany Interactive Youth Theatre, Deptford
All Saints RC School, York
Aberdeenshire Youth Theatre, Aberdeen
Allerton Grange High School, Leeds
Arnold's In Yer Space, Blackpool
Ashcroft High School, Luton
Australian Theatre for Young People

Behind The Scenes Youth Theatre, Buckhaven
Bentley Wood High School, London
Bishop Luffa School, Chichester
Bishop Perowne CE High School, Worcester
Bishop Thomas Grant School, London
Bispham High School Arts College, Blackpool
Blackbird Theatre, Newtownabbey
Blyth Community College, Northumberland
Borders Youth Theatre, Edinburgh
Boston Spa Comprehensive School, Wetherby
Brentford School for Girls, London
Brewhouse Youth Theatre, Burton-upon-Trent
Bridlington School
Bristol Old Vic
British School, Tokyo
Bryanston School, Blandford
Bull Youth Theatre, London

Callington School, Cornwall
Camborne School & Community College, Cornwall
Cap-A-Pie Creative Campus, Durham
Cardinal Langley School, Middleton
Carlton Junior Television Workshop, Birmingham
Castleford High School Technology College
CAT Connections, Cambridge
Challenge College, Bradford
Charles Edward Brooke School, London
Chichester Festival Youth Theatre

Christ's Hospital School, Horsham
Cleeve School, Cheltenham
Coed-y-Lan Comprehensive School, Pontypridd
Commotion (North Ayrshire Youth Theatre], Kilbirnie
Completely Cuckoo Theatre Company, Henley-on-Thames
Cordeaux High School, Louth
Cumberland Youth Theatre, Keswick
Cumberland Youth Theatre North, Keswick

Dolman Youth Theatre, Newport
Dramawise, Whittlesford
Driffield School, Yorkshire
Dumont High School Youth Theatre, USA
Dundee Rep Youth Theatre
Dunfermline Youth Theatre

East Norfolk Sixth Form College, Great Yarmouth
Edwards Theatre Company, Louth
Ellowes Hall School, Dudley
Estover Community College, Plymouth

Fallen Angel Project, Nottingham
Falmouth Community School, Cornwall
Flintshire Youth Theatre, Mold
Fowey Community College, Cornwall
Friends' School, Saffron Walden
Fulwood High School, Lancashire

Gordonstoun School, Elgin
Guiseley School, Leeds

Hall Green Little Theatre (Youth Section), Solihull
Hands on @ the Citadel, St Helens
Harlow College Community Arts Group, Essex
Hazlewood Integrated College, Newtownabbey
Heaton Manor School, Newcastle-upon-Tyne
Hedley Walter High School, Brentford
Hemsworth Arts & Community College, Pontefract
Hope Valley College, Derbyshire

Icknield High School, Luton
Islington Youth Theatre, London

Jackson's Lane Youth Theatre

PARTICIPATING SCHOOLS AND COMPANIES

Kidbrooke School, London
Kildare Youth Theatre @ Crooked House, Newbridge
King Alfred School, London
King Edward's School, Bath
King Edward VI Sixth Form College, Sourbridge

Lacon Childe School, Hereford & Worcester
Lawnswood School, Leeds
Limbo Youth Theatre & Brewery Youth Theatre, Kendal
Limelight Youth Theatre Group, London
Longdean School, Hemel Hempstead
Lyceum Youth Theatre, Edinburgh

MacRobert Arts Centre, Stirling
Manor College of Technology, Hartlepool
Marlborough School, St Albans
McEntree School, London
Methwold High School, Thetford
Monks Dyke Technology College, Louth
More House School, Farnham

New Peckham Varieties, London
Noadswood School, Southampton
Northampton Theatres Youth Theatre
Northolt High School
North Down Youth Drama, Bangor

Old Hall School, Rotherham
Orwell High School, Felixstowe
Our Lady's Catholic High School, Liverpool

Palace Theatre Watford's Youth Theatre
Parsons Mead School, Ashtead
Perins Community School, Alresford
Pilot Youth Theatre, Castleford
Portchester Community School, Fareham
Prior Pursglove 6th Form College, Guisborough
Pyramid Youth Theatre, Stockwell

Queen Elizabeth School, Kirkby Lonsdale

Radley College, Abingdon
Ralph Thoresby High School, Leeds

Ravenswood School, Australia
Ravens Wood School for Boys, Bromley
Reading Youth Theatre
Reigate School, Surrey
Republic, Bodenham
Richmond Schools Youth Theatre
Ryton Comprehensive School, Tyne & Wear

St Bernards School, Barrow-in-Furness
St George's College of Technology, Sleaford
St Julian's School, Newport
St Martin-in-the-Fields High School for Girls, London
St Mary's Youth Theatre, Leeds
St Monica's RC High School, Prestwich
St Wilfrid's RC Comprehensive School, South Shields
Samuel Whitbread Community College, Shefford
Saturday Live, St Marylebone School, London
Sexey's School, Bruton
Shetland Youth Theatre, Lerwick
Shore Thing Youth Theatre, Wimborne
Silver Street Youth Theatre, London
South West Youth Theatre, London
South Wight Youth Theatre, Isle of Wight
Sparkleshark (Sir Frederic Osbourn School), Welwyn Garden City
Stagerite Youth Theatre, York
Stageworks, Woking
Stage 2, Cambridge
Stephen Joseph Theatre 'Rounders', Scarborough
Stockton Riverside College, Cleveland
Stratford High School, Stratford-upon-Avon
Stratton Upper School & Community College, Biggleswade
Strode's College, Egham

Tarleton High School, Lancashire
The Clarendon School Culture Box, Trowbridge
The Company on the Edge, Bideford
The Folkestone School for Girls, Kent
The Freewheelers, Leatherhead
The Howard of Effingham School, Surrey
The Lindsey School & Community Arts College, Cleethorpes
The Loft Theatre Group, Exeter
The Meridian School, Royston
The Rickstones School, Witham

The Young Company, Plymouth
Theatre Antidote, Cyprus
Treo Youth Theatre, Newcastle-upon-Tyne
21st Century Productions, Amersham

Wallington High School for Girls, Surrey
Warwick Park School, Peckham
West Exeter Technology College
Whitecross School, Lydney
Willingdon Community School, Eastbourne
Wrenn School, Wellingborough
Wycombe High School, High Wycombe
Wyndham School, Egremont

Yeovil College
Yorkshire Coast College School of Creative Arts, Scarborough
York Youth Theatre
Youth Lyric, Belfast
Ysgol Aberconwy, Conwy
Ysgol Glan-y-Môr, Burry Port